AQA Biology

GCSE

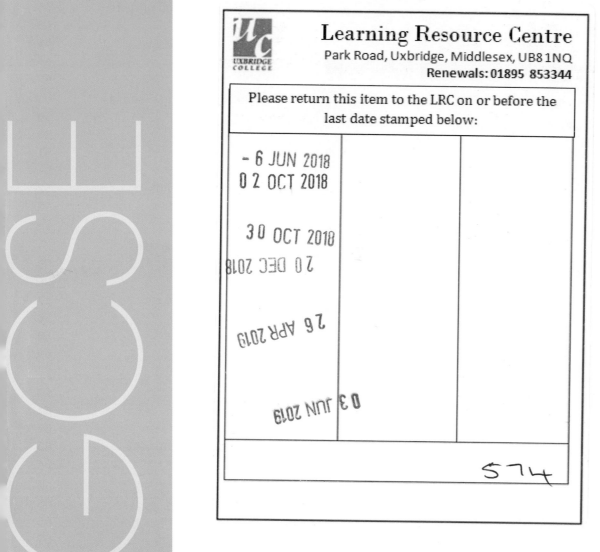

Learning Resource Centre
Park Road, Uxbridge, Middlesex, UB8 1NQ
Renewals: 01895 853344

Please return this item to the LRC on or before the last date stamped below:

- 6 JUN 2018
0 2 OCT 2018

3 0 OCT 2018
2 0 DEC 2018

2 6 APR 2019

0 3 JUN 2019

574

Revision Guide

Niva Miles
Editor: Lawrie Ryan

UXBRIDGE COLLEGE
LEARNING CENTRE

OXFORD
UNIVERSITY PRESS

Contents

Introduction

Key points

- At the start of each topic are the important points that you must remember.
- Anything marked with the **(H)** icon is only relevant to those who are sitting the higher tier exams.

Synoptic link

Synoptic links show how the content of a topic links to other parts of the course. This will support you with the synoptic element of your assessment.

Study tip

Hints giving you advice on things you need to know and remember, and what to watch out for.

On the up

This feature suggests how you can work towards higher grades.

Using maths

This feature highlights and explains the key maths skills you need. There are also clear step-by-step worked examples.

This book has been written by subject experts to match the new 2016 specifications. It is packed full of features to help you prepare for your exams and achieve the very best that you can.

Key words are highlighted in the text. You can look them up in the glossary at the back of the book if you are not sure what they mean.

Many diagrams are as important for your understanding as the text, so make sure you revise them carefully.

Required practical

These practicals have important skills that you will need to be confident with for part of your assessment.

Higher

Anything in the higher tier spreads and boxes must be learnt by those sitting the higher tier exam. If you will be sitting foundation tier, you will not be assessed on this content.

In-text questions check your understanding as you work through each topic.

Summary questions

These questions will test you on what you have learnt throughout the whole chapter, helping you to work out what you have understood and where you need to go back and revise.

Practice questions

These questions are examples of the types of questions you may encounter in your exams, so you can get lots of practice during your course.

You can find brief answers to the summary questions and practice questions at the back of the book. More detailed exam-style feedback on practice questions is also available online.

Checklists

Checklists at the end of each chapter allow you to record your progress, so you can mark topics you have revised thoroughly and those you need to look at again.

Chapter checklist

Tick when you have:

reviewed it after your lesson	✓		
revised once – some questions right	✓	✓	
revised twice – all questions right	✓	✓	✓

Move on to another topic when you have all three ticks

1 Cells and organisation

Living things range from microscopic organisms, to blue whales that can be 30 metres long, and to giant redwood trees that tower over 100 metres. Big or small, all living things are built up of basic building blocks known as cells. Every cell contains a similar mixture of chemical elements combined to make up the molecules of life.

Some organisms are single cells. Many others, including ourselves, contain billions of individual cells working together. In this section you will learn about the characteristics of these cells, and look at how they are organised so that even the largest organisms can carry out all of the functions of life.

I already know...

I will revise...

I already know...	I will revise...
what cells look like under a light microscope.	what we can see under the electron microscope – and how to calculate magnification.
the similarities and differences between plant and animal cells.	the similarities and differences between prokaryotic and eukaryotic cells and orders of magnitude.
the role of diffusion in the movement of materials in and between cells.	the roles of osmosis and active transport in the movement of materials in and between cells.
reproduction in animals and plants.	the type of cell division that forms the gametes and the way normal body cells grow and divide.
the importance of the digestive system.	the way the structure of enzymes is related to their function.
the basic structure and function of the human gas exchange system.	surface area : volume ratios and the adaptations of the alveoli of the lungs for effective gas exchange.
the mechanism of breathing.	the importance of ventilating the lungs and the gills of fish to maintain steep concentration gradients.
the role of the leaf stomata in gas exchange in plants.	how evaporation and transpiration are controlled in plants.

1.1 The world of the microscope

Key points

- Light microscopes magnify up to about ×2000, and have a resolving power of about 200 nm.

- Electron microscopes magnify up to about ×2 000 000, and have a resolving power of around 0.2 nm.

- $\text{magnification} = \dfrac{\text{size of image}}{\text{size of real object}}$

Key word: resolving power

Using units

1 km = 1000 m

1 m = 100 cm

1 cm = 10 mm

1 mm = 1000 µm (micrometres)

1 µm = 1000 nm (nanometres)

Onion cells dividing as seen through a light microscope – magnification ×570

Study tip

Make sure you can work out the magnification, the size of a cell, or the size of the image, depending on the information you are given.

Living things are made of cells. Most cells are too small to see with the naked eye. Microscopes are used to magnify small objects.

Light microscopes	Electron microscopes
use a beam of light to form an image	use a beam of electrons to form an image
can magnify objects up to 2000 times (but school microscopes usually up to about 400 times)	can magnify objects up to 2 000 000 times
can be used to view living objects	cannot be used for living objects
are relatively cheap and easy to carry around	are very expensive and need to be kept in special conditions

1 What forms the image in a typical school microscope?

There are two types of electron microscope.

1 The transmission electron microscope gives 2D images.

2 The scanning electron microscope gives 3D images but gives lower magnifications.

Resolving power

If two dots are very close together they look like one dot. Magnifying the dots allows you to see the two dots separately.

A light microscope allows you to see two dots that are 200 nm apart. The light microscope has a **resolving power** of 200 nm.

A transmission electron microscope can allow you to see two dots that are only 0.2 nm apart. This means that an electron microscope not only has higher magnification but also has a better resolving power than a light microscope.

Calculating magnification, image size, and object size

$\text{magnification} = \dfrac{\text{image size}}{\text{object size}}$

If you know two of the values in the equation, you can calculate the third.

Practise with a regular-shaped object such as a cup. Measure the diameter of the cup (the object). Draw a large circle (your image). Measure the diameter of the circle. Calculate the magnification of your drawing.

2 Measure the length of an onion cell in the photograph. The magnification is ×570. What is the real size of the cell?

Student Book
pages 6–7   **B1**

1.2 Animal and plant cells

Animal cells – structure and function

Animal cells range in size from around 10 μm to 30 μm. Most human cells are like most other animal cells and have structures in common. They have:

- a **nucleus** (diameter 10 μm) to control the cell's activities
- genes on chromosomes within the nucleus that carry the instructions for making proteins
- **cytoplasm** – a liquid gel in which the organelles are suspended, and where many chemical reactions take place
- a **cell membrane** that controls the movement of substances such as glucose and mineral ions into the cell, and other substances such as urea and hormones out of the cell
- **mitochondria** (1–2 μm by 0.2–0.7 μm) where energy is transferred during aerobic respiration
- **ribosomes** where protein synthesis takes place.

> **1** In which part of the cell is energy transferred during respiration?

Plant cells – structure and function

Algae are simple aquatic organisms that have many features similar to plant cells. Plant cells may be larger than animal cells, ranging from 10 μm to100 μm. Plant and algal cells also have:

- a rigid **cell wall** made of **cellulose** for support
- **chloroplasts** (3–5 μm) that contain **chlorophyll** for photosynthesis; the chloroplasts absorb light to make food
- a **permanent vacuole** containing cell sap, which keeps the cell rigid and helps to support the plant.

> **2** What is the function of chloroplasts?

Looking at cells

You can use a light microscope to look at animal cells as well as onion cells and either *Elodea* or algal cells. All the plant cells have a cell wall, cytoplasm, and a vacuole. *Elodea* and algal cells have chloroplasts for photosynthesis, but onion cells do not.

> **3** Onion cells do not look green. Explain why.

Key words: nucleus, cytoplasm, cell membrane, mitochondria, ribosome, algae, cell wall, cellulose, chloroplast, chlorophyll, permanent vacuole

Key points

- Animal cell features that are common to all cells are a nucleus, cytoplasm, cell membrane, mitochondria, and ribosomes.
- Plant and algal cells contain all the structures seen in animal cells as well as a cellulose cell wall.
- Many plant cells also contain chloroplasts and a permanent vacuole filled with sap.

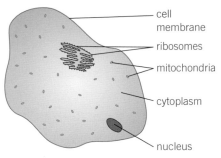

cell membrane
ribosomes
mitochondria
cytoplasm
nucleus

A simple animal cell like this shows the features that are common to all living cells, including human cells

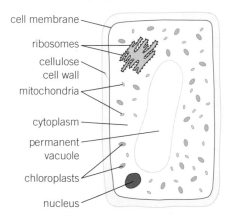

cell membrane
ribosomes
cellulose cell wall
mitochondria
cytoplasm
permanent vacuole
chloroplasts
nucleus

A plant cell has many features in common with an animal cell, as well as others that are unique to plants

Study tips

Practise labelling different types of cell.

Learn the parts of cells and their functions.

1.3 Eukaryotic and prokaryotic cells

Key points

- Eukaryotic cells all have a cell membrane, cytoplasm, and genetic material in a nucleus.

- Prokaryotic cells consist of cytoplasm and a cell membrane surrounded by a cell wall. The genetic material is not in a distinct nucleus. It forms a single DNA loop.

- Prokaryotes may contain one or more extra small rings of DNA called plasmids.

- Bacteria are all prokaryotes.

Synoptic links

For more about bacteria that cause disease, see Topic B5.7.

For more about bacteria that are important in the environment, see Topics B17.2 and B17.3.

Key words: eukaryotic cells, bacteria, prokaryotic cells

Study tip

Design a table to compare animal, plant, and bacterial cell structures and their functions. See the Summary questions for guidance.

Eukaryotic cells

All animals (including human beings), plants, fungi, and protista are eukaryotes. **Eukaryotic cells** contain a cell membrane, cytoplasm, and a nucleus. The nucleus contains chromosomes, which are made of the genetic material called DNA.

Prokaryotic cells

Bacteria are single-celled living organisms. They are examples of **prokaryotic cells**.

- Bacteria are very small (0.2–2 μm) and can be seen only with a powerful microscope.

- Bacterial cells have a cell membrane and a cell wall surrounding the cytoplasm. The cell wall is different from a plant cell wall because it is not made of cellulose.

- Bacteria do not have a nucleus. The genetic material is found in the cytoplasm as a long circle of DNA. Some prokaryotic cells also contain extra small circular rings of DNA called plasmids.

- Some bacteria have a protective slime capsule, others have flagella for movement. Not all bacteria are harmful but some cause diseases in animals and plants. Bacteria may cause stored food to decompose.

- When bacteria multiply they form a colony. Bacterial colonies can be seen with the naked eye.

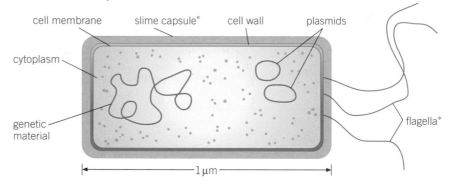

*not always present

Bacteria come in a variety of shapes, but they all have the same basic structure

> **1** Where is the DNA found in a prokaryotic cell?

Orders of magnitude

Orders of magnitude are used to make approximate comparisons between numbers or objects. They are shown using powers of 10.

If a cell is less than 10 times bigger than another cell they have the same order of magnitude – they are similar sizes.

If a cell is 10 times bigger than another it is 10^1 bigger or one order of magnitude bigger.

If the cell is about 100 times bigger than another it is 10^2 or two orders of magnitude bigger.

Example:

A small animal cell has a length of around 10 μm. A large plant cell has a length of around 100 μm.

$$\frac{100}{10} = 10$$

So, a large plant cell is an order of magnitude or 10^1 bigger than a small animal cell.

> **2** What is the order of magnitude of 1 cm compared with 1 mm?

1.4 Specialisation in animal cells

Key points

- As an organism develops, cells differentiate to form different types of cells.

- As an animal cell differentiates to form a specialised cell it acquires different sub-cellular structures to enable it to carry out a certain function.

- Examples of specialised animal cells are nerve cells, muscle cells, and sperm cells.

- Animal cells may be specialised to function within a tissue, an organ, organ systems, or whole organisms.

Study tip

Draw a specialised cell from memory. Label each part. Write a note next to each label stating the function of the part. Check your answers against the Student Book.

A sperm cell

On the up

Practise labelling all types of cell. To achieve the top grades, you need to know the functions of each part and understand why some cells contain specific structures (e.g., muscle cells have many mitochondria to transfer energy for movement).

Large organisms are made of many cells. As the organism develops, some cells become specialised to perform a particular function. The cells become different from each other (they differentiate). Specialised cells may work individually (eggs and sperm) or as part of a tissue, an organ, or a whole organism.

Specialised cells may contain large numbers of particular sub-cellular structures, for example, muscle cells require a lot of energy so they contain many mitochondria.

Nerve cells

Nerve cells are specialised to carry electrical impulses around the bodies of animals. Nerve cells have:

- many dendrites to make connections to other nerve cells

- an axon to carry the impulse from one place to another, such as from your spine to your big toe

- nerve endings or synapses, which pass impulses to other cells by producing transmitter chemicals

- many mitochondria in the synapses to transfer the energy needed to make the transmitter chemicals.

Muscle cells

Muscle cells can contract and relax. Striated (striped) muscle cells are found in the muscles that enable your body to move. Smooth muscle cells are found in the tissues of the digestive system and contract to move food along the gut. So that they can contract, striated muscle cells contain:

- special proteins that slide over each other

- many mitochondria to transfer the energy needed for chemical reactions

- a store of glycogen that can be broken down and used in respiration to transfer energy.

---

1   Muscle cells contain a lot of mitochondria. Why?

2   Which organ system contains nerve cells?

Sperm cells

Sperm cells carry the genetic information from the male parent. They are specialised to move through water or the female reproductive system to reach the egg. Sperm cells have:

- a long tail that whips from side to side to move the sperm

- a middle section full of mitochondria to transfer the energy needed by the tail to move

- an acrosome to store digestive enzymes to break down the outer layers of the egg

- a large nucleus to contain the genetic information.

Key word: sperm

Student Book
pages 12–13

B1

1.5 Specialisation in plant cells

Key points

- Plant cells may be specialised to carry out a particular function.
- Examples of specialised plant cells are root hair cells, photosynthetic cells, xylem cells, and phloem cells.
- Plant cells may be specialised to function within tissues, organs, organ systems, or whole organisms.

A root hair cell

Key words: xylem, phloem

The adaptations of xylem and phloem cells

Study tip

Practise labelling specialised cells. Next to each label, make a note of how the adaptation helps the cell to function.

Like animals, plants have specialised cells to carry out their functions. Specialised plant cells may form part of tissues, organs, organ systems, or whole organisms.

Root hair cells

Root hair cells occur near the tips of roots. They increase the surface area of the root so that it can absorb water and mineral ions efficiently. Root hair cells are close to **xylem** tissue that transports water and mineral ions through the plant. Root hair cells:

- greatly increase the surface area available for water to move into the cell
- have a large permanent vacuole – this speeds up the movement of water by osmosis from the soil across the root hair cell
- have many mitochondria – these transfer the energy needed for the active transport of mineral ions into the root hair cells.

1 What is the main function of a root hair cell?

Photosynthetic cells

Plants can make their own food by photosynthesis. Photosynthetic cells:

- have chloroplasts containing chlorophyll to trap the light needed for photosynthesis
- are often found in continuous layers in the leaf and outer layers of stems
- have a large permanent vacuole that helps keep the cell rigid.

Xylem cells

Xylem tissue has two main functions.

1 The xylem cells transport water and mineral ions from the roots to the stem and leaves.

2 Xylem tissue supports the plant.

- Xylem cells are living when they are first formed.
- Then a chemical called lignin builds up in spirals in the cell walls.
- The cells die leaving long hollow tubes. Water and mineral ions can move up the tubes.
- The spirals and rings of lignin make the tubes of xylem very strong.

Phloem

Phloem is the tissue that transports food made by photosynthesis to the rest of the plant. Phloem cells form tubes but do not become lignified like the xylem.

- The cell walls between phloem cells break down to form sieve plates.
- Phloem cells lose a lot of their structures but are kept alive by companion cells.
- The companion cells contain mitochondria that transfer energy to aid the movement of dissolved food in the phloem.

2 Name the chemical that makes xylem rigid.

1.6 Diffusion

Molecules in gases and liquids move around randomly because of the energy they have.

Diffusion is the spreading out of the particles of a gas, or of any substance in solution (a solute).

The net movement into or out of cells depends on the concentration of the particles on each side of the cell membrane.

- Because the particles move randomly, there will be a net (overall) movement from an area of high concentration to an area of lower concentration.
- The difference in concentration between two areas is called the concentration gradient.
- The larger the difference in concentration, the faster the rate of diffusion.

> 1   What determines the net movement of particles across a cell membrane?

- An increase in temperature causes particles to move faster, which also increases the rate of diffusion.
- Examples of diffusion are:
  - the diffusion of oxygen and glucose into the cells of the body from the bloodstream for respiration
  - the diffusion of carbon dioxide into actively photosynthesising plant cells
  - the diffusion of oxygen and carbon dioxide in opposite directions in the lungs, known as gas exchange
  - the diffusion of simple sugars and amino acids from the gut through cell membranes.

> 2   Describe what is meant by gas exchange in the lungs.

both types of particle can pass through this membrane – it is freely permeable

steep concentration gradient

beginning of experiment

random movement means three blue particles have moved from left to right by diffusion

shallow concentration gradient

beginning of experiment

four blue particles have moved as a result of random movement from left to right – but two have moved from right to left. There is a net movement of two particles to the right by diffusion

This diagram shows the effect of concentration on the rate of diffusion. This is why so many body systems are adapted to maintain steep concentration gradients

Key word: diffusion

Key points

- Diffusion is the spreading out of particles of any substance, in solution or a gas, resulting in a net movement from an area of higher concentration to an area of lower concentration, down a concentration gradient.
- The rate of diffusion is affected by the difference in concentrations, the temperature, and the available surface area.
- Dissolved substances, such as glucose and urea, and gases such as oxygen and carbon dioxide move in and out of cells by diffusion.

Synoptic links

For more about the excretion of urea by the kidney, see Topic B12.3.

For more about gas exchange, see Topic B4.4.

Study tips

Particles move randomly, but the net movement is from a region of high concentration to a region of low concentration.

Always make it clear in which direction there is net movement.

On the up

If you can list the factors that affect diffusion, you can aim for the top grades by being able to predict which way substances will move across a membrane and explain how temperature and the concentration gradient can affect the rate of diffusion.

1.7 Osmosis

- **Osmosis** is the diffusion of water across a **partially permeable membrane**. Just like diffusion, the movement of water molecules is random and requires no energy from the cell.

- The water moves from a region of high water concentration (a **dilute** solution) to a region of lower water concentration (a more **concentrated** solution).

- The cell membrane is partially permeable.

Key points

- Osmosis is a special case of diffusion. It is the movement of water from a dilute to a more concentrated solution through a partially permeable membrane that allows water to pass through.

- Differences in the concentrations of solutions inside and outside a cell cause water to move into or out of the cell by osmosis.

- Animal cells can be damaged if the concentration outside the cell changes dramatically.

---

1 What type of membrane is the cell membrane?

Special scientific terms are used to compare the concentrations of two solutions.

- If the two solutions have the same concentrations they are **isotonic**.

- The solution that is more concentrated (has more solute and relatively less water) is **hypertonic**.

- The solution that is more dilute (has relatively more water and less solute) is **hypotonic**.

---

2 What term is used to refer to two solutions with identical concentrations?

Study tip

Remember that diffusion can refer to any moving particles, but that osmosis refers to the movement of water.

Osmosis in animals

- Animal cells that are surrounded by a hypotonic solution will swell and possibly burst because water moves into the cell by osmosis.

- If the solution around animal cells is hypertonic then water moves out of the cells and they shrink.

- Animals need complex mechanisms to control the concentration of the solutions around their cells to avoid bursting or shrinking.

Synoptic link

For more about the way in which animals control the concentration of their body fluids to prevent osmotic damage, see Topic B12.2.

Investigating osmosis

Model cells can be set up as in the diagrams. The model cells are bags, made of a partially permeable membrane, containing a solution.

a glass tubes — final level
initial level
concentrated sugar solution
water moves into the bag by osmosis
water
partially permeable membrane bags

° sugar molecules
• water molecules

b concentrated sugar solution
water moves out of the bag by osmosis
water
partially permeable membrane bags

3 Explain why water moves into the bag in **a** and out of the bag in **b**.

Key words: partially permeable membrane, osmosis, isotonic, hypertonic, hypotonic

1.8 Osmosis in plants

Key points

- Osmosis is important to maintain turgor in plant cells.
- There are a variety of practical investigations that can be used to show the effect of osmosis on plant tissues.

Key words: turgor, plasmolysis

Micrographs of red onion cells in hypertonic and hypotonic solutions show the effect of osmosis on the contents of the cells

In plants, osmosis is the key to their whole way of life.

Turgor pressure occurs when no more water can enter a cell due to the pressure inside:

water moves into plant cells by osmosis → the vacuole swells → the cytoplasm is pressed against the cell wall → the cell becomes rigid → the leaves and stem become rigid

- As long as the outside solution is hypotonic water moves in and keeps the cells rigid, which supports the plant.
- Plant cells in a hypertonic solution lose water and become flaccid, so the plant wilts.
- When plant cells are placed in hypertonic solutions in a laboratory, a lot of water leaves the cell. The vacuole and cytoplasm shrink, then the membrane pulls away from the cell wall. This is referred to as **plasmolysis**.

plant cell

H_2O H_2O H_2O H_2O

turgid (normal)   flaccid   plasmolysed

Osmosis in plant cells

1   When does turgor pressure occur in a plant cell?

Investigating osmosis in plant cells

Plant tissue reacts so strongly to the concentration of the external solution that you can use it as an osmometer – a way of measuring osmosis. There are lots of ways in which you can investigate the effect of osmosis on plant tissue, each with advantages and disadvantages.

The basis of many experiments is to put plant tissue into different concentrations of salt solutions or sugar solutions. You can even use fruit squash to give you the sugar solution. If plant tissue is placed in a hypotonic solution, water will move into the cells by osmosis. If it is placed in a hypertonic solution, water will move out by osmosis.

These changes can be measured by the effect they have on the tissue sample.

Potato is often used as the experimental plant tissue. It can be cut into cylinders, rectangular 'chips', or smaller discs.

There are different ways of measuring the changes in the plant tissue, such as measuring changes in its mass. (Other methods measure the length or diameter of the sample).

2   If potato chips are placed in pure water, will they get bigger or smaller? Explain your answer.

1.9 Active transport

Key points

- Active transport moves substances from a more dilute solution to a more concentrated solution (against a concentration gradient).
- Active transport requires energy from respiration.
- Active transport allows plant root hairs to absorb mineral ions required for healthy growth from very dilute solutions in the soil against a concentration gradient.
- Active transport enables sugar molecules used for cell respiration to be absorbed from lower concentrations in the gut into the blood where the concentration of sugar is higher.

- Cells may need to absorb substances that are in short supply (i.e., against the concentration gradient).
- Cells use **active transport** to absorb substances across partially permeable membranes against the concentration gradient.
- Active transport requires energy from respiration to move substances against a concentration gradient.

1 Why does active transport require energy?

- Cells are able to absorb ions from dilute solutions. For example, root hair cells absorb mineral ions from the dilute solutions in the soil by active transport.
- Glucose can be absorbed out of the gut and kidney tubules against a large concentration gradient by active transport.
- People with cystic fibrosis have thick, sticky mucus because the active transport system in their mucus cells is not working properly.

2 Name a substance that is moved by active transport into plants from the soil solution.

Synoptic links

You can find out more about cystic fibrosis in Topic B13.9, about the absorption of glucose in the gut in Topic B3.6, and about the absorption of solutes in the kidney in Topic B12.3.

Key word: active transport

Study tips

In diffusion and osmosis molecules move down a concentration gradient from higher to lower concentration.

In active transport molecules move against a concentration gradient from lower to higher concentration.

useful molecule

transport protein

outside cell   inside cell

transport protein rotates and releases molecule inside cell (using energy)

transport protein rotates back again (often using energy)

Active transport uses energy to move substances against a concentration gradient

1.10 Exchanging materials

Key points

- Single-celled organisms have a relatively large surface area to volume ratio so all necessary exchanges with the environment can take place over this surface.
- In multicellular organisms, many organs are specialised with effective exchange surfaces.
- Exchange surfaces usually have a large surface area and thin walls, which give short diffusion distances.
- In animals, exchange surfaces will have an efficient blood supply or, for gaseous exchange, be ventilated.

Synoptic links

You use the idea of surface area to volume ratio when you study the adaptations of animals and plants for living in a variety of different habitats in Topics B16.7 and B16.8.

You can find out much more about gas exchange in the lungs in Topic B4.4, and about the adaptations of the small intestine in Topic B3.2.

You can find out more about the transpiration stream in Topic B4.8.

Study tips

Make sure you understand why the surface area to volume (SA : V) ratio decreases as the size of the organism increases.

Learn the features of an exchange surface that make exchange more efficient. SA : V ratio is a very important concept in biology.

Materials such as oxygen and soluble food molecules need to reach all cells, and metabolic waste materials must be removed efficiently.

- Small organisms have a large surface area to volume ratio. Single-celled organisms are tiny and can gain enough of materials such as oxygen by diffusion through their surface.
- As organisms increase in size, their surface area to volume ratio decreases.
- Large, complex, organisms have many cells that are not in contact with the environment; so they have special exchange surfaces to obtain all the food and oxygen they need.
- Efficient exchange surfaces have a large surface area, thin membranes or a short diffusion path, and an efficient transport system – the blood supply in animals.
- Gaseous exchange surfaces in animals must be **ventilated**. Oxygen is absorbed by the **alveoli** in the lungs when air is drawn in during breathing. The alveoli have a large surface area and a good blood supply to carry the oxygen away and maintain a concentration gradient.
- The villi of the small intestine have a large surface area, a short diffusion path, and a good blood supply to absorb soluble food molecules.
- Fish have gills. which are the gaseous exchange surface between the water and the blood. A flap, the operculum, acts as a pump to maintain the flow of water over the gills. The blood carries the oxygen away to maintain a concentration gradient.

1   Why do large organisms need specialised exchange surfaces?

- Plants have long, thin roots to increase the surface area for water absorption. The root hair cells increase the surface area even more.
- Plant leaves are modified for efficient gaseous exchange. The leaves are flat and thin with internal air spaces and **stomata** to allow gases in and out of the leaves.

2   How are leaves adapted to increase their surface area?

Using units

It is important to understand that larger organisms have a smaller surface area to volume (SA : V) ratio. The SA : V ratio of a cube with sides 1 cm long is 6 : 1. The SA : V ratio for a cube with sides 3 cm long is 2: 1.

1 cm
1 cm   1 cm
SA : V ratio is 6 : 1

3 cm
3 cm
3 cm   3 cm
SA : V ratio is 54 : 27 or 2 : 1

3   Calculate the SA : V ratio of a cube with sides 2 cm long.

Key words: ventilated, alveoli, stomata

1. Copy and complete **Table 1** to show the cell structures and their functions in plant, animal, and prokaryotic cells. The first line has been done for you. [6 marks]

Table 1

Cell structure	Function	In animal cell?	In plant cell?	In prokaryotic cell?
nucleus	controls cell activities	✓	✓	✗

2. 1 mm contains 1000 μm. What is the order of magnitude of the mm? [1 mark]

3. Why do some cells have a large number of ribosomes? [1 mark]

4. What is the difference between diffusion and osmosis? [2 marks]

5. Name the features that increase the surface area of the lungs. [1 mark]

6. What are the features of an efficient exchange surface? [3 marks]

7. Give two differences between active transport and diffusion. [2 marks]

8. What is meant by the term hypotonic? [1 mark]

9. Give an example of active transport in:

   a plants   [1 mark]   **b** a human. [1 mark]

10. What is meant by turgor pressure and why is it important? [2 marks]

11. Explain why animals that normally live in fresh water may die if placed in seawater. [4 marks]

12. Explain in detail what happens to plant cells when placed in a hypertonic solution. [4 marks]

13. **a** Calculate the surface area to volume ratio of the rectangular block of modelling clay shown in **Figure 1**. [6 marks]

    b How could you increase the surface area without changing the volume of the block? [1 mark]

2 cm
6 cm
4 cm

Figure 1

Chapter checklist

✓

Tick when you have:

reviewed it after your lesson   ✓ ☐ ☐

revised once – some questions right   ✓ ✓ ☐

revised twice – all questions right   ✓ ✓ ✓

Move on to another topic when you have all three ticks

1.1 The world of the microscope   ☐ ☐ ☐
1.2 Animal and plant cells   ☐ ☐ ☐
1.3 Eukaryotic and prokaryotic cells   ☐ ☐ ☐
1.4 Specialisation in animal cells   ☐ ☐ ☐
1.5 Specialisation in plant cells   ☐ ☐ ☐
1.6 Diffusion   ☐ ☐ ☐
1.7 Osmosis   ☐ ☐ ☐
1.8 Osmosis in plants   ☐ ☐ ☐
1.9 Active transport   ☐ ☐ ☐
1.10 Exchanging materials   ☐ ☐ ☐

2.1 Cell division

The cell cycle

- Cell division is necessary for the growth and development of an organism, and for the repair of damaged tissues.
- The cell divides in a series of stages called the **cell cycle**. The length of the cycle can vary. In embryos it is very short as cells divide rapidly to form a new organism. In adults the process slows down but some cells, such as hair follicles, skin, blood, and the lining of the digestive system, continue to divide rapidly.
- **Mitosis** is one stage in the cell cycle, which results in two identical cells being produced from the original cell.

There are three stages in the cell cycle:

1 The longest stage. The cells grow, increase in mass, and carry out normal cell activities. At the end of stage 1 the cells replicate their DNA to make two copies of every chromosome. They also make more sub-cellular structures such as mitochondria, ribosomes, and chloroplasts.

2 Mitosis: in this process one set of chromosomes is pulled to each end of the dividing cell and the nucleus divides.

3 The cytoplasm and cell membrane divide to form two new identical cells.

1 What happens to the chromosomes during mitosis?

The information in the cells

- The chromosomes contain the genes (made of DNA), which must be passed on to each new cell.
- Human body cells have 23 pairs of chromosomes. One of each pair is from your mother, the other from your father. Eggs and sperm (gametes) have 23 chromosomes each, and combine to form the 46 chromosomes in body cells.
- When offspring are produced by asexual reproduction, their cells are produced by mitosis from the parent cell. They contain exactly the same genes as the parent.

2 A cell has nine pairs of chromosomes. The cell divides by mitosis. How many chromosomes are in each new cell?

Key points

- In body cells, chromosomes are found in pairs.
- Body cells divide in a series of stages called the cell cycle.
- During the cell cycle the genetic material is doubled. It then divides, forming two identical nuclei in a process called mitosis.
- Before a cell can divide, it needs to grow, replicate the DNA to form two copies of each chromosome, and increase the number of subcellular structures.
- In mitosis one set of chromosomes is pulled to each end of the cell and the nucleus divides. Finally the cytoplasm and cell membranes divide to form two identical cells.
- Mitotic cell division is important in the growth, repair, and development of multicellular organisms.

Synoptic links

For more information on genes, see Topics B13.5, B13.7, B13.8, and B13.9.

There is more about DNA in Topic B13.4.

Key words: cell cycle, mitosis

Study tip

Remember – two genetically identical cells are produced when the nucleus divides by mitosis.

MITosis = **M**aking **I**dentical **T**wo

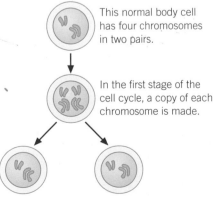

This normal body cell has four chromosomes in two pairs.

In the first stage of the cell cycle, a copy of each chromosome is made.

The cell divides in two to form two daughter cells, each with a nucleus containing four chromosomes identical to the ones in the original parent cell.

Two identical cells are formed by mitotic division in the cell cycle. This cell is shown with only two pairs of chromosomes rather than 23

2.2 Growth and differentiation

Key points

- In plant cells, mitosis takes place throughout life in the meristems found in the shoot and root tips.
- Many types of plants cell retain the ability to differentiate throughout life.
- Most types of animal cell differentiate at an early stage of development.

Synoptic links

There is more about specialised cells that result from differentiation in Topics B1.4 and B1.5.

Topic B3.1 has more about the results of differentiation.

Plant and animal cloning are described in Topics B14.5 and B14.6.

Key words: differentiate, stem cell, adult stem cell, cloning

Study tip

Make sure you understand the terms 'differentiation', 'meristem', and 'cloning'.

On the up

If you can explain how using tissue culture creates a clone of a plant, you can achieve the top grades if you can also explain why it is easier to clone a plant than an animal.

Organisms start as one cell, which divides by mitosis. The growth of an organism is a result of cell enlargement and cell division. An adult human contains trillions of cells.

The cells of a multicellular organism are not all the same. As cells grow, divide, and develop, they **differentiate**. This means they change and form different types of cell.

- In early development of animal and plant embryos the cells are unspecialised and are called **stem cells**.
- Most animal cells differentiate early in development and cell division is mainly for repair and replacement.
- Some differentiated cells cannot divide so they are replaced by **adult stem cells**, such as those found in the bone marrow.
- Plants cells can differentiate throughout the life of the plant as it continues to grow. Actively dividing plant tissues are called meristems, found at the growing points of plants. The cells produced by mitosis in the meristem then elongate and differentiate.
- Producing genetically identical offspring is known as **cloning**. Plants are easy to clone because the cells can become unspecialised, divide by mitosis, and then differentiate into the various types of plant cell.
- It is difficult to clone animals because once the cells are differentiated they cannot become unspecialised again.

1   What is a meristem?
2   Why do cells need to differentiate?

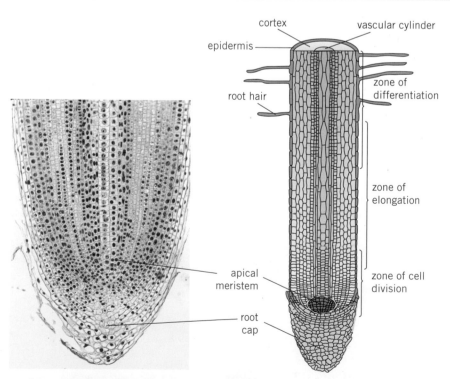

The main zones of division, elongation, and differentiation in a plant root

2.3 Stem cells

- Stem cells are unspecialised cells that are found in the human embryo and in adult bone marrow.

- An egg and sperm fuse to form a **zygote**. This cell divides many times to form a ball of cells – the embryo. The inner layers of the ball are **embryonic stem cells**.

- Layers of cells in the embryo differentiate into all the cells the body needs.

- When stem cells change into all the different types of body cell, such as nerve cells or muscle cells, we say the cells differentiate.

- **Adult stem cells** in the bone marrow can change into other types of cell, such as blood cells.

- Researchers hope that human stem cells can be made to differentiate into many types of cell. The cells formed could then be used to treat conditions such as:

  - paralysis, by differentiating into new nerve cells

  - macular degeneration in the eye, to restore lost vision

  - diabetes, by producing cells that are sensitive to blood sugar and can produce insulin.

Key points

- Embryonic stem cells (from human embryos) and adult stem cells (from adult bone marrow) can be cloned and made to differentiate into many different types of cell.

- Treatment with stem cells may be able to help conditions such as paralysis and diabetes.

- Stem cells from plant meristems are used to produce new plant clones quickly and economically for research, horticulture, and agriculture.

Synoptic links

There is more about the spinal nerves in Topic B10.2, and about the eye in Topic B10.5.

Topics B11.2 and B11.3 have more about insulin and the control of blood glucose levels.

There is more about cloning plants in Topic B14.5.

Key words: zygote, embryonic stem cells, adult stem cells

Study tip

Make sure you understand how stem cells can be used to benefit humans and plants.

On the up

To achieve the top grades, you should be able to name and evaluate the arguments for and against stem cell research.

1 Where are embryonic stem cells found?

The stem cells from plant meristems can be used to make clones of the mature parent plant very quickly and economically. There are benefits of cloning plants.

- Rare plants can be saved from extinction.

- Large populations of genetically identical plants can be produced for scientific research.

- In horticulture, large numbers of exotic plants can be produced for sale.

- In agriculture, plants can be produced with special features, such as resistance to disease.

2 Where are stem cells found in plants?

2.4 Stem cell dilemmas

Key points

- Treatment with stem cells, from embryos or adult cell cloning, may be able to help with conditions such as diabetes.

- In therapeutic cloning, an embryo is produced with the same genes as the patient, so the stem cells produced are not rejected and may be used for medical treatment.

- The use of stem cells has some potential risks, and some people have ethical or religious objections.

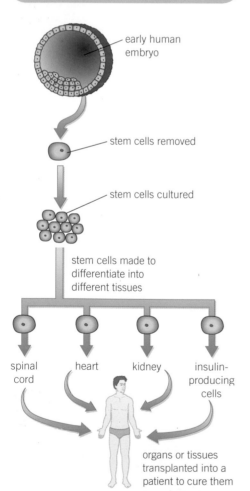

early human embryo

stem cells removed

stem cells cultured

stem cells made to differentiate into different tissues

spinal cord   heart   kidney   insulin-producing cells

organs or tissues transplanted into a patient to cure them

This shows one way in which scientists hope embryonic stem cells might be formed into adult cells and used as human treatments in the future

Problems with stem cell research

There are many potential benefits when using stem cells in human medicine, but there are also risks, as well as social and ethical issues.

Embryonic stem cells come from aborted embryos or spare embryos from fertility treatment.

- Some people believe this is a violation of the embryo's rights as it cannot give permission – this is an ethical objection.

- Other people believe we should not interfere with the natural processes of reproduction – this is a religious objection.

- Some people think a lot of money, which could be used to treat other medical conditions, is wasted on stem cell research – this is both an ethical and a social problem.

- Scientists are finding it difficult to 'persuade' stem cells to differentiate – development of the process is proving slow and expensive.

- Because embryonic stem cells divide rapidly there is concern that they could cause cancer.

- Embryonic stem cells are preferred to adult stem cells. It is possible that adult stem cells could transmit viruses to another person or trigger an immune response.

> 1 Give one ethical objection to using embryonic stem cells.

The future of stem cell research

- It is hoped that human stem cells can be made to differentiate into many types of cell. The cells formed could then be used to treat conditions such as paralysis (e.g., by differentiating into new nerve cells). This area of research is called **therapeutic cloning**. It has already been successful in producing new organs, such as tracheas.

- Therapeutic cloning involves the development of an embryo cloned from the adult who needs treatment. The cells would be genetically identical to that adult so the risk of rejection is reduced.

- Scientists have discovered stem cells in previously unknown areas of the body, such as the tubes connecting the liver and the pancreas to the small intestine. They hope to develop insulin-producing cells from these stem cells to treat type 1 diabetes.

> 2 What is the advantage of therapeutic cloning?

Key word: therapeutic cloning

Study tip

Make lists of the advantages and disadvantages of stem cell research.

1. Where are chromosomes found? [1 mark]

2. Name the chemical that forms a gene. [1 mark]

3. Which type of cell division produces two identical cells? [1 mark]

4. How many chromosomes are found in the nucleus of a human sperm cell? [1 mark]

5. Name the tissue that continues to divide in plants. [1 mark]

6. Give one place where stem cells are found in adult humans. [1 mark]

7. Name two medical conditions that could be treated with stem cells. [2 marks]

8. Describe what happens when a cell differentiates. [1 mark]

9. Name two uses of cloning in plants. [2 marks]

10. What is therapeutic cloning? [2 marks]

11. Give two reasons why some people object to the use of stem cells. [2 marks]

12. Suggest why scientists are finding it difficult to produce nerve cells from stem cells. [1 mark]

Chapter checklist

Tick when you have:

reviewed it after your lesson	✔	☐	☐
revised once – some questions right	✔	✔	☐
revised twice – all questions right	✔	✔	✔

Move on to another topic when you have all three ticks

2.1 Cell division

2.2 Growth and differentiation

2.3 Stem cells

2.4 Stem cell dilemmas

3.1 Tissues and organs

Cells are the building blocks of organisms. As a multicellular organism develops the cells **differentiate** to perform particular jobs.

Tissues

A **tissue** is a group of cells with similar structure and function.

Animal tissues include:

- muscular tissue, which can contract to bring about movement
- glandular tissue, to produce substances such as enzymes or hormones
- epithelial tissue, which covers some parts of the body.

> **1** What is a tissue?

Organs

Organs are made of tissues. The stomach is an organ made of:

- muscular tissue to churn the stomach contents
- glandular tissue to produce digestive juices
- epithelial tissue to cover the outside and the inside of the stomach.

The pancreas is an organ. The pancreas has two types of glandular tissue, producing:

- hormones to control blood sugar
- some of the digestive enzymes.

Organ systems

Multicellular organisms are made up of **organ systems** that work together.

- Each organ system is made up of several organs that work together to perform a particular function.
- Organ systems include the digestive system, circulatory system, and gas exchange system.
- These systems have organs that are adapted to be efficient exchange surfaces. These have large surface areas, short diffusion paths, rich blood supplies, and mechanisms for ventilating surfaces or for moving materials.

> **2** What is the function of muscular tissue in the stomach?

Key points

- A tissue is a group of cells with similar structure and function.
- Organs are collections of tissues performing specific functions.
- Organs are organised into organ systems, which work together to form organisms.

The pancreas, showing the tissue that makes hormones (stained yellow) and the tissue that makes enzymes (stained red)

Synoptic link

For more information on specialised cells, see Topics B1.4 and B1.5.

Key words: differentiate, tissue, organ, organ system

Study tips

Learn the organisation of a multicellular organism:

cells → tissues → organs → organ systems → whole body

On the up

To achieve the top grades, you should be able to define the terms and be able to relate levels of organisation to familiar organ systems in order to give examples of cells, tissues, and organs.

gullet (part of the digestive system)

small intestine (organ, part of digestive system)

stomach (organ, part of digestive system)

folded lining

epithelial and glandular tissue

epithelial layer containing blood vessels

muscle layers

The stomach contains several different tissues, each with a different function in the organ

3.2 The human digestive system

Key points

- Organ systems are groups of organs that perform specific functions in the body.
- The digestive system in a mammal is an organ system in which several organs work together to digest and absorb food.

Synoptic link

Topic B1.10 gives the adaptations of the villi in the small intestine as an exchange surface.

Key words: digestive system, enzyme

The **digestive system** is responsible for changing the food you eat from insoluble molecules into soluble molecules, then absorbing them into the blood.

The digestive system is a muscular tube that includes:

- glands, such as the pancreas and salivary glands, that produce digestive juices containing **enzymes**
- the stomach, where digestion occurs
- the liver, which produces bile
- the small intestine, where digestion occurs, and which also has a large number of villi where the absorption of soluble food occurs
- the large intestine, where water is absorbed from the undigested food, producing faeces.

1 Name two glands in the digestive system.

The villi are adapted to absorb soluble food efficiently. Villi have:

- a very large surface area to absorb soluble food molecules by diffusion and active transport.
- a thin wall to provide a short diffusion path,
- a good blood supply to carry the food molecules away to maintain a concentration gradient,

2 Where does absorption of the digested food occur?

The large surface area of the villi of the small intestine helps make it possible to absorb the digested food molecules from the gut into the blood

Study tip

Practise labelling the human digestive system. Cover the labels with paper and write your own labels next to the lines.

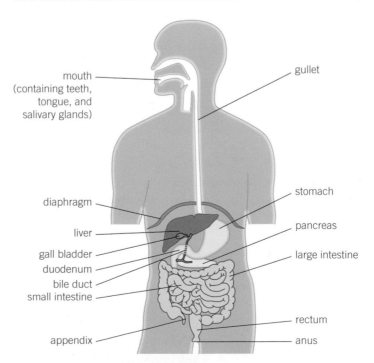

mouth (containing teeth, tongue, and salivary glands)

gullet

diaphragm

stomach

liver

pancreas

gall bladder

large intestine

duodenum

bile duct

small intestine

rectum

appendix

anus

The main organs of the human digestive system

3.3 The chemistry of food

Key points

- Carbohydrates are made up of units of sugar.
- Simple sugars are carbohydrates that contain only one or two sugar units – they turn blue Benedict's solution brick red on heating.
- Complex carbohydrates contain long chains of simple sugar units bonded together. Starch turns yellow-red iodine solution blue-black.
- Lipids consist of three molecules of fatty acids bonded to a molecule of glycerol. A cloudy white layer with the ethanol test indicates the presence of lipids in solutions.
- Protein molecules are made up of long chains of amino acids. Biuret reagent turns from blue to purple in the presence of proteins.

Lipids are made of three molecules of fatty acids joined to a molecule of glycerol

Key words: carbohydrates, simple sugars, lipids, fatty acids, glycerol, proteins, amino acids, denatured

Study tips

Evaluate the food tests and results on a table. Make sure you can spell the names of the reagents.

Don't confuse Benedict's and Biuret. Protein and Biuret both contain the letter 'r'.

Carbohydrates

All **carbohydrates** are made of units of sugar.

- Glucose has one unit of sugar. Sucrose has two sugar units linked together. These are **simple sugars**.
- Starch and cellulose are made of long chains of simple sugar units that are bonded together. These are complex carbohydrates.

1 What is a complex carbohydrate?

Lipids

- **Lipids** are molecules made of three molecules of **fatty acids** linked to a molecule of **glycerol**.

Proteins

- **Proteins** are made of long chains of **amino acids**. The long chains are folded to form a specific shape. Other molecules can fit into these specific shapes. If the protein is heated the shape is changed and the protein is **denatured**.
- Each protein has a specific function. Some proteins are structural components of tissues, such as muscles. Other proteins are hormones, antibodies, or enzymes.

Carbohydrates are all based on simple sugar units

Amino acids are the building blocks of proteins. They can join in an almost endless variety of ways to produce different proteins

2 What happens to a protein molecule if it is heated?

Food tests

You can identify the main food groups using standard food tests.

- Carbohydrates:
  - iodine test for starch – yellow-red iodine solution turns blue-black if starch is present.
  - Benedict's test for sugars – blue Benedict's solution turns brick red on heating if a sugar such as glucose is present.
- Protein: Biuret test – blue Biuret reagent turns purple if protein is present.
- Lipids: ethanol test – ethanol added to a solution gives a cloudy white layer if a lipid is present.

3 What results would you expect if you tested some egg white with:
a iodine solution **b** Benedict's solution **c** Biuret solution?

Safety: Wear eye protection. Ethanol is highly flammable and harmful.

3.4 Catalysts and enzymes

Key points

- Catalysts increase the rate of chemical reactions without changing chemically themselves.
- Enzymes are biological catalysts. They catalyse specific reactions in living organisms due to the shape of their active site. This is the lock and key theory of enzyme action.
- Enzymes are proteins. The amino acid chains are folded to form the active site, which matches the shape of a specific substrate molecule.
- The substrate binds to the active site and the reaction is catalysed by the enzyme.
- Metabolism is the sum of all the reactions in a cell or in the body.

Key words: catalyst, active site, metabolism

Study tip

Remember that it is the unique shape of the active site of the enzyme that allows it to bind with the substrate.

On the up

To achieve the top grades, you should be able to explain:

- why the shape of an enzyme is vital for its function
- how enzymes speed up reactions
- how enzymes control metabolism.

You should also be able to plan an experiment to investigate how different catalysts affect the rate of a reaction and identify the key variables.

- Chemical reactions in cells are controlled by proteins called enzymes.
- Enzymes are biological **catalysts** – they speed up reactions.
- Enzymes are large proteins. The shape of an enzyme is vital for its function. The enzyme has an area called the **active site** where its substrate molecule can fit.
- The substrate is held in the active site and may be joined to another molecule or may be broken down into smaller molecules.
- The lock and key theory is a simple model of how enzymes work.

Enzymes act as catalysts using the 'lock and key' mechanism shown here

- Enzymes can:
  - build large molecules from many smaller ones, such as building starch from glucose molecules
  - change one molecule into another one, such as converting one type of sugar into another
  - break down large molecules into smaller ones – the digestive enzymes do this.
- **Metabolism** is the sum of all the reactions that take place in a cell or in the whole body.

1   Name the area of an enzyme where other molecules can fit.

Breaking down hydrogen peroxide

You can investigate the effect of manganese(IV) oxide (a chemical catalyst) and liver (containing catalase enzyme) on the breakdown of hydrogen peroxide.

2   Which is the better catalyst, catalase or manganese(IV) oxide? Use the graph below to explain your answer.

3.5 Factors affecting enzyme action

Key points

- Enzyme activity is affected by temperature and pH.
- High temperatures denature the enzyme, changing the shape of the active site.
- pH can affect the shape of the active site of an enzyme and make it work very efficiently or stop it working.

Key word: denatured

Study tip

Always use the term **denatured** to describe an enzyme that has changed shape and stopped working.

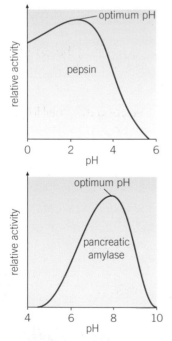

These two digestive enzymes need very different pH levels to work at their maximum rate. Pepsin is found in the stomach, along with hydrochloric acid, whilst pancreatic amylase is in the first part of the small intestine along with alkaline bile

The effect of temperature on enzyme action

- Reactions take place faster when it is warmer. At higher temperatures the molecules move around more quickly and so collide with each other more often, and with more energy.

- Enzyme-catalysed reactions are similar to other reactions – when the temperature is increased the rate of an enzyme-catalysed reaction increases. However, after increasing the temperature beyond a certain point the rate no longer increases.

- If the temperature gets too high the enzyme stops working because the active site changes shape. The enzyme becomes **denatured**.

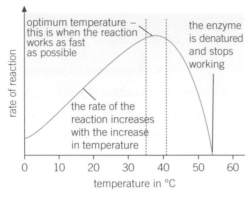

The effect of temperature on the rate of an enzyme-controlled reaction

1 What is meant by the term 'denatured'?

The effect of pH on enzyme action

- Each enzyme works best at a particular pH. Some enzymes work best in acid conditions, such as those found in the stomach, while others need neutral or alkaline conditions.

- The folded shape of the protein molecule that forms an enzyme is held together by forces. A change in pH affects these forces, which in turn changes the shape of the active site.

- At the optimum pH the active site has the best shape so that the enzyme works most efficiently.

- When the pH is too acidic or too alkaline, the enzyme becomes denatured as the shape of the active site changes.

2 What three words do we use to describe the pH of solutions?

Drawing graphs

Scientists use graphs to convert tables of figures into a form that makes it easy to interpret results and see trends.

You can show the results of enzyme-controlled reactions as a line graph.

A rate of reaction always involves time.

Student Book
pages 46–47

B3

3.6 How the digestive system works

The food you eat contains large, insoluble molecules such as starch (a carbohydrate), protein, and lipid. The large molecules must be digested into smaller, soluble molecules that can be absorbed into the blood.

Digestive enzymes:

- are produced by specialised cells in glands and in the lining of the small intestine
- pass out of the glands into the cavity of the digestive system – they work *outside* the cells, unlike most enzymes
- come into contact with the food so it is digested.

The digestive system is a long, hollow, muscular tube. The digestive system:

- breaks the food into smaller pieces to increase the surface area for enzymes to work on
- mixes the food with digestive juices that contain the enzymes
- has muscles to move the food along
- has areas with different levels of pH, for example, the mouth and small intestine are alkaline whilst the stomach is acidic
- absorbs the small, soluble food molecules into the blood in the small intestine.

1 Where are digestive enzymes produced?

Each type of food is digested by a specific enzyme.

- **Amylase** (a **carbohydrase**) is produced by the salivary glands, the pancreas, and the small intestine. Amylase catalyses the digestion of starch into sugars in the mouth and small intestine.
- **Proteases** are produced by the stomach, the pancreas, and the small intestine. Proteases catalyse the breakdown of proteins into **amino acids** in the stomach and small intestine.
- **Lipase** is produced by the pancreas and the small intestine. Lipase catalyses the breakdown of lipids (fats and oils) to **fatty acids** and **glycerol**.

2 Which enzymes digest protein?

Key points

- Digestion involves the breakdown of large, insoluble molecules into soluble substances. These smaller molecules can then be absorbed into the blood across the wall of the small intestine.
- Digestive enzymes are produced by specialised cells in glands and in the lining of the digestive system.
- Carbohydrases, such as amylase, catalyse the breakdown of carbohydrates to simple sugars.
- Proteases catalyse the breakdown of proteins to amino acids.
- Lipases catalyse the breakdown of lipids to fatty acids and glycerol.

Synoptic links

Topics B1.6, B1.7, B1.8, and B1.9 give more information on moving substances in and out of cells.

For more on adaptations for effective absorption, see Topic B1.10.

Key words: amylase, carbohydrase, protease, amino acid, lipase, fatty acid, glycerol

Study tips

Learn three examples of digestive enzyme reactions.

- Amylase: starch → sugars
- Protease: protein → amino acids
- Lipase: lipids → fatty acids + glycerol

The effect of pH on the rate of reaction of amylase

Investigating the effect of different pH on the rate of reaction of amylase helps show why the varying pH of the digestive system is so important.

When you have completed an investigation into the rates of enzyme reactions you should know: the names of the enzyme, substrate, and product(s); the range of pH you used; how you measure when the substrate has been broken down; how you control other variables; why each piece of apparatus is important.

3.7 Making digestion efficient

Key points

- The protease enzymes of the stomach work best in acid conditions. The stomach produces hydrochloric acid, which maintains a low pH.
- The enzymes made in the pancreas and the small intestine work best in alkaline conditions.
- Bile is produced by the liver, stored in the gall bladder, and released through the bile duct. It neutralises acid and emulsifies fats.

Key word: bile

Study tips

Make sure you understand that:

- hydrochloric acid gives the stomach a low pH suitable for the protease secreted there to work efficiently
- alkaline bile neutralises the acid and gives a high pH for the enzymes from the pancreas and small intestine to work well
- bile is *not* an enzyme as it does *not* break down fat molecules.

Instead it emulsifies the fat into tiny droplets, which increases the surface area for lipase to increase the rate of digestion.

Study tip

Make a table of all the chemicals, including enzymes, involved in digestion, where they are produced, and their functions.

Human digestive enzymes work best at body temperature, 37 °C, so the temperature in the digestive system is optimum. Different enzymes have different optimum pH levels.

- Protease enzymes in the stomach work best in acid conditions. Glands in the stomach wall produce hydrochloric acid to create very acidic conditions.
- Other proteases, amylase, and lipase work best in the small intestine where the conditions are slightly alkaline.

---

1 Are conditions in the stomach acidic, neutral, or alkaline?

Food leaving the stomach is very acidic so its pH must be changed. To do this the liver produces **bile** that is stored in the gall bladder and released into the small intestine when food enters.

Bile:

- neutralises the stomach acid
- makes the conditions in the small intestine slightly alkaline
- emulsifies fats (breaks large drops of fats into smaller droplets) to increase the surface area of the fats for lipase enzymes to act upon.

---

2 Where is bile stored?

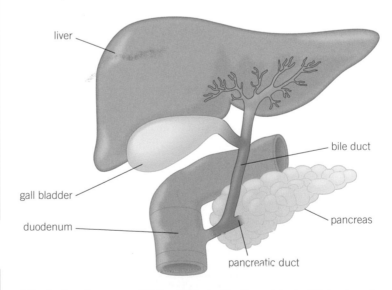

Bile drains down small bile ducts in the liver. Most of it is stored in the gall bladder until it is needed

1. Which two factors can alter the shape of an enzyme? [2 marks]

2. Name the two types of molecule that form a lipid. [2 marks]

3. Name the molecules that bond together to form a protein. [1 mark]

4. Name the enzymes that digest: **a** starch **b** proteins **c** lipids. [3 marks]

5. Where is bile made? [1 mark]

6. What is meant by the term 'digestion of molecules'? [2 marks]

7. Name the tissues found in the stomach and give their function. [6 marks]

8. Why does increasing the temperature increase the rate of a reaction? [3 marks]

9. Enzymes are catalysts. The rate of an enzyme-catalysed reaction increases as the temperature increases. Explain why. [2 marks]

10. Explain why some catalysts can work at 100 °C but enzymes cannot. [2 marks]

11. Explain fully how bile helps in the digestion process. [4 marks]

12. Describe the effect of pH on an enzyme. [4 marks]

13. **Figure 1** shows what happened to similar-sized chunks of meat when placed in:

    a hydrochloric acid
    b pepsin (a protease from the stomach)
    c both pepsin and hydrochloric acid.

    The tubes were left for a few hours.
    Describe and explain the differences in each tube. [4 marks]

Figure 1 *Meat was placed in:* **a** *hydrochloric acid,* **b** *pepsin,* **c** *pepsin and hydrochloric acid*

Chapter checklist

Tick when you have:

reviewed it after your lesson ✓ ☐ ☐

revised once – some questions right ✓ ✓ ☐

revised twice – all questions right ✓ ✓ ✓

Move on to another topic when you have all three ticks

3.1 Tissues and organs ☐ ☐ ☐

3.2 The human digestive system ☐ ☐ ☐

3.3 The chemistry of food ☐ ☐ ☐

3.4 Catalysts and enzymes ☐ ☐ ☐

3.5 Factors affecting enzyme action ☐ ☐ ☐

3.6 How the digestive system works ☐ ☐ ☐

3.7 Making digestion efficient ☐ ☐ ☐

Student Book
pages 52–53

B4

4.1 The blood

Multicellular organisms need a transport system to move material between exchange surfaces. The human circulatory system consists of the blood, the blood vessels, and the heart.

Blood is a tissue. The liquid **plasma** contains **red blood cells**, **white blood cells**, and **platelets**.

Blood plasma transports many substances, including:

- carbon dioxide from the organs to the lungs
- soluble products of digestion from the small intestine to other organs
- **urea** from the liver to the kidneys, where urine is made.

1 Give an example of a gas transported by plasma.

Red blood cells:

red
blood
cell

- are biconcave discs and do not have a nucleus
- contain the red pigment called **haemoglobin**
- use their haemoglobin to combine with oxygen, which forms oxyhaemoglobin in the lungs
- carry the oxygen to all the organs, where the oxyhaemoglobin splits back into haemoglobin and oxygen.

White blood cells:

white
blood
cell

- have a nucleus
- form part of the body's defence system against microorganisms.

Some white blood cells produce antibodies, some produce antitoxins, and others engulf microorganisms.

Platelets:

platelets

- are small fragments of cells
- do not have a nucleus
- help the blood to clot at the site of a wound.

2 What is the function of platelets?

Blood clotting is a series of enzyme-controlled reactions.

- The final reaction causes fibrinogen to change into fibrin.
- Fibrin forms a network of fibres that trap blood cells and form a clot.
- The clot dries and forms a scab.

Key points

- The blood, the blood vessels, and the heart make up the circulatory system. This transports substances to and from the body cells.
- Plasma has blood cells suspended in it and transports proteins and other chemicals around the body.
- Your red blood cells contain haemoglobin that binds to oxygen to transport it from the lungs to the tissues.
- White blood cells help to protect the body against infection.
- Platelets are cell fragments that start the clotting process at wound sites.

Synoptic links

Topic B3.6 has more about how digested food molecules get into the transport system.

See Topic B4.5 for more about how oxygen and carbon dioxide enter and leave the blood.

Topic B9.1 explains how oxygen is used in the cells and how carbon dioxide is produced.

Key words: plasma, red blood cells, white blood cells, platelets, urea, haemoglobin

Study tip

Make a list of the different types of blood cell and note their functions.

4.2 The blood vessels

Key points

- Blood flows around the body in the blood vessels. The main types of blood vessel are arteries, veins, and capillaries.
- Substances diffuse in and out of the blood in the capillaries.
- Valves prevent backflow, ensuring that blood flows in the right direction.
- Human beings have a double circulatory system.

Key words: arteries, veins, capillaries, double circulatory system

Study tip

Remember that arteries always carry blood away from the heart. Veins carry blood back to the heart.

Blood flows round the body in three main types of blood vessel: **arteries**, **veins**, and **capillaries**.

Arteries:

- carry blood away from the heart
- have thick walls containing muscle and elastic tissue.

Veins:

- carry blood towards the heart
- have thinner walls than arteries
- often have valves along their length to prevent backflow of blood.

Capillaries:

- are narrow, thin-walled vessels
- carry the blood through the organs
- allow the exchange of substances with all the living cells in the body.

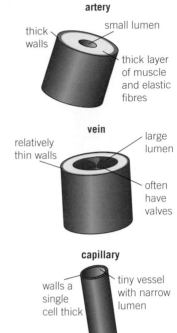

The three main types of blood vessel

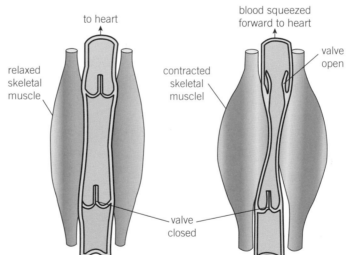

How the valves and the muscles between them ensure that blood in veins flows from the body towards the heart

UXBRIDGE COLLEGE LEARNING CENTRE

1   What is the difference in structure between an artery and a vein?
2   Why do veins have valves?

Double circulation

In humans and other mammals the blood vessels are arranged into a **double circulatory system.**

- One transport system carries blood from your heart to your lungs and back again.
- The other transport system carries blood from your heart to all other organs of your body and back again.

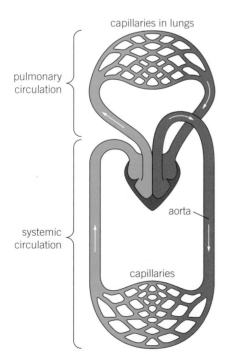

The two separate circulatory systems supply the lungs and the rest of the body

4.3 The heart

The heart is a muscular organ that pumps blood around the body. It is made up of two pumps held together.

- Arteries carry blood away from the heart. Veins carry blood back to the heart.
- The right pump forces deoxygenated blood to the lungs where it picks up oxygen and loses carbon dioxide.
- After returning to the heart, the oxygenated blood is then pumped to the rest of the body by the left pump, which needs a bigger force.
- The heart has four chambers. The upper ones are the **atria**. The right atrium receives blood from the **vena cava**. The left atrium receives blood from the **pulmonary vein**.
- The atria contract together to move blood into the lower chambers, the **ventricles**. When the ventricles contract they force blood out of the heart. The right ventricle pushes blood into the **pulmonary artery**. The left ventricle pushes blood into the **aorta**.
- The left ventricle has the thicker wall. Valves in the heart prevent the blood from flowing in the wrong direction.

Key points

- The heart is an organ that pumps blood around the body.
- Heart valves keep the blood flowing in the right direction.
- Stents can be used to keep narrowed or blocked arteries open.
- Statins reduce cholesterol levels in the blood, reducing the risk of coronary heart disease.

Key words: atria, vena cava, pulmonary vein, ventricles, pulmonary artery, aorta, coronary arteries, stent, statins

Study tips

Practise labelling diagrams of the heart.

Make sure you can evaluate information about treatments to reduce the effects of coronary heart disease.

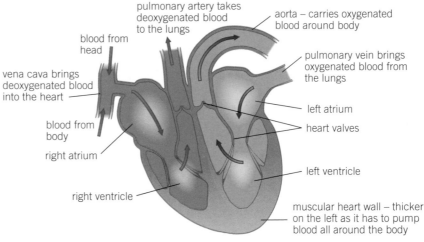

The structure of the heart

1 What is the function of valves in the heart?

- The heart muscle is supplied with oxygenated blood via the **coronary arteries**.
- Coronary heart disease occurs when the coronary arteries become blocked or narrower due to a buildup of fatty material inside them.
- Doctors can use a **stent** to open up the arteries, allowing the blood to deliver nutrients and oxygen to the heart muscle again.
- Bypass surgery can also be used to replace damaged coronary arteries with lengths of vein.
- **Statins** are prescribed to lower cholesterol, which in turn reduces the fatty buildup in arteries.

2 Why are statins prescribed by doctors?

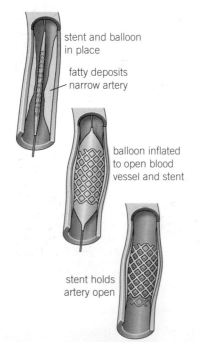

A stent being positioned in an artery

4.4 Helping the heart

Key points

- Damaged heart valves can be replaced using biological or mechanical valves.

- The resting heart rate is controlled by a group of cells in the right atrium that form a natural pacemaker.

- Artificial pacemakers are electrical devices used to correct irregularities in the heart rhythm.

- Artificial hearts are occasionally used to keep patients alive while they wait for a transplant, or for their heart to rest as an aid to recovery.

Study tips

Learn the position of the natural pacemaker, and why a person may need an artificial one.

Make lists of the advantages and disadvantages of an artificial heart.

On the up

To achieve the top grades, you should be able to explain how a natural pacemaker maintains the heartbeat. You should also be able to evaluate in detail the different methods used in the treatment of heart problems.

Doctors, scientists, and engineers have developed ways to solve problems with damaged hearts.

- Leaky valves mean the blood could flow in the wrong direction. Artificial or animal valves can be inserted in the heart to replace damaged valves.

Adults have a natural resting heart rate of about 70 beats per minute. The natural resting heart rate is controlled by a group of cells that act as a pacemaker.

The natural pacemaker is located in the right atrium.

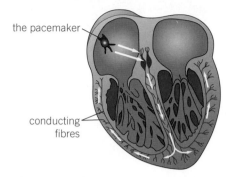

The pacemaker region controls the basic rhythm of your heart

---

1 In which chamber of the heart is the natural pacemaker found?

Sometimes the rhythm of the heart becomes irregular if the natural pacemaker does not work properly.

- An artificial pacemaker is an electrical device that can be fitted in the chest to correct irregularities in the heart rate.

- If a person has a very weak or diseased heart they may require a transplant. Donors are not always available so artificial hearts are being developed.

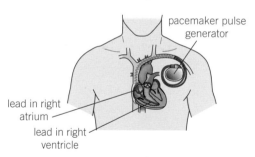

An artificial pacemaker is positioned under the skin of the chest with wires running to the heart itself

Artificial hearts can be used to:

- keep patients alive while waiting for a heart transplant

- allow the heart to rest as an aid to recovery.

One disadvantage of an artificial heart or artificial valve is that the person needs drugs to prevent the blood from clotting.

This artificial heart uses air pressure to pump blood around the body

---

2 Why do patients with artificial valves need drugs?

4.5 Breathing and gas exchange

Key points

- The lungs are in your chest cavity, protected by your ribcage, and separated from your abdomen by the diaphragm.
- The alveoli provide a very large surface area and a rich supply of blood capillaries. This means gases can diffuse into and out of the blood as efficiently as possible.

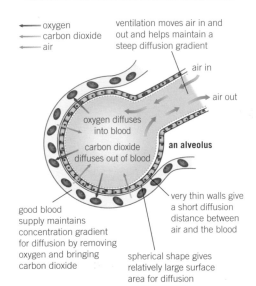

→ oxygen
→ carbon dioxide
→ air

ventilation moves air in and out and helps maintain a steep diffusion gradient

air in

air out

oxygen diffuses into blood

carbon dioxide diffuses out of blood

an alveolus

good blood supply maintains concentration gradient for diffusion by removing oxygen and bringing carbon dioxide

very thin walls give a short diffusion distance between air and the blood

spherical shape gives relatively large surface area for diffusion

The alveoli are adapted so that gas exchange can take place as efficiently as possible in the lungs

Synoptic links

There is more about diffusion and concentration gradients in Topic B1.6, and about exchange surfaces in Topic B1.10.

Key word: capillaries

Study tip

Learn the sequences for breathing in and out.

- Moving air into and out of the lungs is called ventilating the lungs, or breathing.
- The lungs contain the exchange surface of the breathing system.
- The lungs are situated in the thorax, inside the ribcage and above the diaphragm, which separates the lungs from the abdomen.

When you breathe in:

- the intercostal muscles, between the ribs, contract, moving the ribcage up and out
- the muscles of the diaphragm contract and the diaphragm flattens
- the volume of the thorax increases
- the pressure in the thorax decreases and air is drawn into your lungs.

When you breathe out:

- the intercostal muscles of the ribcage and the diaphragm relax
- the ribcage moves down and in and the diaphragm becomes domed
- the volume of the thorax decreases
- the pressure increases and air is forced out.

1 Which muscles contract when you breathe in?

Adaptations of the alveoli

Your lungs are adapted to make gas exchange more efficient.

- Oxygen is absorbed from the air into the blood in the lungs. Carbon dioxide is removed from the blood to the air.
- Efficient exchange surfaces have a large surface area, thin walls or a short diffusion path, and an efficient transport system.
- The lungs contain the gaseous exchange surface. The surface area of the lungs is increased by the alveoli (air sacs).
- The alveoli have a large surface area, thin walls, and a good blood supply.
- The lungs are ventilated to maintain a steep concentration gradient.
- Oxygen diffuses into the many **capillaries** surrounding the alveoli, and carbon dioxide diffuses back out into the lungs to be breathed out.

2 Which structures increase the surface area of the lungs?

breathing in

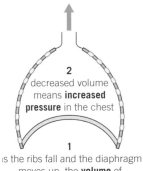

3
atmospheric air at higher pressure than the chest – so air is drawn into the lungs

2
increased volume means **lower pressure** in the chest

1
as the ribs move up and out and the diaphragm flattens, the **volume** of the chest **increases**

breathing out

3
the pressure in the chest is higher than outside – so air is forced out of the lungs

2
decreased volume means **increased pressure** in the chest

1
is the ribs fall and the diaphragm moves up, the **volume of** the chest **gets smaller**

Ventilation of the lungs

Student Book
pages 62–63

B4

4.6 Tissues and organs in plants

Key points

- Plant tissues are collections of cells specialised to carry out specific functions.
- The structure of the tissues in plant organs is related to their functions.
- The roots, stem, and leaves form a plant organ system for the transport of substances around the plant.

Plant tissues

Plant tissues are collections of cells that are specialised to carry out specific functions.

Plant tissues include:

- **epidermal** tissue, which covers the plant
- **palisade mesophyll**, which has many chloroplasts and can photosynthesise
- **spongy mesophyll**, which has some chloroplasts, many air spaces between the cells, and a large surface area for diffusion of gases
- **xylem**, which transports water and dissolved mineral ions from the root to the rest of the plant
- **phloem**, which transports dissolved food substances from the leaves to the rest of the plant.

1   What is the function of palisade mesophyll tissue?

Synoptic links

The specialised plant cells that make up plant tissues and organs are covered in Topic B1.5, and plant meristems are covered in Topic B2.3.

Plant organs

- The plant tissues are arranged to form organs.
- Each plant organ has its own functions.
- Stems, roots, and leaves are plant organs.
- The plant organs form a plant organ system to transport substances around the plant.

2   Name a plant organ.

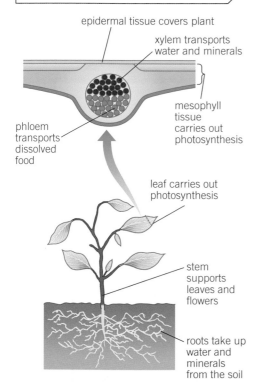

Some of the main plant organs

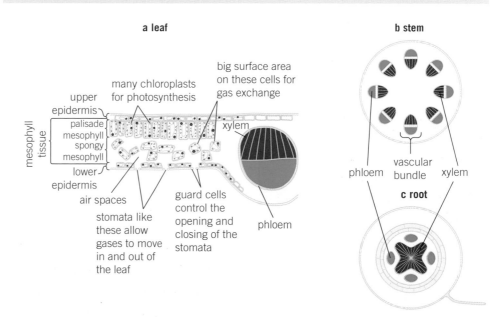

Plants have specific tissues to carry out particular functions. They are arranged in organs such as: **a** leaves, **b** the stem, and **c** roots

Study tip

Make sure you can label the tissues in a leaf. Learn the function of each tissue.

Key words: epidermal, palisade mesophyll, spongy mesophyll, xylem, phloem

4.7 Transport systems in plants

Flowering plants have separate transport systems.

- Phloem tissue carries dissolved sugars from the leaves to the rest of the plant, including the growing regions and the storage organs. This process is called **translocation**.
- Xylem tissue transports water and mineral ions from the roots to the stem, leaves, and flowers.

1 What are the names of the two transport tissues in flowering plants?

The importance of transport in plants

- All the cells in the plant need the sugar produced in photosynthesis for respiration.
- The sugar and mineral ions are needed for growth.
- Water is needed for photosynthesis.
- Water is needed to support the cells, particularly in young plants and in the leaves.

2 What is meant by 'translocation'?

Evidence for movement through xylem

You can demonstrate the movement of water up the xylem by placing celery stalks in water containing a coloured dye. After a few hours, slice the stem in several places – you will see the coloured circles where the water and dye have moved through the xylem.

Key word: translocation

Key points

- Plants have separate transport systems.
- Xylem tissue transports water and mineral ions from the roots to the stems and leaves.
- Phloem tissue transports dissolved sugars from the leaves to the rest of the plant, including the growing regions and storage organs.

The phloem and xylem are arranged in vascular bundles in the stem

Synoptic link

For information on phloem and xylem cells, see Topic B1.5.

4.8 Evaporation and transpiration

Water loss from the leaves

- Gases diffuse in and out of leaves through tiny holes called stomata. The size of the stomata is controlled by the **guard cells** that surround them.
- Water is absorbed from the soil by the roots. The water passes through the plant to the cells in the leaves.
- In the leaves, water evaporates from the cells in the leaf into the air spaces between them. This water vapour diffuses out of the plant through the stomata on the leaf surface when the stomata are open. This is **transpiration**.
- The movement of the water through the plant is called the transpiration stream.
- The guard cells can close the stomata to prevent excessive water loss.

1 By what process does water vapour move out of the leaves?
2 What is the function of guard cells?

Key points

- The loss of water vapour from inside a plant from the surface of its leaves is known as transpiration.
- Water is lost through the stomata, which open to let in carbon dioxide for photosynthesis.
- The stomata and guard cells control gas exchange and water loss.

Key words: guard cells, transpiration

Student Book
pages 68–69

B4

4.9 Factors affecting transpiration

Key points

● Factors that increase the rate of photosynthesis or increase stomatal opening will increase the rate of transpiration. These factors include temperature, humidity, air flow, and light intensity.

● Transpiration is more rapid in hot, dry, windy, or bright conditions.

Synoptic link

There is more about plant adaptations to reduce transpiration in harsh environments in Topic B16.8.

Study tips

Make sure you know the difference between diffusion, evaporation, transpiration, and the transpiration stream.

Learn the factors that affect the rate of transpiration.

A plant could dehydrate if the rate of evaporation in the leaves is greater than the rate of water uptake by the roots.

Factors that increase the rate of photosynthesis, increasing the opening of stomata to let carbon dioxide into the leaf, will also increase the rate of transpiration. These factors include:

● temperature – as temperature increases, the molecules move faster so more water evaporates and the rate of diffusion of water from the leaf also increases; as temperature increases, the rate of photosynthesis also increases, so more stomata are open

● humidity – the rate of diffusion of water from the leaf is faster in dry air than in damp air

● air flow – windy conditions increase the rate of evaporation and keep a steep concentration gradient between the inside and outside of the leaf by blowing away the water vapour

● light intensity – more light means there will be an increase in the rate of photosynthesis.

So transpiration is more rapid in hot, dry, windy, or bright conditions.

A potometer is used to show the water uptake of a plant under different conditions

1 Why does an increase in temperature increase the rate of transpiration?

Plants can control water loss.

● Plants have a waxy, waterproof cuticle on the leaves that can be very thick and shiny in hot environments.

● Most of the stomata are on the underside of the leaf.

● Wilting of the whole plant can also reduce water loss. The leaves collapse and hang down, which reduces their surface area.

● The stomata can close, which stops photosynthesis but prevents more water loss and further wilting.

2 Where are most of the stomata?

open stomata   closed stomata

The size of the opening of the stomata is controlled by the guard cells. This in turn controls the diffusion of carbon dioxide into the leaf and the diffusion of water vapour and oxygen out of the leaf

1. What prevents the backflow of blood in the circulatory system? [1 mark]

2. Name the tissues found in a leaf. [5 marks]

3. What is the function of phloem? [1 mark]

4. What type of blood vessel carries blood to the heart? [1 mark]

5. **a** Name the types of cells found in the blood. [3 marks]

   b Name the liquid that transports them. [1 mark]

6. Give two differences in the structure of arteries and veins. [2 marks]

7. **a** Where is the natural pacemaker found in the heart? [1 mark]

   b What is the function of the pacemaker? [1 mark]

8. Explain why the left ventricle can generate more force than the right ventricle. [1 mark]

9. What features of an alveolus make it an efficient exchange surface? [3 marks]

10. Identify the route the blood would take when travelling from the body to the lungs and back to the body. Include the names of all the blood vessels and heart chambers. [4 marks]

11. Explain why plants wilt. [5 marks]

12. Describe and explain the sequence of events that draws air into the lungs. [6 marks]

13. Look at the diagram of the potometer in Topic B4.9. Suggest how you could use the potometer to compare transpiration rates in still air and windy conditions. [5 marks]

Chapter checklist

Tick when you have:

reviewed it after your lesson ✓ ☐ ☐

revised once – some questions right ✓ ✓ ☐

revised twice – all questions right ✓ ✓ ✓

Move on to another topic when you have all three ticks

4.1 The blood ☐ ☐ ☐
4.2 The blood vessels ☐ ☐ ☐
4.3 The heart ☐ ☐ ☐
4.4 Helping the heart ☐ ☐ ☐
4.5 Breathing and gas exchange ☐ ☐ ☐
4.6 Tissues and organs in plants ☐ ☐ ☐
4.7 Transport systems in plants ☐ ☐ ☐
4.8 Evaporation and transpiration ☐ ☐ ☐
4.9 Factors affecting transpiration ☐ ☐ ☐

01 Look at **Figure 1**.

Figure 1

Study tips

Questions **01** and **03.1** test your knowledge. Thorough revision is essential to gain maximum marks.

Practise labelling diagrams and write down the functions of the parts next to the label.

01.1 What is structure **X**? [1 mark]

01.2 A sperm cell is adapted for its function.
What is the function of the tail? [1 mark]

01.3 Explain why a sperm cell has many mitochondria. [2 marks]

01.4 The acrosome contains enzymes.
What is the purpose of these enzymes? [2 marks]

01.5 In what way is the structure of a root hair cell the same as that of a sperm? [2 marks]

01.6 In what way is the structure of a root hair cell different from that of a sperm? [2 marks]

01.7 A drawing of a root hair cell is 30 mm long. The magnification of the drawing is × 500.
What is the real size of the root hair cell in micrometres? [3 marks]

02 The heart pumps blood around the body. This causes blood to leave the heart at high pressure.
The graph in **Figure 2** shows blood pressure measurements for a person at rest.
The blood pressure was measured in an artery and in a vein. Use the information in the graph to answer the following questions.

Study tips

Question **02** has a graph and calculations. You could lose marks by not reading the axes carefully.

Always check your readings and remember that for **02.3** you must multiply by 4 to find the number of beats per minute. If you use a calculator, make sure you tap in the correct numbers. It is too easy to write an answer of the wrong order of magnitude if you assume the answer on the calculator is correct.

Figure 2

02.1 Which blood vessel, **A** or **B**, is the artery?
Give **two** reasons for your answer. [2 marks]

02.2 How many times did the heart beat in 15 seconds? [1 mark]

02.3 Use your answer from **02.2** to calculate the person's heart rate per minute. [1 mark]

02.4 During exercise, the heart rate increases. This supplies useful substances to the muscles and removes waste materials from the muscles at a faster rate.
Name **two** useful substances that must be supplied to the muscles at a faster rate during exercise. [2 marks]

02.5 Name **one** waste substance that must be removed from the muscles at a faster rate during exercise. [1 mark]

03 Cystic fibrosis is the UK's most common life-threatening inherited disease. In individuals who have the condition, the internal organs, especially the lungs and digestive system, become clogged with thick, sticky mucus resulting in chronic infections and inflammation in the lungs and difficulty digesting food.
The mucus covers the cells in the lungs and digestive system. Substances cannot cross the membranes easily.

03.1 Select the correct word or words from the list below to complete the sentences.

> **active transport   cytoplasm   diffusion   high   impermeable**
>
> **low nucleus   osmosis   porous   selectively permeable**

The cells in the lungs and digestive system are similar to all animal cells. Surrounding the cell is a _____ _____ membrane.
Solutes or gases pass across this outer layer by a process of _____ from a region of _____ concentration and enter the _____. inside the cell.
In the cell, chemical reactions take place that require water.
Water enters the cell by a process called _____ from a region of _____ solute concentration. [6 marks]

03.2 Explain why people with cystic fibrosis have difficulty digesting food. [2 marks]

03.3 Explain why cystic fibrosis is a life-threatening condition. [4 marks]

Study tips

Questions **01** and **03** feature parts that ask you to 'Explain why'.

Remember, you always need to give a reason for your answer. Words such as 'because' or 'so' are needed.

For example, in **03.2** you may realise that the mucus blocks the surface of the intestine, but for full marks you should say 'so the digestive enzymes cannot reach the food'.

2 Disease and bioenergetics

Communicable diseases are caused by pathogens – microorganisms that can be spread from one organism to another. In this section you will learn how we defend ourselves from the pathogens that attack us, and how our lifestyles affect our risk of developing non-communicable diseases such as heart disease and cancer.

You will also learn about photosynthesis in plants – the process where they use light to make sugar from carbon dioxide and water. You will also look at respiration – all living organisms use respiration to transfer the energy they need to carry out the reactions required for life.

I already know...

I will revise...

I already know...	I will revise...
the consequences of imbalances in the diet.	more about the impact of obesity on human health.
the importance of bacteria in the human digestive system.	the role of bacteria and other pathogens in human and plant diseases, and how to calculate the effect of antibacterial chemicals by measuring the area of zones of inhibition.
the impact of exercise and smoking on the human gas exchange system.	how exercise and smoking can affect the health of other systems of the body.
the effects of recreational drugs on behaviour, health, and life processes.	how to interpret data to understand the effect of lifestyle factors including diet, alcohol, and smoking on the incidence of non-communicable diseases at local, national, and global levels.
the basic principles of photosynthesis.	how to measure and calculate the rate of photosynthesis, and how different factors affect the rate of photosynthesis.
the differences between aerobic and anaerobic respiration.	how an oxygen debt builds up during anaerobic respiration in your muscles.

5.1 Health and disease

Student Book
pages 74–75

Key points

- Health is a state of physical and mental well-being.
- Diseases, both communicable and non-communicable, are major causes of ill health.
- Other factors including diet, stress, and life situations may have a profound effect on both mental and physical health.
- Different types of diseases may and often do interact.

Scatter graphs can show a correlation between stress and depression

Synoptic links

There is more about diseases in Chapters B6 and B7.

Topic B7.2 has more about cancer.

Key words: communicable (infectious) diseases, pathogens, non-communicable diseases

Study tip

Make a spider diagram with 'disease' at the centre. Link as many ideas as you can from this chapter to remind you of the causes of disease.

Your health is a state of physical and mental well-being.

Communicable (infectious) diseases (e.g., tuberculosis and flu) are caused by **pathogens**, such as bacteria and viruses, that can be passed from one person to another.

Non-communicable diseases (e.g., heart disease and arthritis) cannot be transmitted from one person to another.

Other factors can also affect health.

Diet

- Too little food or the wrong nutrients can lead to starvation, anaemia, or rickets, for example.
- Too much food or the wrong type of food can lead to obesity, some cancers, or type 2 diabetes.

Stress

- Too much stress is linked to an increased risk of heart disease, certain cancers, and mental health problems.

Life situations

- Depending on the part of the world where you live, you will have an increased risk of certain health problems (e.g., malaria in tropical regions).
- Gender, financial status, ethnic group, and the number of children in a family also affect which disease people are most at risk from.
- If free health care is provided, this will reduce the risk and effect of many conditions.
- Local sewage and rubbish disposal systems are important for a healthy population.

> **1** What is a communicable disease?

A person can have different types of disease and health conditions at the same time, and these often interact.

- Viruses living in cells, such as the human papilloma virus, can trigger changes that lead to cancers.
- Defects in the immune system can make someone more likely to have a communicable disease.
- Immune reactions can trigger allergies.
- Severe physical health issues can lead to mental health problems, such as depression.
- Malnutrition can lead to deficiency diseases, a weakened immune system, obesity, cardiovascular disease, type 2 diabetes, or cancer.

> **2** Give an example of a type of disease caused by malnutrition.

5.2 Pathogens and disease

Key points

- Communicable diseases are caused by microorganisms called pathogens, which include bacteria, viruses, fungi, and protists.
- Bacteria and viruses reproduce rapidly inside your body. Bacteria can produce toxins that make you feel ill.
- Viruses live and reproduce inside your cells, causing cell damage.
- Pathogens can be spread by direct contact, by air, or by water.

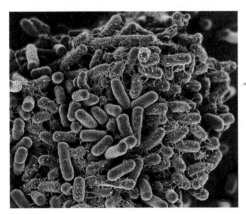

Many bacteria are very useful to humans but some, such as this strain of E. coli, *are pathogens and cause disease*

Synoptic links

Topic B1.3 covers the structure of bacteria.

For more information on bacteria that are resistant to antibiotics, see Topic B15.8.

Key words: communicable diseases, viruses

Communicable diseases or infectious diseases are caused by microorganisms called pathogens. These include bacteria, **viruses**, fungi, and protists.

- Bacteria and viruses are the pathogens that cause most communicable diseases in humans. Viruses and fungi cause most diseases in plants.
- When bacteria or viruses enter the body they reproduce rapidly.
- Bacteria can make you feel ill by producing toxins (poisons) and may also damage the body cells.
- Viruses are much smaller than bacteria and reproduce inside cells, damaging and destroying the cells.

1 How do viruses make you feel ill?

Pathogens can be spread in a variety of ways.

Air
- Bacteria, viruses, and fungal spores can be spread through the air from one animal or plant to another.
- Humans spread pathogens when they cough or sneeze. The droplets of water carrying the pathogens are inhaled by another person. This is called droplet infection.

Direct contact
- Sexually transmitted infections can be passed by sexual contact.
- Some pathogens are transmitted by skin contact or enter via cuts, scratches, or needle punctures.
- Animals such as mosquitoes can act as vectors and carry pathogens from one individual to another.
- If a portion of a diseased plant is left in a field it could infect the whole crop.

Water
- Drinking contaminated water can allow pathogens to enter the digestive system.
- Fungal spores in splashes of water can spread plant diseases.

2 What is 'droplet infection'?

5.3 Growing bacteria in the lab

Bacteria multiply rapidly by simple cell division called **binary fission**. Millions of bacteria become visible as a colony. A culture is produced when scientists encourage bacteria to multiply in suitable conditions.

Pure cultures of non-pathogenic (safe) bacteria can be used for laboratory investigations. A culture of bacteria can be used to investigate the effect of antibiotics on the bacteria, for example. You need an uncontaminated culture of microorganisms for an investigation. Strict health and safety procedures are used to protect yourself and others. Contamination might come from your skin, the air, the soil, or the water around you. If the culture is contaminated other bacteria could grow, including pathogens.

Growing cultures

To culture (grow) microorganisms in a laboratory, you need to do the following.

- Use **agar gel** or liquid containing nutrients as a **culture medium**. A nutrient broth solution contains carbohydrate as an energy source, various minerals, and sometimes other chemicals.

- Pour hot, sterile agar gel into a Petri dish. When cold this provides a solid, sterile medium.

- **Inoculate** the sterile agar. This means introducing the bacteria using a sterilised wire loop.

- Provide warmth and oxygen.

- Keep the dish incubated at no higher than 25 °C in school laboratories (35 °C may be used in industry).

> **1** Why do industrial laboratories use 35 °C instead of 25 °C as in schools?

It is important to keep the culture uncontaminated.

- Kill all the bacteria on the equipment – pass metal loops through a flame; boil solutions and agar.

- Use the sterilised metal loop to inoculate the agar.

- Prevent microorganisms from the air getting into the Petri dish.

- You should also prevent microorganisms leaving the Petri dish during and after your investigation, in case there has been a **mutation** producing a new and dangerous pathogen.

> **2** How do you make sure that unwanted microorganisms do not contaminate a pure culture of bacteria?

Key points

- An uncontaminated culture of microorganisms can be grown using sterilised Petri dishes and agar. You sterilise the inoculating loop before use and fix the lid of the Petri dish to prevent unwanted microorganisms getting in.

- Uncontaminated cultures are needed so you can investigate the effect of chemicals, such as disinfectants and antibiotics, on a specific microorganism.

- Cultures should be incubated at a maximum temperature of 25 °C in schools and colleges to reduce the likelihood of pathogens growing that might be harmful to humans.

To culture microorganisms safely, use a sterilised loop to transfer a suspension of bacteria to sterile agar

Key words: binary fission, agar gel, culture medium, inoculate, mutation

Synoptic link

For more on mitosis, the process behind binary fission, see Topic B2.1.

Study tip

Make sure you understand why each step in preparing a culture medium is important.

5.4 Preventing bacterial growth

Bacteria multiply by binary fission. They split into two about every 20 minutes at the right temperature and with enough nutrients. Cell division in some bacteria could be much slower than this.

- The rate of division may change if there is a change in the temperature, available nutrients, oxygen levels, or pH.
- You can calculate the number of bacteria in a population of bacteria after a given time if you know the mean division time.

Bacterial growth can be prevented by:

- raising or lowering the temperature
- disinfectants – these are chemicals used to kill bacteria in the environment
- antiseptics – these are chemicals used to kill bacteria on human skin
- antibiotics – these are chemicals used as drugs to kill bacteria inside the body.

> **1** If a bacterium has a mean division time of 20 minutes, how many bacteria would there be after three hours, starting with one bacterium?

Investigating the effect of disinfectants and antibiotics

You can set up a culture plate and add circles of filter paper soaked in different types or concentrations of disinfectant or antibiotic to see their effect on the bacteria. An area of clear agar indicates that the bacteria have been killed or cannot grow. You can measure this zone of inhibition and use the results to compare the effect of different antiseptics or antibiotics on the growth of the bacteria.

> **2** Why is there a clear area around some of the circles of filter paper?

Calculating the effect of disinfectants and antibiotics on bacterial growth

Measure the diameter of any clear circles of agar around your filter paper circles (see diagram). Divide the diameter by 2 to find the radius of the circle. Now you can work out the areas of the circles of clear jelly using πr^2 and use these to compare the effectiveness of the different chemicals.

Key points

- Bacteria multiply by simple cell division as often as every 20 minutes if they have enough nutrients and a suitable temperature.
- You can investigate the effects of disinfectants and antibiotics on bacterial growth using agar plates and calculating the cross-sectional area of colonies grown, or of clear areas of agar.

Synoptic link

There is more about preventing the spread of disease in Chapter B6.

Study tip

Make sure you know the difference between disinfectants, antiseptics, and antibiotics.

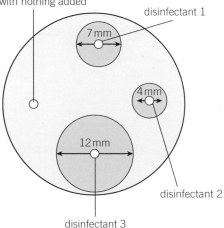

circle of filter paper with nothing added

disinfectant 1

7 mm

4 mm

12 mm

disinfectant 2

disinfectant 3

Investigating the effect of disinfectants on bacteria growth. The untreated filter paper acts as a control

Measuring the impact of different chemicals on bacterial growth

Chemical treatment	Measured diameter of clear circle in mm to 1 dp	Calculated radius of clear circle (D/2 = r) in mm to 1 dp	Calculated surface area of clear circle (πr^2) in mm to 1 dp
none	0.0	0.0	0.0
disinfectant 1	7.0	3.5	38.5
disinfectant 2	4.0	2.0	12.6
disinfectant 3	12.0	6.0	113.1

5.5 Preventing infections

Our modern understanding of pathogens comes from the work of pioneering doctors and scientists in the 19th century, such as Ignaz Semmelweis, Louis Pasteur, and Joseph Lister.

- Ignaz Semmelweiss was a doctor working before bacteria and viruses had been discovered. He realised that infection could be transferred from person to person in a hospital.

- Semmelweiss told his staff to wash their hands between treating patients. This reduced the number of deaths. We now know that he was right, but at the time, other doctors did not take him seriously.

---

1 Why did it take a long time for other doctors to accept the ideas of Semmelweiss?

- Louis Pasteur showed that microorganisms cause disease. He developed **vaccines** against anthrax and rabies.

- Joseph Lister started to use antiseptics to destroy pathogens in operating theatres.

There are a number of key ways to help prevent the spread of communicable diseases.

Hygiene

- Hand washing, especially after using the toilet, before cooking, or after contact with an animal or someone who has an infectious illness.

- Using disinfectants on kitchen work surfaces, toilets, etc.

- Keeping raw meat away from food that is eaten uncooked.

- Coughing or sneezing into a handkerchief, tissue, or your hands (then washing them).

- Maintaining the hygiene of people and agricultural machinery to help prevent the spread of plant diseases.

Isolating infected individuals

- If someone has an infectious disease such as Ebola they need to be kept in isolation to prevent the pathogen being passed on.

- Small plants infected with diseases can be moved and destroyed.

Destroying or controlling vectors

Some communicable diseases are passed on by vectors.

- Mosquitoes, houseflies, and rats carry many human pathogens between people.

- Aphids and some beetles transmit plant pathogens.

- Destroying the vectors controls the spread of disease.

Vaccination

- A small amount of a harmless form of a specific pathogen is introduced into your body. This prepares the immune system so you are protected from future infection.

- Plants cannot be vaccinated against disease as they do not have an immune system.

---

2 Why is it not possible to vaccinate plants?

Key points

- The spread of disease can be prevented by:
  - simple hygiene measures
  - destroying vectors
  - isolating infected individuals
  - vaccination.

Synoptic link

There is more about preventing communicable diseases in Topic B6.1.

Key word: vaccines

Study tip

Learn the methods that are used to prevent or reduce the spread of communicable diseases.

On the up

To achieve the top grades, you should be able to use your scientific knowledge to explain in detail how different methods reduce or prevent the spread of disease.

5.6 Viral diseases

Viruses can infect and damage all types of cells.

Measles

- The main symptoms of measles are fever and a red skin rash.

- It is spread by droplet infection.

- Measles is a serious disease that can be fatal.

- An infected person should be isolated.

- Measles can be prevented by vaccination.

A measles rash is now a rare sight in the UK

> 1   How can doctors prevent measles?

HIV/AIDS

- HIV is a virus that can lead to AIDS.

- The early symptoms may be mild and flu-like.

- HIV attacks the immune system eventually resulting in AIDS. It may take several years to develop AIDS, depending on a person's general health, level of nutrition, and access to antiretroviral drugs. In sub-Saharan Africa most people with HIV infection do not have access to these drugs.

- HIV is spread by direct sexual contact or by infected blood (from shared needles) or breast milk.

- The spread of HIV can be prevented by using condoms, screening blood before transfusion, and bottle-feeding babies of infected mothers. There is no vaccine.

Tobacco mosaic virus (TMV)

- TMV is a plant pathogen of plants such as tomatoes and tobacco.

- It discolours the leaves and destroys the cells so the plant cannot photosynthesise.

- TMV is spread by contact between diseased and healthy plants and by animal vectors.

- There is no treatment so farmers grow TMV-resistant strains of crops.

- Its spread can be reduced by good field hygiene and pest control.

> 2   What causes a plant with TMV to die?

Key points

- Measles virus is spread by droplet infection. It causes fever and a rash and can be fatal. There is no cure. Isolation of patients and vaccination prevents spread.

- HIV initially causes flu-like illness. Unless it is successfully controlled with antiretroviral drugs the virus attacks the body's immune cells. Late stage HIV infection, or AIDS, occurs when the body's immune system becomes so badly damaged it can no longer deal with other infections or cancers.

- HIV is spread by sexual contact or by the exchange of body fluids, such as blood, which occurs when drug users share needles.

- Tobacco mosaic virus is spread by contact and vectors. It damages leaves and reduces photosynthesis. There is no treatment. Spread is prevented by field hygiene and pest control.

Study tip

Learn the names of viral diseases.

Tobacco mosaic virus causes a typical pattern of damage in many different types of plants

5.7 Bacterial diseases

- Bacterial diseases affect animals and plants.
- Antibiotics can be used to kill bacteria.
- Some bacteria are becoming resistant to many antibiotics.

Salmonella food poisoning

- *Salmonella* are bacteria that can be found in raw meat, poultry, eggs, and egg products.
- The bacteria cause *Salmonella* food poisoning.
- Infection is spread by undercooked food or poor food hygiene.
- Symptoms are fever, abdominal cramps, vomiting, and diarrhoea.
- Prevention is by vaccinating chickens and good food hygiene, particularly keeping raw chicken away from food that is not going to be cooked.

> **1** Why should chicken be cooked thoroughly?

Gonorrhoea

- Gonorrhoea is a **sexually transmitted disease (STD)**, or STI (sexually transmitted infection).
- STDs are spread by unprotected sexual contact with an infected person.
- Early symptoms are discharge from the penis or vagina and pain on urination.
- The disease may become symptomless and some people have no symptoms at all.
- Untreated gonorrhoea can lead to infertility, pelvic pain, and ectopic pregnancies. Babies born to infected mothers may have severe eye infections or blindness.
- Treatment is with antibiotics, but some strains of the bacteria are resistant.
- Prevention is by using condoms, limiting sexual partners, and treating all partners of an infected person with antibiotics.

> **2** What is meant by 'STD'?

Bacterial disease in plants

- There are relatively few bacterial diseases of plants. Most are found in tropical and sub-tropical regions.
- *Agrobacterium tumefaciens* is a bacterium that causes crown galls.
- The galls contain a mass of unspecialised cells that are produced when the bacteria insert plasmids into the plant cells.
- The gall cells are new, undifferentiated, and genetically modified cells.
- Scientists can manipulate the bacteria by inserting desirable genes into the cell. These genes are then carried by the bacteria into the plant by natural processes. This results in genetic modification of the plant.

> **3** What is inside a plant gall?

Key points

- *Salmonella* is spread through undercooked food and poor hygiene. Symptoms include fever, abdominal cramps, diarrhoea, and vomiting caused by the toxins produced by the bacteria. In the UK, poultry are vaccinated against *Salmonella* to control the spread of disease.
- Gonorrhoea is a sexually transmitted disease. Symptoms include discharge from the penis or vagina and pain on urination. It is treated using antibiotics, although many strains are now resistant. Using condoms and limiting sexual partners prevents its spread.
- There are relatively few bacterial diseases of plants but *Agrobacterium tumefaciens* causes galls.

Synoptic links

See Topic B1.3 for more on orders of magnitude.

There is more about antibiotics in Topic B6.2, and about antibiotic resistance in Topic B15.8.

Key word: sexually transmitted disease (STD)

Study tip

Learn examples of bacterial diseases and be sure you can distinguish them from viral diseases.

5.8 Diseases caused by fungi and protists

Fungi and protists are important pathogens.

There are only a few fungal diseases of humans. Athlete's foot is a well-known example. In plants, fungal diseases are common and can ruin whole crops.

Rose black spot is a fungal disease of rose leaves.

- Symptoms are purple or black spots on the leaves.
- The leaves turn yellow and drop early so there is less photosynthesis. This weakens the plant and it will not produce healthy flowers.
- The disease is spread when the fungus spores are carried by the wind. When the spores land on a plant they are spread by splashes of water when it rains.
- To reduce the spread of the fungus, gardeners remove and burn affected leaves and stems. Fungicides are chemicals used to prevent the spread of black spot.
- Horticulturists have bred types of roses that are relatively resistant to black spot.

1 Which part of the plant is affected by black spot?

Diseases caused by protists

Protists are a type of single-celled organism. Some cause diseases.

Vectors are usually needed to transfer the protist to the host.

Malaria is a disease caused by a parasitic protist that lives and feeds on other living organisms.

- The protist is spread when a person is bitten by a female mosquito. The mosquito is the vector.
- The protists reproduce sexually in the mosquito and asexually in the human body.
- When a person is bitten, the protist enters the person's bloodstream and:
  - is carried to the liver and then enters red blood cells
  - bursts out of the red blood cells, causing fever and shaking, and may cause death
  - is carried to another person after a mosquito bites an infected person (to obtain a meal of blood).

2 What is an insecticide?

Key points

- Rose black spot is a fungal disease spread in the environment by wind and water. It damages leaves so they drop off, affecting growth as photosynthesis is reduced. Spread is controlled by removing affected leaves and by using chemical sprays, but this is not very effective.
- Malaria is caused by parasitic protists and is spread by the bite of female mosquitoes. It damages blood and liver cells, causes fevers and shaking, and can be fatal. Some drugs are effective if given early but the protists are becoming resistant. Spread is reduced by preventing the vectors from breeding and using mosquito nets to prevent people from being bitten.

Drugs to treat malaria, by killing parasites in the blood, must be given early, but not everyone has access to them.

The protists are becoming resistant to the drugs. The best methods of preventing malaria target the mosquito by:

- using insecticide-impregnated insect nets to stop mosquitoes from biting people
- using insecticides to kill adult mosquitoes
- preventing them from breeding by removing standing water
- spraying standing water with insecticides to kill the mosquito larvae.

Synoptic link

There is more about asexual and sexual reproduction in Topics B13.1–B13.3.

Study tip

Make a list of the precautions you might take to avoid catching malaria when travelling.

Student Book
pages 90–91

B5

5.9 Human defence responses

B5

Key points

- Your body has several lines of defence against the entry of pathogens. These include the skin (barrier and antimicrobial), the nose, the trachea, the bronchi, and the stomach.
- Your white blood cells help to defend you against pathogens by ingesting them and by making antibodies and antitoxins.

Synoptic links

There is more about the production of acid in the stomach in Topic B3.7, about blood and clotting in Topic B4.1, and about the structure of the breathing system in Topic B4.5.

Study tip

Remember the three functions of white blood cells.

Your body has several ways to prevent pathogens from entering and causing disease.

The skin acts as a barrier by covering the tissues underneath. It also produces antimicrobial secretions to kill pathogenic bacteria, and heals quickly when cut because the blood clots and produces a scab.

The respiratory system starts with the nose and continues with the trachea and bronchioles.

- Hairs and mucus in the nose trap pathogens and dirt particles.
- The trachea and bronchioles secrete mucus to trap pathogens. Cilia beat to waft the mucus back up to the throat where it is swallowed.

The stomach produces acid, which kills pathogens in the mucus you have swallowed and in the food you eat.

White blood cells in the immune system defend the body in three ways:

- They can ingest pathogens. Then they digest and destroy them.
- They produce antibodies to help destroy particular pathogens.
- They produce antitoxins to counteract the toxins (poisons) that pathogens produce.

---

1 Name the chemical that kills bacteria in the stomach.
2 How do white blood cells defend the body?

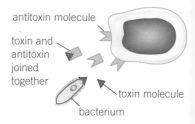

White blood cells ingest bacteria, make antibodies, and make antitoxins

Student Book
pages 92–93

B5

5.10 More about plant diseases

Key points

- Plants can be infected by a range of viral, bacterial, and fungal pathogens and can be damaged by insect pests.
- Plants can be damaged by a range of ion deficiency conditions.

The global loss of food crops to plant pathogens is 15–40% a year.

Plants can be damaged by viruses, bacteria, fungi, and insect pests.

- Insect pests may destroy the plant directly, or act as vectors of disease.
- Some plant pests such as nematode worms and insect larvae feed on the roots of plants so they cannot absorb water and mineral ions efficiently.

Aphids:

- insert their sharp mouthparts to feed on the sugar-rich sap in the phloem, depriving the plant cells of nutrients, which damages and weakens the plant

H Plant diseases can be detected by a range of symptoms. They can be identified in a number of ways including using gardening manuals and laboratory tests, some involving monoclonal antibodies.

Synoptic links

There is more about the phloem in Topic B4.7.

H There is more about DNA analysis in Topic B15.10, and about monoclonal antibodies in Topics B6.5 and B6.6.

Key words: aphids, chlorosis

Study tips

Learn what happens when plants are deficient in nitrate or magnesium.

Find photographs of diseased plants and try to describe the symptoms that are visible. Look for chlorosis and pest damage.

Aphids can destroy plants, but ladybirds destroy aphids

Chlorosis in a leaf due to magnesium ion deficiency in the soil

- act as vectors, transferring pathogens from diseased to healthy plants
- can be destroyed with chemical pesticides or by biological pest control, for example, ladybirds are released to eat the aphids and their larvae.

1   What do aphids eat?

Mineral deficiencies in the soil can lead to some plant diseases.

Mineral ion	Why needed	Deficiency
nitrate	To convert sugars to protein	Plant will not grow properly – it will be stunted
magnesium	To make chlorophyll	Leaves are yellow (**chlorosis**) so less photosynthesis so less growth

2   Why does a lack of magnesium cause chlorosis?

Detecting disease

Fast detection, by recognising symptoms, leads to early treatment and reduces the spread of plant diseases.

Symptoms of disease in plants include:

- stunted growth (e.g., nitrate deficiency)
- spots on leaves (e.g., black spot fungus on roses)
- areas of decay or rotting (e.g., black spot on roses, blights on potatoes)
- growths (e.g., crown galls caused by bacterial infections)
- malformed stems and leaves (e.g., due to aphid or nematode infestation)
- discoloration (e.g., yellowing or chlorosis in magnesium deficiency or mosaic patterns resulting from tobacco mosaic virus)
- presence of visible pests (e.g., aphids, caterpillars).

Early treatment is important to kill pests or fungi, or to replace mineral ions.

If untreatable the diseased plants must be removed quickly.

Recognising the symptoms of disease can be difficult so gardeners use manuals to compare healthy and diseased plants.

When the symptoms of disease occur in crop plants or forest trees, experts observe the symptoms in the natural environment. Samples of diseased materials can be analysed in the laboratory using techniques including DNA analysis to identify the pathogen.

Plant scientists, foresters, farmers, and market gardeners can use testing kits that contain monoclonal antibodies to identify the presence of certain plant pathogens, for example, the fungal pathogen *Botrytis*.

Higher

5.11 Plant defence responses

Plants have evolved some very effective defences against the attacks of pathogens, insects, and larger herbivores.

Physical barriers

- The cellulose cell walls that strengthen plant cells help resist invasion by microorganisms.
- The tough waxy cuticle on the surfaces of leaves is a barrier to pathogen entry.
- Bark on trees, and a layer of dead cells on the outside of stems, form a protective layer.
- If pathogens infect the leaves of deciduous trees, the pathogens fall off the tree with the leaves during leaf fall.

> **1** Name the part of a plant cell that acts as a barrier to prevent microorganisms entering.

Chemical barriers

- Many plants produce antibacterial chemicals that protect them against invading pathogens.
- Some plants produce poisons that deter herbivores.

Plant defence mechanisms

Plants often have special adaptations to protect them from being eaten. Sometimes they have combinations of two or more of these adaptations:

- poisons
- thorns
- hairy stems and/or leaves
- drooping or curling when touched
- mimicry.

Key points

- Physical plant defences against invasion by microorganisms include cellulose cell walls, tough waxy cuticles, and layers of bark or dead cells (or dead leaves) that fall off.
- Chemical plant defences include antibacterial chemicals and poisons to deter herbivores.
- Many plants have mechanical adaptations against herbivores, such as thorns and hairs, leaves that droop or curl when touched, and mimicry to trick animals.

On the up

If you can classify plant defences as physical, chemical, or mechanical, you can achieve the top grades by being able to explain in detail how plant defence responses work.

Plant defence mechanisms: poisons act as a chemical defence while thorns, hairy stems and leaves, drooping or curling, and mimicry are all mechanical adaptations for defence

> **2** Name one example of a plant defence mechanism.

1. Give three ways in which pathogens are spread. [3 marks]

2. Match each disease to the correct pathogen. Write the letters with the numbers.

   A malaria   **B** measles   **C** *Salmonella* food poisoning   **D** rose black spot

   1 virus   **2** fungus   **3** protist   **4** bacteria [4 marks]

3. Name the type of cell division carried out by bacteria. [1 mark]

4. What is a vector? [1 mark]

5. Name two features of plants that prevent them from being eaten. [2 marks]

6. Describe the ways in which the structure of a tree is designed to prevent pathogen entry. [4 marks]

7. How does your respiratory system remove the pathogens you breathe in? [5 marks]

8. Describe and explain the effect in plants of:

   a nitrate deficiency [3 marks]

   b magnesium deficiency. [4 marks]

9. Describe how you would prepare a pure culture of bacteria from a colony on agar gel in a flask of nutrient broth before leaving it to grow. [6 marks]

10. **a** What is a zone of inhibition? [1 mark]

    b Calculate the area of a zone of inhibition with a diameter of 4 mm to 1 decimal place. [4 marks]

11. **a** How do aphids damage a plant? [2 marks]

    b Explain the advantage of using ladybirds instead of insecticides to kill aphids. [5 marks]

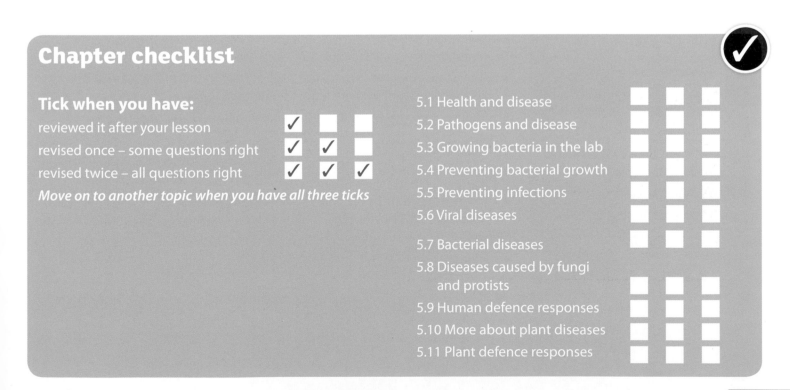

Chapter checklist

Tick when you have:

reviewed it after your lesson	✓	☐	☐
revised once – some questions right	✓	✓	☐
revised twice – all questions right	✓	✓	✓

Move on to another topic when you have all three ticks

5.1 Health and disease	☐	☐	☐
5.2 Pathogens and disease	☐	☐	☐
5.3 Growing bacteria in the lab	☐	☐	☐
5.4 Preventing bacterial growth	☐	☐	☐
5.5 Preventing infections	☐	☐	☐
5.6 Viral diseases	☐	☐	☐
5.7 Bacterial diseases	☐	☐	☐
5.8 Diseases caused by fungi and protists	☐	☐	☐
5.9 Human defence responses	☐	☐	☐
5.10 More about plant diseases	☐	☐	☐
5.11 Plant defence responses	☐	☐	☐

6.1 Vaccination

Key points

- If a pathogen enters the body the immune system tries to destroy the pathogen.

- Vaccination involves introducing small amounts of dead or inactive forms of a pathogen into your body to stimulate the white blood cells to produce antibodies. If the same live pathogen re-enters the body, the white blood cells respond quickly to produce the correct antibodies, preventing infection.

- If a large proportion of the population is immune to a pathogen, the spread of the pathogen is much reduced.

- Dead or inactive forms of a pathogen are used to make a **vaccine**. Vaccines can be injected into the body. The process is called vaccination (immunisation).

- The white blood cells react by producing antibodies, as they would if you were infected by a live pathogen.

- This response makes the person immune. It prevents subsequent infection because if the body meets this pathogen, it responds quickly by producing more antibodies.

- Specific antibodies recognise a particular antigen (usually a protein shape) on the pathogen.

- The MMR vaccine prevents measles, mumps, and rubella. It is one of several vaccines given to children and young people, to protect them and the population.

- Most people in a population need to be vaccinated to protect society from very serious diseases. This is known as herd immunity.

1   What is meant by vaccination?

2   How do antibodies 'recognise' antigens?

Key word: vaccine

6.2 Antibiotics and painkillers

Key points

- Painkillers and some other medicines treat the symptoms of disease, but do not kill the pathogens that cause it.

- Antibiotics cure bacterial diseases by killing the bacterial pathogens inside your body.

- The use of antibiotics has greatly reduced deaths from infectious diseases.

- The emergence of strains of bacteria resistant to antibiotics is a matter of great concern.

- Antibiotics do not destroy viruses because viruses reproduce inside the cells. It is difficult to develop drugs that can destroy viruses without damaging your body cells.

- Antibiotics kill infective bacteria in the body. They destroy the bacteria without damaging the body cells. Antibiotics cannot be used to treat viral diseases.

- Some antibiotics kill a wide range of bacteria. Other antibiotics are specific to particular bacteria or types of bacteria.

- Viruses are difficult to kill because they reproduce inside the body cells, so any treatment for viral infections could also damage the body cells.

- Painkillers and some other drugs treat the symptoms of a disease but do not kill the pathogen. They are often used to treat the symptoms of viral diseases.

- Your immune system will usually overcome the viral pathogens.

1   Why is it not possible to treat viral diseases with antibiotics?

- Strains of bacteria have evolved that are resistant to some or all of the available antibiotics. This means the antibiotics cannot kill the bacteria and the disease cannot be cured.

- Scientists need to find new drugs to kill the antibiotic-resistant bacteria.

2   Why are doctors concerned about the emergence of antibiotic-resistant bacteria?

6.3 Discovering drugs

Key points

- Traditionally drugs were extracted from plants (e.g., digitalis) or from microorganisms (e.g., penicillin).

- Penicillin was discovered by Alexander Fleming from the *Penicillium* mould.

- Most new drugs are synthesised by chemists in the pharmaceutical industry. However, the starting point may still be a chemical extracted from a plant or fungus.

- Many drugs still used today were extracted from plants or microorganisms.

- Penicillin is an antibiotic that was found in the mould *Penicillium*. It was discovered by Alexander Fleming but developed by other scientists as an antibiotic.

- Scientists in the pharmaceutical industry often use chemicals extracted from plants or fungi to develop new drugs.

- Digitalis and digoxin are drugs extracted from the foxglove plant. Digoxin is still used to strengthen the heartbeat, alongside more modern drugs. Aspirin was first prepared from a compound found in the bark of the willow tree. Scientists are hoping that microorganisms in the soil might reveal new antibiotics to kill antibiotic-resistant bacteria.

1 Who discovered penicillin?
2 Name a plant that produces a chemical used as a medicine to treat the heart.

Synoptic link

There is more about the development of antibiotic resistance in bacteria in Topic B15.8.

6.4 Developing drugs

Key points

- New medical drugs are extensively tested for efficacy, toxicity, and dosage.

- New drugs are tested in the laboratory using cells, tissues, and live animals.

- Preclinical testing of new drugs takes place in a laboratory on cells, tissues, and live animals. Clinical trials use healthy volunteers and patients. Low doses are used to test for safety, followed by higher doses to test for optimum dose.

- In double blind trials, some patients are given a placebo. Neither the doctor nor the patient knows who is given the drug and who has the placebo.

- Scientists test large numbers of substances to see if they might cure a disease or relieve symptoms.

- Researchers test new drugs to make sure they are effective, safe, stable, and can be taken into the body and removed easily.

- **Preclinical testing** is carried out in laboratories on cells and tissues or organs. If the drug seems to work it is then tested on animals.

- **Clinical trials** then take place on healthy human volunteers and finally on patients.

- Healthy people are given very low doses of the drug to find out if it is safe.

- In some trials with patients, a **placebo** is used. A placebo does not contain a drug. Some patients have the drug, and others are given the placebo. This is to check that the drug being tested really does have an effect on the patient.

- In a double-blind trial, neither the doctor nor the patient knows who is given a drug and who has the placebo.

- People taking part in a drug trial are asked to report any side effects.

1 Why is it important to test new drugs?
2 What is a clinical trial?

Key words: preclinical testing, clinical trials, placebo

Study tip

List the stages of testing a drug.

6.5 Making monoclonal antibodies

- Monoclonal antibodies are a form of medical treatment that relies on the immune system.
- Monoclonal antibodies are proteins. If all the antibodies come from one type of cell, they are monoclonal.
- Some white blood cells (lymphocytes) make antibodies naturally, but cannot divide so they cannot be used to produce the antibodies to make medicines.
- Tumour cells do not usually make antibodies, but they can divide rapidly to make a clone of cells.

Stages in making monoclonal antibodies

- Mouse lymphocytes are stimulated to make a particular antibody.
- Scientists combine a mouse lymphocyte with a tumour cell to make a **hybridoma**.
- Single hybridoma cells divide to make a large number of identical cells that all produce the same antibodies.
- These antibodies are collected and purified.
- They are monoclonal because they are produced from a single clone of cells.

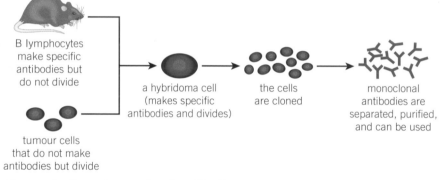

B lymphocytes make specific antibodies but do not divide

tumour cells that do not make antibodies but divide

a hybridoma cell (makes specific antibodies and divides)

the cells are cloned

monoclonal antibodies are separated, purified, and can be used

The production of monoclonal antibodies

- Monoclonal antibodies are produced to target particular cells or chemicals in the body.

Using monoclonal antibodies

- Pregnancy tests rely on monoclonal antibodies that bind to a hormone produced in early pregnancy.
- Monoclonal antibodies are used to diagnose disease. Specific antibodies are produced that bind to the antigens on a pathogen or on a particular type of cancer cell.
- Monoclonal antibodies are also used to measure and monitor the levels of hormones and other chemicals in the blood for diagnoses in hospitals.
- In research, scientists can locate specific molecules in a cell by adding fluorescent markers to a monoclonal antibody.
- Monoclonal antibodies are used to treat diseases.

1 What is an antibody?

2 What is a hybridoma?

Key points

- Monoclonal antibodies are produced from a single clone of cells. Each type is specific to one binding site on a specific protein antigen so they can target specific cells in the body or specific chemicals.
- Monoclonal antibodies are produced by stimulating mouse lymphocytes to make a specific antibody. Large amounts of the specific monoclonal antibody can be collected and purified.
- Monoclonal antibodies are used:
  - for diagnosis in pregnancy tests
  - in labs to measure levels of hormones and other chemicals in the blood to detect pathogens for research
  - to identify or locate specific molecules in cells or tissue.

Key word: hybridoma

On the up

If you can describe what monoclonal antibodies are and know some of their uses, you can achieve the top grades by being able to explain why hybridoma cells are used and explain in detail how pregnancy tests work.

6.6 Uses of monoclonal antibodies

Monoclonal antibodies are used in the treatment of disease.

- Some have been developed to target the specific antigens on certain cancer cells.
- The monoclonal antibody could carry radioactive substances, a toxic drug, or another chemical directly to the cancer cells without damaging other body cells.
- Some can trigger the immune system to recognise and destroy cancer cells.
- Some can block receptors on the surface of cancer cells to stop them dividing.

Key points

- Monoclonal antibodies are used in the treatment of diseases.
- They have been developed against the antigens on cancer cells.
- If a monoclonal antibody is bound to a radioactive substance, a toxic drug, or a chemical that stops cells growing and dividing, it will deliver the substance to the cancer cells without harming other cells in the body.
- Monoclonal antibodies have created more side effects than expected and are not yet as widely used as hoped when they were first developed.

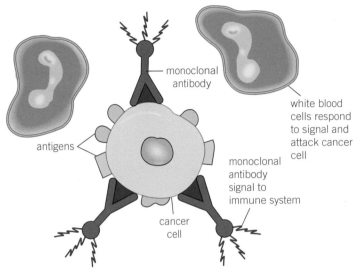

Monoclonal antibodies can trigger the immune system by *making cancer cells more noticeable*

- The main advantage of using monoclonal antibodies is that they target specific diseased cells without damaging healthy cells. In conventional cancer treatment the drugs and radiotherapy also damage healthy cells.
- Disadvantages of using monoclonal antibodies include:
  - side effects – it is hoped that using human cells in hybridomas will reduce these
  - they are expensive to produce.

Synoptic links

There is more about the immune system and antibodies in Topic B5.9, about how cancer cells grow and develop in Topic B7.2, and about clones of cells in Topic B2.3.

Study tip

Research other examples of the use of monoclonal antibodies. Make sure you understand what they are and how they work.

1 Give three ways that monoclonal antibodies can act to treat a diseased cell.
2 What is the main advantage of using monoclonal antibodies to treat cancer?

On the up

If you can outline the advantages and disadvantages of using monoclonal antibodies, you can achieve the top grades by being able to explain in detail how the methods of using them to treat cancer work.

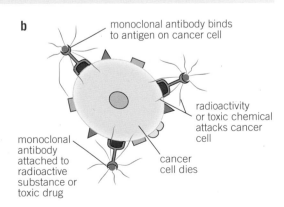

*Monoclonal antibodies may bind to receptors on cancer cells, removing the stimulus to grow and divide (**a**) or they may carry drugs or radioactive therapies to cancer cells (**b**)*

1 What does a vaccine contain? [1 mark]

2 **a** What is an antibiotic? [1 mark] **b** Give an example. [1 mark]

3 Name two drugs that are extracted from plants. [2 marks]

4 What makes a treatment 'a good medicine'? [4 marks]

5 Describe how the polio vaccine works to protect you against polio. [6 marks]

6 Why are antibiotics unable to cure viral diseases? [2 marks]

7 Why is it important to find new antibiotics? [2 marks]

8 Explain what is meant by a double-blind clinical trial. [2 marks]

9 Suggest one disadvantage of using monoclonal antibodies. [1 mark]

10 What observation was made by Alexander Fleming that prompted him to discover the idea of antibiotics? [2 marks]

11 **H** Describe how monoclonal antibodies are produced. Use **Figure 1** to help you. [6 marks]

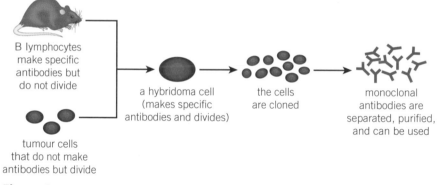

B lymphocytes make specific antibodies but do not divide

a hybridoma cell (makes specific antibodies and divides)

the cells are cloned

monoclonal antibodies are separated, purified, and can be used

tumour cells that do not make antibodies but divide

Figure 1

12 **H** Describe how monoclonal antibodies can be used to trigger the immune system to destroy cancer cells. Use the diagram on page 53 to help you. [6 marks]

Chapter checklist

Tick when you have:

reviewed it after your lesson ✔ ☐ ☐

revised once – some questions right ✔ ✔ ☐

revised twice – all questions right ✔ ✔ ✔

Move on to another topic when you have all three ticks

6.1 Vaccination ☐ ☐ ☐

6.2 Antibiotics and painkillers ☐ ☐ ☐

6.3 Discovering drugs ☐ ☐ ☐

6.4 Developing drugs ☐ ☐ ☐

6.5 Making monoclonal antibodies ☐ ☐ ☐

6.6 Uses of monoclonal antibodies ☐ ☐ ☐

Student Book
pages 112–113 **B7**

7.1 Non-communicable diseases

Non-communicable diseases cannot be passed from one person to another.

Risk factors that are linked to an increased rate of disease include:

- age
- genetic make-up
- aspects of lifestyle such as diet, obesity, level of exercise, and inhaling **carcinogens** in tobacco smoke
- environmental factors such as **ionising radiation**, UV light from the sun, and second-hand tobacco smoke.

> **1** Name an environmental factor that can cause disease.

Causal mechanisms

- Sometimes scientists can see a link between two factors. A rise in one factor might lead to a rise or fall in the other. For example, scientists noticed that the more cigarettes a person smoked, the more chance they would have of developing lung cancer or cardiovascular disease. The scientists saw a **correlation** between smoking and lung cancer.

- Once scientists notice a correlation they need to carry out more research to show there is a **causal mechanism** between the two factors. A causal mechanism explains how one factor influences another through a biological process.

- Scientists have shown that the causal mechanism of increased rates of lung cancer from smoking is the action of the carcinogens in tobacco smoke on cells in the lungs.

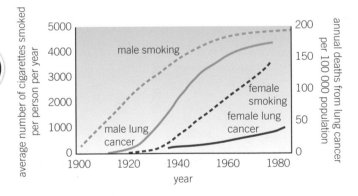

This graph shows the number of deaths from lung cancer and the average number of cigarettes smoked. In the UK, 86% of lung cancer cases are linked to smoking

- For some non-communicable diseases, it has not yet been possible to prove a causal mechanism.

> **2** Why is tobacco smoke thought to be the causal mechanism in lung cancer?

- There is a high human and financial cost of non-communicable diseases to an individual, a local community, a nation, or globally. For example, reducing the numbers of people who smoke could reduce the cost of health provision in a country.

Key points

- A non-communicable disease cannot be passed from one individual to another.
- Risk factors are aspects of a person's lifestyle, or substances present in a person's body or environment, that have been shown to be linked to an increased rate of a disease.
- For some non-communicable diseases, a causal mechanism for some risk factors has been proven, but not in others.

Key words: carcinogens, ionising radiation, correlation, causal mechanism

Study tip

Make sure you can explain the difference between a correlation and a causal mechanism.

On the up

If you can describe whether a link is causal, you can achieve the top grades by being able to explain why a correlation does not prove a causal mechanism.

7.2 Cancer

Tumours

The process of mitosis is normally well controlled when cells divide. However, sometimes a cell will change, due to mutations in the genetic material, and start to divide in an uncontrolled way.

- A mass of abnormally growing cells is called a **tumour**.
- A **benign tumour** grows in one place. Although it does not invade other tissues, it can be dangerous if it grows in tissue such as the brain and compresses it.
- **Malignant tumour** cells can spread to healthy tissue. Malignant tumours are **cancer**.
- Some malignant cells may enter the bloodstream and circulate to other parts of the body, forming secondary tumours.

1 What is a tumour?

Causes of cancer include:

- genetic factors, for example, for some breast cancers
- mutations in genes caused by carcinogens, such as carcinogens in tobacco smoke causing lung cancer
- ionising radiation, for example UV light causing skin cancers
- virus infections, such as HPV, which causes cervical cancer.

2 Which cancer can be caused by UV light?

- Cancer can be treated with radiotherapy and chemotherapy.

15 mm	10 mm	10 mm	30 mm
asymmetry	border irregularity	colour	diameter: 1/4 inch or 6 mm

Melanomas are malignant tumours often triggered by exposure to UV radiation. Over 2000 people a year die from melanomas in the UK alone, so it is important to know the signs to look out for

Key points

- Benign and malignant tumours result from abnormal, uncontrolled cell division.
- Benign tumours form in one place and do not spread to other tissues.
- Malignant tumours are cancers. The cancerous cells invade neighbouring tissues and may spread in the blood to different parts of the body, where they form secondary tumours.
- Lifestyle risk factors for various types of cancer include smoking, obesity, common viruses, and UV exposure. There are also genetic risk factors for some cancers.

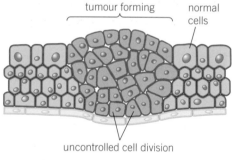

tumour forming   normal cells

uncontrolled cell division

A tumour forms when there is uncontrolled cell division

Key words: tumour, benign tumour, malignant tumour, cancer

Synoptic links

For mitosis and the cell cycle, see Topic B2.1.

There is more about the use of monoclonal antibodies to treat cancer in Topic B6.6.

Study tip

Make sure you know the difference between a benign tumour and a malignant tumour.

7.3 Smoking and the risk of disease

The smoke from cigarettes contains about 4000 chemicals. About 150 of these chemicals have been linked to disease.

Tobacco smoke contains:

- nicotine, which is the addictive substance in the smoke
- carbon monoxide, a toxic gas, which replaces oxygen in red blood cells
- tar, which is a sticky black substance that accumulates in the lungs and is also carcinogenic
- chemicals that anaesthetise the cilia in the airways, preventing them from wafting up the mucus.

1   Name the three main components of tobacco smoke that cause health problems.

Here are the problems caused by smoking:

- The blood carries less oxygen around the body because of carbon monoxide attaching to red blood cells. This can lead to breathlessness.
- If a pregnant woman smokes, her baby will also receive less oxygen, leading to premature births, low birth weight, or stillbirths.
- Mucus containing dirt and pathogens builds up in the airways because it is not removed. This leads to infection and coughing.
- Tar and other chemicals lead to bronchitis because they inflame the bronchi.
- Tar can damage the alveoli, causing chronic obstructive pulmonary disease (COPD), which in turn leads to severe breathlessness and death.
- Tar causes other cancers of the respiratory system including cancers of the throat, larynx, and trachea.
- A causal link has been shown between smoking and cardiovascular disease. The blood vessels in the skin narrow. Nicotine increases the heart rate. Some chemicals damage the lining of blood vessels, increasing the risk of clots, and other chemicals cause an increase in blood pressure. A combination of these factors leads to heart attacks and strokes.

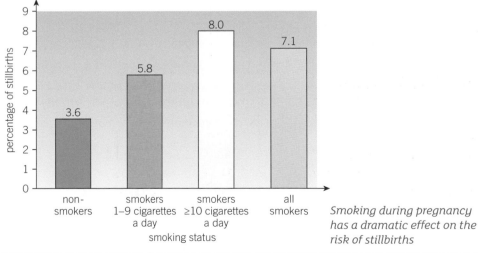

Smoking during pregnancy has a dramatic effect on the risk of stillbirths

2   What does COPD stand for?

Key points

- Smoking can cause cardiovascular disease including coronary heart disease, lung cancer, and lung diseases such as bronchitis and COPD.
- A fetus exposed to smoke has a restricted oxygen supply, which can lead to premature birth, low birth weight, and even stillbirth.

Synoptic links

See Topic B4.5 for the structure of the breathing system, and Topic B4.1 for the way oxygen is carried around the body.

There is more about cancer in Topic B7.2, about coronary heart disease and how it can be treated in Topic B4.3, and about the clotting of the blood in Topic B5.9.

Study tips

Make sure you know the difference between the effects of carbon monoxide, nicotine, tar, and other carcinogens. Learn what these chemicals do to the body.

Be sure you can explain why smokers develop coughs.

On the up

To achieve the top grades, you should also be able to suggest possible causal mechanisms to explain trends shown in data, and explain how the causal link between smoking and lung cancer was identified.

7.4 Diet, exercise, and disease

Key points

- Diet affects your risk of developing cardiovascular and other diseases directly through cholesterol levels and indirectly through obesity.
- Exercise levels affect the likelihood of developing cardiovascular disease.
- Obesity is a strong risk factor for type 2 diabetes.

Synoptic links

See Topic B9.2 for the effect of fitness on the body.

There is more about type 1 and type 2 diabetes in Topics B11.2 and B11.3.

Your weight and the amount of exercise you do can affect your risk of developing various diseases.

- Eating too much food for your energy needs will make you overweight and possibly obese.
- Obesity can lead to type 2 diabetes, high blood pressure, or heart disease.
- People who exercise regularly have bigger muscles, bigger hearts, and bigger lungs than those who do not exercise.
- Regular exercise reduces your risk of developing cardiovascular disease:
  - by lowering blood cholesterol levels and reducing fatty deposits in the blood vessels
  - by building muscle tissue, which increases your metabolic rate and means you are less likely to be overweight
  - by improving the blood supply to the heart so the heart is fitter.

1 What is one high risk factor for type 2 diabetes?

2 Give a reason why the heart is fitter if you exercise regularly.

7.5 Alcohol and other carcinogens

Key points

- Alcohol can damage the liver and cause cirrhosis and liver cancer.
- Alcohol can cause brain damage and death.
- Alcohol taken in by a pregnant woman can affect the development of her unborn baby.

Synoptic links

Topic B3.7 explains the role of the liver.

For more about the brain, see Topic B10.4.

Study tip

Make a list of the short-term and long-term effects of alcohol on the body.

Alcohol

Alcohol (ethanol) is a commonly used social drug. Alcohol is very addictive.

- Alcohol enters the bloodstream and reaches all parts of the body including the brain and liver.
- Large amounts of alcohol affect the nervous system, slowing reactions, reflexes, and thought processes. Very large amounts can cause death.
- The liver breaks down the alcohol. However, over a long period of heavy drinking the liver becomes damaged and the person may have cirrhosis caused by scar tissue in the liver. Long-term drinking can also lead to liver cancer.
- Long-term alcohol abuse can also cause damage to the brain.
- If a pregnant woman drinks alcohol it can pass across the placenta to the fetus. The alcohol can cause physical problems such as facial deformities and heart problems. After birth the baby may have developmental and learning problems. This is called fetal alcohol syndrome.

1 Why are pregnant women advised not to drink alcohol?

Ionising radiation

Radioactive materials are a source of ionising radiation and are carcinogenic.

- Radiation penetrates the cells and damages the chromosomes, leading to mutations in the DNA.
- Sources of radiation include UV light from the sun, radon gas, medical and dental X-rays, and accidents at nuclear power stations.

1. What are the main treatments for cancer? [2 marks]

2. Give two examples of ionising radiation. [2 marks]

3. Why is carbon monoxide harmful? [2 marks]

4. What is the main cause of type 2 diabetes? [1 mark]

5. Name the two main organs that are damaged by long-term alcohol consumption. [2 marks]

6. **a** Which type of cell division leads to two identical cells? [1 mark]

   b What changes take place in cell division when a tumour is formed? [3 marks]

7. How does cancer spread from one part of the body to another? [3 marks]

8. Why do smokers find it difficult to give up smoking? [2 marks]

9. Look at **Figure 1**.

   a Name the three diseases that affect the lungs. [3 marks]

   b Which of these diseases is communicable? [1 mark]

   c What was the total number of deaths from lung disease in 2012? [1 mark]

   d How do the total deaths from lung disease compare with the combined deaths from coronary heart disease and stroke? [2 marks]

10. Explain why babies who are born to mothers who smoke have lower than average birth weights. [5 marks]

11. Describe and explain the effects experienced by a person who drinks several units of alcohol in a 2-hour period. [6 marks]

12. Describe how COPD leads to death. [6 marks]

13. What is the evidence for a causal link between smoking cigarettes and cardiovascular disease? [4 marks]

Figure 1 *The leading causes of death globally in 2012 (World Health Organization). Non-communicable diseases (blue bars) contribute to more deaths than communicable diseases (pink bars)*

Chapter checklist

Tick when you have:

reviewed it after your lesson ✔ ☐ ☐

revised once – some questions right ✔ ✔ ☐

revised twice – all questions right ✔ ✔ ✔

Move on to another topic when you have all three ticks

7.1 Non-communicable diseases ☐ ☐ ☐

7.2 Cancer ☐ ☐ ☐

7.3 Smoking and the risk of disease ☐ ☐ ☐

7.4 Diet, exercise, and disease ☐ ☐ ☐

7.5 Alcohol and other carcinogens ☐ ☐ ☐

8.1 Photosynthesis

Key points

- Photosynthesis is an endothermic reaction.
- During photosynthesis energy is transferred from the environment to the chloroplast by light. It is used to convert carbon dioxide and water into sugar (glucose). Oxygen is also formed and released as a by-product.
- Photosynthesis can be summarised as follows:

carbon dioxide + water $\xrightarrow{\text{light}}$ glucose + oxygen

- Leaves are well adapted to allow the maximum amount of photosynthesis to take place.

Photosynthesis can be carried out only by green plants and algae.

- Chlorophyll in the chloroplasts absorbs the Sun's light.
- The equation for photosynthesis is:

carbon dioxide + water $\xrightarrow{\textbf{light energy}}$ glucose + oxygen

- Photosynthesis is an **endothermic reaction**. Energy is transferred from the environment when the light is absorbed by the chlorophyll.
- The process for photosynthesis is:
  1. Carbon dioxide is taken in by the leaves, and water is taken up by the roots.
  2. The chlorophyll traps the light energy needed for photosynthesis.
  3. This energy is used to convert the carbon dioxide and water into **glucose** (a sugar).
- Oxygen is released as a by-product of photosynthesis.

The oxygen produced during photosynthesis is vital for life on Earth. You can demonstrate that it is produced using water plants such as this Cabomba

Synoptic link

For more about the structure and function of plant cells, see Topic B1.5.

Key words: photosynthesis, endothermic reaction, glucose

Study tip

Learn the word equation for photosynthesis.

- Some of the glucose is converted into insoluble starch for storage.

1 Where does the energy for photosynthesis come from?

Leaves are well adapted for photosynthesis.

- Leaves are broad and flat so they have a large surface area, and thin so the diffusion path is short.
- The guard cells open the stomata so that gases can diffuse in and out of the air spaces inside the leaves.
- The photosynthetic cells in the leaves contain chlorophyll.
- The veins contain xylem, which brings water to the leaves, and phloem, which takes the glucose away.

2 What is the function of the veins in leaves?

8.2 The rate of photosynthesis

Key point

● The rate of photosynthesis may be affected by light intensity, temperature, level of carbon dioxide, and amount of chlorophyll.

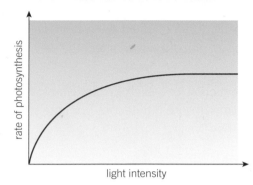

Investigating the effect of light intensity on the rate of photosynthesis

Study tip

Make sure you understand what is meant by a limiting factor.

Key word: limiting factor

Light intensity and the inverse square law

As the distance of the light from the plant increases, the light intensity decreases.

That is an inverse relationship – as one factor goes up, the other goes down. However the relationship between distance and light intensity is not linear.

Use the equation:

$$\text{light intensity} \propto \frac{1}{\text{distance}^2}$$

If you double the distance between the light and the plant the intensity falls by $\frac{1}{2^2} = \frac{1}{4}$

● A lack of light would slow down the rate of photosynthesis, because light transfers the energy for the process. Even on sunny days, light may be limited to plants that are shaded by trees.

● If it is cold, then enzymes do not work as effectively and this will slow down the rate of photosynthesis.

● If there is too little carbon dioxide, then the rate of photosynthesis will slow down. Carbon dioxide may be limited in an enclosed space, such as in a greenhouse on a sunny day where there is plenty of light available but the plants use up the carbon dioxide.

1 Why does photosynthesis slow down in cold conditions?

● Anything that stops the rate of photosynthesis increasing above a certain level is a **limiting factor**.

● Some plants have patches of white among the green parts of the leaves. A variegated leaf will have less photosynthetic activity than one that is completely green.

Light intensity and rate of photosynthesis

You can investigate the effect of light intensity on the rate of photosynthesis of a water plant by:

● counting the bubbles of oxygen released per minute

● collecting the total volume of oxygen released and calculating the volume collected per minute.

2 Give two reasons why collecting the total volume of gas is likely to be more accurate than counting bubbles.

If the light source (lamp) is near the plant, the rate of photosynthesis will be fast.

As the lamp is moved further away the rate will slow down, becoming limited by the intensity of the light.

When the lamp is very close to the plant the rate of photosynthesis will level off because another factor, such as carbon dioxide availability, could be limiting the reaction.

3 As the lamp is moved nearer to the plant, which other factor will also increase with the light?

The results can be plotted on a graph showing the effect of light intensity on the rate of photosynthesis.

Study tip

Learn how to apply the inverse square law to photosynthesis investigations. **H**

8.3 How plants use glucose

Key points

- Plant and algal cells use the glucose produced during photosynthesis:
  - for respiration
  - to convert into insoluble starch for storage
  - to produce fats or oils for storage
  - to produce cellulose to strengthen cell walls
  - to produce amino acids for protein synthesis.
- Plants and algal cells also need nitrate ions absorbed from the soil or water to make the amino acids used to make proteins.

Synoptic links

For more on the cellulose wall in plant cells, see Topics B1.2 and B1.7.

There is more about respiration in cells in Topic B9.1.

For more information on transport in plants, see Topic B4.7.

For more on osmosis in plants, see Topic B1.7.

See Topic B3.3 for the Biuret test for proteins and the iodine test for starch.

On the up

If you can describe all the ways plants use glucose, including how they make proteins, you can achieve the top grades by being able to explain how and why plants convert glucose to starch for storage.

The uses of soluble glucose

- The glucose produced by photosynthesis may be:
  - converted into insoluble starch for storage in organs such as a potato tuber
  - used for respiration
  - converted into fats and oils for storage
  - used to produce cellulose, which strengthens cell walls
  - used to produce proteins.
- Glucose is stored as insoluble starch so that it does not affect the water balance of the plant. High concentrations of dissolved glucose would affect the way water moves by osmosis.
- Plant and algal cells also need a supply of mineral ions, such as nitrate ions, in order to produce protein from glucose. Plants absorb nitrate ions from the soil. Algae absorb nitrate ions from the water they live in.

1 Name three substances used for storage in plants.

- Carnivorous plants such as the Venus flytrap are adapted to live in nutrient-poor soil.
- The Venus flytrap obtains most of its nutrients from the animals, such as insects, that it catches and digests. The plant obtains nitrates by digesting animal protein.

2 What is meant by the term 'carnivorous plant'?

Study tips

Look back at the tests for sugar, starch, protein, and lipids. Leaves can be tested for the presence of starch after removing the chlorophyll.

Student Book
pages 130–131 **B8**

8.4 Making the most of photosynthesis

Key points

- The factors that limit the rate of photosynthesis interact and any one of them may limit photosynthesis.

- Limiting factors are important in the economics of commercial greenhouses. The aim is to enhance the conditions to gain the maximum rate of photosynthesis whilst still maintaining profit.

One piece of American research showed the crop yield for tomatoes was almost doubled in a greenhouse

Study tip

Make a list of the factors that are controlled in a commercial greenhouse.

On the up

If you can describe how greenhouses increase plant growth, to achieve the top grades you should be able to explain in detail how greenhouses can help control limiting factors and increase the rate of photosynthesis.

- The more a plant photosynthesises, the more biomass it makes and the faster it grows.

- The factors that limit the rate of photosynthesis interact and any one of them may limit the process.

- It is difficult to control limiting factors in fields where crops are growing. Farmers use greenhouses and polytunnels to increase the yields of their crops. The conditions are varied to ensure that plants photosynthesise for as long as possible:

  - the temperature is maintained at the optimum for enzyme action

  - carbon dioxide levels are increased so they do not become a limiting factor

  - artificial lighting can be used to extend the hours, and the months, when plants photosynthesise

  - the levels of nutrients such as nitrate ions must be monitored to ensure optimum growth.

1 Why is maintaining a steady, optimum temperature important in a greenhouse?

- In some greenhouses the plants are grown in a solution of mineral ions instead of soil so that they never run out of essential ions. This system is called hydroponics.

- Using greenhouses can be costly in terms of buildings, electricity (used for heating and lighting), and control systems, such as computers, but higher yields mean more profits.

2 What is likely to be the most expensive requirement in keeping a greenhouse running?

1. Write the word equation for photosynthesis. [2 marks]

2. Name the green pigment in plants and algae. [1 mark]

3. Name three factors that affect the rate of photosynthesis. [3 marks]

4. Name the insoluble storage carbohydrate found in potato tubers. [1 mark]

5. Describe a simple method to investigate photosynthesis for a given factor. [3 marks]

6. Describe three adaptations of a leaf for photosynthesis. [3 marks]

7. Why do plants require nitrate ions? [2 marks]

8. **a** What is meant by a limiting factor?

   b Give one example of a factor that limits photosynthesis. [2 marks]

9. In an investigation to find the effect of light intensity on the rate of photosynthesis, a student set up the following apparatus: he placed a water plant in a boiling tube, filled the tube with water containing dissolved sodium hydrogencarbonate, and supported the tube in a rack. Then he placed a lamp 40 cm from the plant and counted the oxygen bubbles it gave off in 1 minute. He moved the lamp towards the plant 10 cm at a time and counted the bubbles for each position of the lamp.

   a What is the independent variable in this investigation? [1 mark]

   b What is the dependent variable? [1 mark]

   c What other factor will change as the lamp moves nearer the plant in the boiling tube? [1 mark]

   d How could the student reduce the effect of the factor named in **c**? [1 mark]

   e Which factor will become limiting? [1 mark]

   f How could the student reduce the effect of the limiting factor? [1 mark]

   g What other measurement did the student make, apart from number of bubbles, to calculate the rate of photosynthesis? [1 mark]

10. **H** Using the inverse law, what is the change in light intensity when a lamp is moved from 40 cm to 20 cm from a plant? [2 marks]

11. **H** Explain how tomato growers can reduce the effects of limiting factors in order to obtain larger crops. [5 marks]

12. **H** What factors do tomato growers need to take into account to maximise their profits? [6 marks]

Chapter checklist

Tick when you have:

reviewed it after your lesson ☑ ☐ ☐

revised once – some questions right ☑ ☑ ☐

revised twice – all questions right ☑ ☑ ☑

Move on to another topic when you have all three ticks

8.1 Photosynthesis

8.2 The rate of photosynthesis

8.3 How plants use glucose

8.4 Making the most of photosynthesis

Student Book
pages 134–135   **B9**

9.1 Aerobic respiration

Aerobic respiration takes place all the time in plant and animal cells. Aerobic respiration is an **exothermic reaction** using glucose and oxygen to transfer energy. The energy transferred is needed for all living processes. Carbon dioxide and water are produced as waste products. Most of the chemical reactions of aerobic respiration take place in the mitochondria and are controlled by enzymes.

- The equation for aerobic respiration is:
  glucose + oxygen → carbon dioxide + water (energy transferred to the environment)

$$C_6H_{12}O_6 + \quad 6O_2 \quad \rightarrow \quad 6CO_2 \quad + 6H_2O \text{ (energy transferred to the environment)} \quad \boxed{H}$$

1 Where does aerobic respiration take place in the cell?

The transferred energy may be used by the organism to:

- build larger molecules from smaller ones

- enable muscle contraction in animals

- maintain a constant body temperature in colder surroundings in mammals and birds

- move materials such as mineral ions into cells against a concentration gradient (active transport)

- build sugars, nitrates, and other nutrients into amino acids and then proteins in plants.

2 Why is energy needed to make proteins from amino acids?

Investigating respiration

- Investigations involving aerobic respiration use limewater (which turns cloudy white) to detect the carbon dioxide produced.

- It is also possible to detect a rise in temperature when respiration is occurring.

3 Why do we not plan investigations with living organisms to prove that they need oxygen for aerobic respiration?

Key points

- Cellular respiration is an exothermic reaction that occurs continuously in living cells.
  - Aerobic respiration is summarised as:
    glucose + oxygen →
    carbon dioxide + water (energy transferred to the environment).
  - The energy transferred supplies all the energy needed for living processes.

Synoptic links

See Topic B1.2 for more about mitochondria, and Topic B1.4 for more about adaptations of active cells in Topic B1.4.

For active transport and the movement of mineral ions into root hair cells see Topic B1.9, for uses of energy see Topics B18.8 and B18.9, and for temperature control see Topic B12.1.

Key words: aerobic respiration, exothermic reaction

Study tips

Make sure you know the word equation for aerobic respiration.
Remember that aerobic respiration takes place in the mitochondria.

On the up

You can achieve the top grades if you are able to plan an investigation and explain why the controls are necessary.

cytoplasm — Where enzymes are made. Location of reactions in anaerobic respiration.

cell wall

nucleus — Holds genetic code for enzymes involved in respiration.

chloroplast

mitochondrion — Contains the enzymes for aerobic respiration.

cell membrane — Allows gases and water to pass freely into and out of the cell. Controls the passage of other molecules.

typical plant cell   **typical animal cell**

Aerobic respiration takes place in the mitochondria, but other parts of the cell play vital roles

9.2 The response to exercise

Key points

- The energy that is transferred during respiration is used to enable muscles to contract.

- During exercise the human body responds to the increased demand for energy.

- Body responses to exercise include:

  - an increase in the heart rate, the breathing rate, and the breath volume

  - conversion of glycogen stores in the muscles to glucose for cellular respiration

  - an increase in the flow of oxygenated blood to the muscles.

- These responses act to increase the rate of supply of glucose and oxygen to the muscles and the rate of removal of carbon dioxide from the muscles.

Synoptic links

For more about the heart see Topic B4.3, and for more about the lungs and breathing see Topic B4.4.

Key word: glycogen

On the up

If you can choose the best way to display data and calculate percentage changes, you can achieve the top grades by being able to justify the choice of a chart or graph used to display the data.

- When you exercise, your muscles need more energy so that they can contract.

- You need to increase the rate at which oxygen and glucose reach the muscle cells for aerobic respiration. You also need to remove the extra waste carbon dioxide produced more quickly.

  glucose + oxygen → carbon dioxide + water (energy transferred to the environment)

$$C_6H_{12}O_6 + 6O_2 \rightarrow 6CO_2 + 6H_2O \text{ (energy transferred to the environment)} \quad \boxed{H}$$

  - The heart rate increases and the blood vessels supplying the muscles dilate (widen). This allows more blood containing oxygen and glucose to reach the muscles.

  - Your breathing rate and the depth of each breath also increase. This allows a greater uptake of oxygen and release of carbon dioxide at the lungs.

The changes measured in the heart and breathing rate before, during, and after a period of exercise

  - Muscles store glucose as **glycogen**. The glycogen can be converted back to glucose for use during exercise.

1 Which sugar is needed by the muscles for aerobic respiration?

The heart and lung functions change during exercise whether you are fit or not

	Unfit person	Fit person
amount of blood pumped out of the heart during each beat at rest in cm³	64	80
volume of the heart at rest in cm³	120	140
resting breathing rate in breaths per minute	14	12
resting pulse rate in beats per minute	72	63

2 Use information from the table above to describe the differences between a fit person and an unfit person.

Study tips

You need to be clear about:

- the difference between the rate and the depth of breathing
- the difference between the breathing rate and the rate of respiration.

9.3 Anaerobic respiration

- If you use muscles over a long period then they will get tired (fatigued) and stop contracting efficiently. For example, this might happen when you lift a weight repeatedly for a few minutes or when you go jogging.

- When your muscles cannot get enough oxygen for aerobic respiration, they start to respire anaerobically (without oxygen).

- In **anaerobic respiration** the glucose is not completely broken down and **lactic acid** is produced.
  glucose → lactic acid (energy transferred to the environment)

- Less energy is transferred from the glucose in anaerobic respiration.

- One cause of muscle fatigue is the build-up of lactic acid. This creates an **oxygen debt**.

- Blood flowing through the muscles removes the lactic acid.

> 1   What is produced during anaerobic respiration in muscle cells?

Oxygen debt

When the exercise has finished all the lactic acid must be completely broken down to carbon dioxide and water. To do this you need to take in extra oxygen for a while after you stop exercising.

The extra oxygen needed is known as the oxygen debt.

lactic acid + oxygen → carbon dioxide + water

Everyone gets an oxygen debt if they exercise hard, but if you are fit you can pay it off faster

> 2   How is an oxygen debt repaid?

Plants and microorganisms also respire anaerobically.

- Plant cells and yeast cells produce ethanol and carbon dioxide.
  glucose → ethanol + carbon dioxide (energy transferred to the environment)
  $C_6H_{12}O_6 → 2C_2H_5OH + 2CO_2$

- Anaerobic respiration in yeast cells is called fermentation.

- Some microorganisms, such as bacteria used in yoghurt production, produce lactic acid in anaerobic respiration.

Key points

- If muscles work hard for a long time, they become fatigued and do not contract efficiently. If they do not get enough oxygen, they will respire anaerobically.

- Anaerobic respiration is respiration without oxygen. When this takes place in animal cells, glucose is incompletely broken down to form lactic acid.

- The anaerobic breakdown of glucose transfers less energy than aerobic respiration.

- **H** After exercise, oxygen is still needed to break down the lactic acid that has built up. The amount of oxygen needed is known as the oxygen debt.

- Anaerobic respiration in plant cells and some microorganisms, such as yeast, results in the production of ethanol and carbon dioxide.

Study tip

Learn the word equations for aerobic and anaerobic respiration.

Key words: anaerobic respiration, lactic acid, oxygen debt

Study tip

Make sure you understand why we continue to puff and pant after vigorous exercise.

9.4 Metabolism and the liver

The metabolism of an organism is the sum of all the reactions that take place in a cell or in the body.

Some of the most common metabolic reactions include the conversion of small molecules into larger molecules:

- glucose to starch, glycogen, or cellulose
- fatty acids and glycerol to lipids
- glucose and nitrate ions to amino acids
- amino acids to protein

Other common metabolic reactions are:

- the reactions of respiration and photosynthesis
- the breakdown of excess proteins in the liver to form urea.

Some of the energy transferred by respiration is used to bring about movement. Some is used to build up or break down molecules.

Mammals and birds also use energy from respiration to maintain a constant body temperature.

> **1** Which set of metabolic reactions transfers energy so that it can be used for other processes in the organism?

The role of the liver

The liver is a large organ that has many different functions.

Excess amino acids are changed to urea in the liver. The amino group is removed from the amino acid in the process of deamination. This forms ammonia, a toxic substance, which is then converted to urea. The urea passes in the blood to the kidneys and is excreted (removed) in the urine.

amino acids $\xrightarrow[\text{in liver}]{\textbf{deamination}}$ ammonia $\longrightarrow$ urea $\xrightarrow[\text{to kidneys}]{\textbf{in blood}}$ urine

Poisonous substances such as ethanol are detoxified in the liver. The breakdown products are transported in the blood to the kidneys, so they can be excreted in the urine.

Old red blood cells are broken down and the iron is stored to make new red blood cells.

Lactic acid, produced by the muscles in anaerobic respiration, is transported in the blood to the liver. Here it is converted to glucose. The oxygen debt is repaid once the lactic acid has been converted to glucose and the glucose has been completely broken down in aerobic respiration to carbon dioxide and water. Excess glucose can be stored as glycogen in the liver.

> **2** Name the process that removes the amino group from an amino acid.

Higher

Key points

- Metabolism is the sum of all the reactions in the body.
- The energy transferred by respiration in cells is used by the organism for the continual enzyme-controlled processes of metabolism that synthesise new molecules.
- Metabolism includes the conversion of glucose to starch, glycogen, and cellulose. Metabolism also includes the formation of lipid molecules, and the use of glucose and nitrate ions to form amino acids, which are used to synthesise proteins, and the breakdown of excess proteins to form urea.
- **H** Blood flowing through the muscles transports lactic acid to the liver, where it is converted back to glucose.

Synoptic links

Topic B3.3 covers the reactions that build up carbohydrates, proteins, and lipids.

For photosynthesis, see Topics B8.1 and B8.3.

For the role of the liver in digestion, see Topic B3.7.

There is more about the kidneys and the formation of urine in Topic B12.3.

Study tip

Learn the functions of the liver.

Study tip

Learn the metabolic sequence involved when the liver produces urea from amino acids.

1. Write the word equation for aerobic respiration. [2 marks]

2. Where does aerobic respiration take place in cells? [1 mark]

3. Why do muscles respire? [2 marks]

4. What is meant by 'anaerobic'? [1 mark]

5. In plant metabolism, glucose can be converted into larger molecules. Name two of them. [2 marks]

6. Describe two ways your breathing changes during exercise. [2 marks]

7. Why do muscles store glycogen? [4 marks]

8. **a** What is fermentation? [1 mark]

   b How do humans benefit from fermentation in yeast cells? [4 marks]

9. Why do blood vessels in the muscles dilate during exercise? [5 marks]

10. What are the disadvantages of anaerobic respiration compared with aerobic respiration? [3 marks]

11. **H** Explain what is meant by an oxygen debt. [3 marks]

12. What measurements would you take to test your level of fitness?
    Explain how each measurement indicates fitness. [6 marks]

13. **H** **a** Describe how urea is produced. [6 marks]

    b Explain why urea must be excreted and how this is achieved in humans. [4 marks]

Chapter checklist ✔

Tick when you have:

reviewed it after your lesson	✓	☐	☐
revised once – some questions right	✓	✓	☐
revised twice – all questions right	✓	✓	✓

Move on to another topic when you have all three ticks

9.1 Aerobic respiration ☐ ☐ ☐

9.2 The response to exercise ☐ ☐ ☐

9.3 Anaerobic respiration ☐ ☐ ☐

9.4 Metabolism and the liver ☐ ☐ ☐

01 Plants carry out photosynthesis.

01.1 Name the gas used in photosynthesis. [1 mark]

01.2 Name the food made in photosynthesis. [1 mark]

A gardener wants to grow bigger tomato plants in his greenhouse.

01.3 Ⓗ Name **three** factors the gardener can change to speed up the rate of photosynthesis of the plants. [3 marks]

01.4 Ⓗ Explain why the gardener in **01.3** cannot immediately see if the rate of photosynthesis has increased. [2 marks]

02 Penicillin is an antibiotic.

02.1 Explain why doctors prescribe antibiotics. [2 marks]

02.2 Influenza (flu) is caused by a virus.
It is difficult to treat diseases caused by a virus. Explain why. [2 marks]

02.3 Penicillin is produced by a fungus. The fungus is grown in fermenters containing nutrients. The graph in **Figure 1** shows the relationship between the growth of the fungus and the production of penicillin.

Figure 1

Explain the shapes of the curves for the growth of the fungus and the production of penicillin. [6 marks]

03 Cancer is a non-communicable disease that can affect many parts of the body.

03.1 How is a cancer tumour formed? [2 marks]

Study tips

In questions such as **02.3** you need to write in a logical order and use the correct scientific terms to gain full marks.

Do not be put off if you have not been taught about fermenters. This question is about comparing the growth of the fungus and the penicillin production. Read the question carefully – you are told that the fermenter contains nutrients. The fungus needs food to grow before it can produce penicillin. Some of the nutrients will then be used to make the penicillin. Use this information to explain why penicillin production lags behind fungal growth and remember to use figures from the graph.

03.2 Using the diagrams in **Figure 2** to help you, describe how a tumour can spread from the skin to the liver. [4 marks]

skin

capillary

liver

Figure 2

03.3 What is the most likely cause of skin cancer? [1 mark]

03.4 Lung cancer is a common cancer that causes many deaths every year. Scientists have made a causal link between smoking tobacco and lung cancer.
What is a causal link? [2 marks]

03.5 An electronic cigarette or e-cigarette is a hand-held electronic device that vaporises a flavoured liquid. The user inhales the vapour.
The fluid in the e-cigarette is usually made of nicotine, propylene glycol, glycerine, and flavourings.
Both e-cigarettes and cigarettes made of tobacco contain chemicals.
Which chemical is addictive? [1 mark]

03.6 Suggest **one** benefit to tobacco smokers if they change to e-cigarettes. [1 mark]

03.7 Give **one** reason why some people think e-cigarettes should not be widely available. [1 mark]

04 Ⓗ Monoclonal antibodies are used in medical treatment.
04.1 What type of chemical is an antibody? [1 mark]
04.2 Which human cells make antibodies? [1 mark]
04.3 What is a hybridoma? [1 mark]
04.4 Describe how monoclonal antibodies are produced. [5 marks]
04.5 Give **one** use of monoclonal antibodies. [1 mark]

3 Biological responses

The ability to respond to the world around you is key to survival. Your body needs awareness of the conditions outside and inside your body to coordinate your responses. Everything works towards keeping your internal conditions stable and within very narrow ranges.

It isn't just human beings that need complex coordination and control systems. Plants also need to respond to the world around them so they grow in the right direction and make as much food as possible. In humans, the nervous system controls most of our rapid responses, and our hormones control everything from our reproduction to the rate of our metabolism. In plants, most control is through the action of hormones.

I already know...

I will revise...

I already know...	I will revise...
the basic structure of neurones.	the differences between sensory and motor neurones and their roles in coordination and control.
that tissues can be organised into organs with particular functions in the body.	the arrangement of tissues in the human eye and how they are adapted to their functions.
the importance of light to plants for photosynthesis.	how plants respond to unilateral light and gravity to ensure they capture as much light as possible.
the basic processes of human reproduction.	how reproduction is controlled by hormones and how hormones can be used in the artificial control of fertility.
how the rate of enzyme action is affected by temperature changes.	how body temperature is maintained within a narrow range through homeostasis.
that urea is produced as a waste product from the breakdown of excess protein in the liver.	how the kidneys work to remove urea from the body in the urine.

10.1 Principles of homeostasis

Key points

- Homeostasis is the regulation of the internal conditions of a cell or organism to maintain optimum conditions for function, in response to internal and external changes.

- Homeostasis is important for maintaining optimal conditions for enzyme action and all cell functions.

- In the human body homeostasis includes control of blood glucose concentration, body temperature, and water levels.

- The automatic control systems may involve nervous or chemical responses.

- All control systems include receptors, coordination centres, and effectors.

Synoptic links

For more about the effect of temperature and pH changes on enzyme activity, see Topic B3.5.

See Chapter B11 for more about the role of the hormonal system, and Chapter B12 for some specific homeostatic systems.

Key words: homeostasis, receptors, stimuli, coordination centres, effectors

Study tip

Make sure you can explain the term 'homeostasis' and can give examples.

- The process by which your body maintains a constant internal environment is called **homeostasis**.

- It is important to maintain optimal conditions for enzyme action and all cell functions.

- Homeostasis relies on automatic control systems such as your nervous system, hormones, and body organs.

Internal conditions that are controlled include:

- water content
- body temperature
- blood glucose concentration.

---

1 Name one internal condition that is controlled by homeostasis.

- Water leaves the body all the time as you breathe out and sweat. Excess water is removed in the urine by the kidneys.

- Your body must keep the core body temperature constant so that your enzymes will work properly.

- Glucose is the energy source for cells. The level of glucose in your blood is controlled by the pancreas.

All control systems in the body have the following key features.

- **Receptors** detect **stimuli** in the external or internal environment. The receptor cells may be part of the nervous or hormonal control system.

- **Coordination centres**, which include the brain, spinal cord, and organs such as the pancreas.

- **Effectors**, which are usually muscles or glands that bring about a response to the stimulus.

---

2 Name two types of effector in the body.

B10

10.2 The structure and function of the human nervous system

Key points

- The nervous system uses electrical impulses to enable you to react quickly to your surroundings and coordinate your behaviour.
- Cells called receptors detect stimuli (changes in the environment).
- Impulses from receptors pass along sensory neurones to the brain or spinal cord (CNS). The brain coordinates the response, and impulses are sent along motor neurones from the brain (CNS) to the effector organs.

- The nervous system has receptor cells to detect stimuli.
- The receptor cells are found in sense organs such as the eye, ear, nose, tongue, and skin.
- In the eye, light stimulates receptors, and electrical impulses then pass to the brain along **neurones** (nerve cells). Other stimuli include sound, chemicals, temperature changes, touch, and pain.
- The brain coordinates responses to many stimuli.

1 Which stimuli are detected by the skin?

- The brain and spinal cord form the **central nervous system (CNS)**.
- **Nerves** contain bundles of neurones. **Sensory neurones** carry impulses from receptors to the CNS.
- **Motor neurones** carry impulses from the CNS to **effectors** that respond to the impulses. Effectors may be muscles or glands. Muscles respond by contracting and glands respond by secreting (releasing) chemicals.

Synoptic link

For more about nerve cells, see Topic B1.4.

2 How do impulses pass from a receptor to the CNS?

The way your nervous system works can be summed up as:

$$\text{stimulus} \rightarrow \text{receptor} \rightarrow \text{sensory neurone} \rightarrow \text{coordinator (CNS)} \rightarrow$$
$$\text{motor neurone} \rightarrow \text{effector} \rightarrow \text{response}$$

Key words: neurones, nerves, central nervous system (CNS), sensory neurones, motor neurones, effectors

Sensory nerves carry impulses to the CNS. The information is processed and impulses are sent out along motor nerves to produce an action.

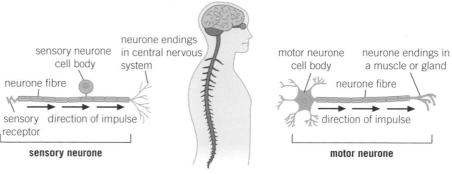

Study tips

Learn the difference between a nerve and a neurone. Remember that a sensory neurone carries impulses to the CNS, and a motor neurone carries the impulse from the CNS to a muscle or gland.

The rapid responses of your nervous system allow you to respond to your surroundings quickly – and in the right way

Measuring reaction times

There are many ways to investigate how quickly nerve impulses travel in your body. Two simple methods are:

- to use the ruler drop test
- to use digital sensors to measure how quickly you react to a visual stimulus.

People claim that activities such as drinking cola, talking on the phone, and listening to music affect reaction times. You can use these simple techniques to investigate the effect a factor has – or does not have – on human reaction times.

10.3 Reflex actions

Key points

- Reflex actions are automatic and rapid and do not involve the conscious parts of the brain.

- Reflexes involve sensory, relay, and motor neurones.

- Reflex actions control everyday bodily functions, such as breathing and digestion, and help you to avoid danger.

- The main stages of a reflex arc are:
  stimulus → receptor → sensory neurone → relay neurone → motor neurone → effector → response

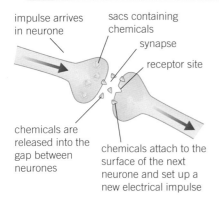

impulse arrives in neurone

sacs containing chemicals

synapse

receptor site

chemicals are released into the gap between neurones

chemicals attach to the surface of the next neurone and set up a new electrical impulse

When an impulse arrives at the junction between two neurones, chemicals are released that cross the synapse and arrive at receptor sites on the next neurone. This starts up a new electrical impulse in the next neurone

The main steps involved in reflex actions (**reflexes**) are as follows.

- A receptor detects a stimulus (e.g., a sharp pin).
- A sensory neurone transmits the impulse to the CNS.
- A relay neurone in the CNS passes the impulse on.
- A motor neurone is stimulated.
- The motor neurone passes the impulse to an effector (muscle or gland).
- Action is taken (the response).

1   What is the function of a relay neurone?

At the junction between two neurones is a gap called a synapse. Chemicals transmit the impulse across the gap.

The sequence from receptor to effector is a **reflex arc**.

2   Name a type of effector.

Reflex actions protect you from danger because they happen automatically and rapidly. They do not involve the conscious parts of the brain, and this speeds up the response.

You do not have to think about breathing and moving food along the digestive system. These body movements are types of reflex action.

Key words: reflexes, reflex arc

Study tip

Cover the labels in the diagram below showing a reflex arc and practise labelling the diagram. Remember that the stimulus and effector will vary, but the rest of the diagram will always be the same.

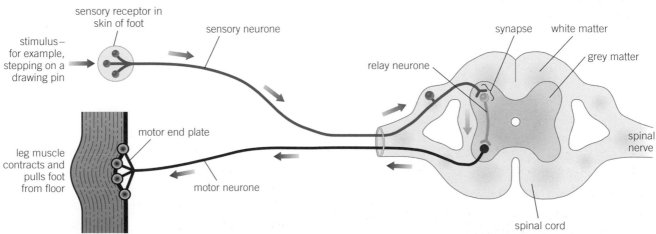

sensory receptor in skin of foot

stimulus – for example, stepping on a drawing pin

sensory neurone

synapse   white matter

relay neurone

grey matter

motor end plate

leg muscle contracts and pulls foot from floor

motor neurone

spinal nerve

spinal cord

The reflex action that moves your foot away from a sharp object can save you from a nasty injury

10.4 The brain

Key points

- The brain is made up of billions of interconnected neurones that control complex behaviour.
- It has different regions, for example the cerebral cortex, the cerebellum, and the medulla, each having different functions.
- **(H)** Scientists map regions of the brain to their functions by studying patients with brain damage, by electrically stimulating different areas of the brain, and by using MRI scanning techniques.

Synoptic links

There is more about the pituitary gland and its hormones in Topics B11.1 and B12.3.

For more about thermoregulation, see Topic B12.1.

Key words: cerebral cortex, cerebellum, medulla

Study tips

Learn what each part of the brain controls:

- cerebral cortex – memory and thought
- cerebellum – movement
- medulla – heartbeat and breathing.

Study tip

H

Make sure you can describe why it is difficult to study the brain and to treat it. Learn the methods scientists use to study the brain.

The brain:

- is made of billions of interconnected neurones
- receives impulses from sensory neurones all over your body and coordinates the responses
- controls complex behaviour and is responsible for your thoughts and feelings
- has different regions that carry out different functions.

The brain has different regions.

- The **cerebral cortex** is concerned with consciousness, intelligence, memory, and language.
- The **cerebellum** is concerned mainly with the coordination of muscular activity.
- The **medulla** is concerned with unconscious activities, such as controlling the heartbeat and breathing.

The pituitary gland, which produces hormones such as ADH, is linked to the brain.

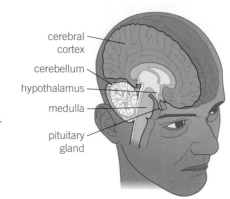

The brain is very complex – it coordinates and controls much of your behaviour

1 Which region of the brain is mainly concerned with movement?

Finding out about the brain

Scientists have been able to map the regions of the brain to particular functions by:

- studying patients with brain damage
- electrically stimulating different parts of the brain
- using magnetic resonance imaging (MRI) scanning techniques to monitor brain activity after injury or as someone completes a task.

2 What type of scanner can be used to monitor brain activity?

Problems with the brain

The brain is very delicate and complex so it is very difficult to investigate or treat brain disorders without causing unintended damage.

- Drugs do not always pass through the membranes surrounding the brain.
- Surgery is difficult because the function of each area of the brain is not fully understood.

Higher

10.5 The eye

The eye is a sense organ. The structures of the eye are designed to focus light onto the retina. The receptor cells in the retina are sensitive to light intensity and colour.

The main structures of the eye

- The sclera is the tough, white outer layer that prevents damage to the eye.

- The cornea is a transparent area at the front of the sclera. The cornea lets light into the eye. The curved surface of the cornea changes the direction of the light rays so they are refracted towards the retina.

- The muscles of the iris contract and relax to control the size of the pupil, the hole through which the light enters the eye.

  - In dim light the pupil is enlarged to let in as much light as possible.

  - In bright light the iris makes the pupil small to reduce the amount of light entering the eye. Too much light could damage the receptor cells in the retina.

- The lens is a clear disc held in place by **suspensory ligaments** and the **ciliary muscles**. The lens changes the direction of the light so that the image is focused on the retina.

- When light hits the retina, the light-sensitive cells are stimulated. They send impulses to the brain along sensory neurones in the optic nerve.

1 What is the function of the iris?

Focusing the light

- The light that enters the eye is focused by refraction.

- The light changes direction as it passes through the cornea, the jelly in the eyeball, and the lens.

- The cornea and jelly refract the light a fixed amount.

- The shape of the lens can be changed by the contraction or relaxation of the ciliary muscles. The change in shape alters the amount of refraction depending on whether the light is entering from a near or a distant object.

Key points

- The eye is a sense organ containing receptors in the retina that are sensitive to light intensity and colour.

- The tough outer sclera has a transparent region at the front called the cornea that lets light in and refracts (changes the direction of) light towards the retina.

- The muscular iris controls the size of the pupil and the amount of light entering the eye.

- The ciliary muscles and suspensory ligaments change the shape of the lens to finely focus light on to the retina.

- The optic nerve carries impulses from the retina to the brain.

Key words: suspensory ligaments, ciliary muscles

bright light
- circular muscles contract
- radial muscles relax
- pupil constricts

circular muscles contract

dim light
- circular muscles relax
- radial muscles contract
- pupil dilates

radial muscles contract

The ever-changing size of the pupil affects the amount of light that reaches the retina

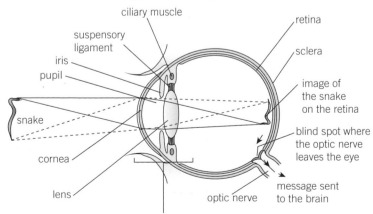

The human eye is a complex and effective sense organ. Each structure is closely related to its function. When an image falls on the light-sensitive cells of the retina and impulses are sent through the optic nerve to the brain, you are able to see

Study tip

Make a table showing the structures that make up the eye and their functions.

10.6 Common problems of the eye

Key points

- Accommodation is the process of changing the shape of the lens of the eye to focus on near or distant objects.

- To focus on close objects the ciliary muscles contract, the suspensory ligaments loosen, and the lens becomes thicker so it can refract light rays strongly.

- To focus on distant objects the ciliary muscles relax, the suspensory ligaments are pulled tight, and the lens is pulled thin so it only refracts the light rays slightly.

- Sight defects can be treated using:
  - spectacle lenses to refract the light rays so they focus on the retina
  - hard or soft contact lenses
  - laser surgery
  - replacement lenses in the eye.

Key words: myopia, hyperopia

Study tip

Make sure you know the difference between myopia and hyperopia and how to correct them.

1 What is accommodation?
2 What type of lens is used to correct **a** myopia? **b** hyperopia?

Accommodation – seeing near and far

- The light rays from close objects are spreading out or diverging very strongly. The light rays from distant objects are travelling in almost parallel rays.

- Accommodation is the process of changing the shape of the lens to focus on near or distant objects. To focus on a distant object, the ciliary muscles relax so the suspensory ligaments are pulled tight and the lens is pulled flat and thin. To focus on a nearby object, the ciliary muscles contract so the suspensory ligaments loosen. The lens is then thicker and more curved. It refracts light rays more strongly.

Focusing on a distant object — lens less convex (flatter)

Focusing on a nearby object — lens more convex (rounded)

Accommodation in the eye

Common defects of the eye

Myopia is short sightedness. **Hyperopia** is long sightedness.

Myopia
rays not focused on retina
rays now correctly focused
concave lens

Hyperopia
rays not focused on retina
rays now correctly focused
convex lens

The eyes of short-sighted people focus light from distant objects in front of the retina, making the objects difficult to see clearly. A simple concave lens can make all the difference

The eyes of long-sighted people focus light from nearby objects behind the retina, making the objects difficult to see clearly. A simple convex lens can make all the difference

New technology

- **Hard or soft contact lenses** are placed on the surface of the eye. They must be kept sterile to prevent eye infections. Some are disposable.

- **Laser eye surgery**: in myopia, it is used to reduce the thickness of the cornea so it refracts light less strongly in hyperopia, lasers change the curve of the cornea so it refracts light from nearby objects more effectively.

- **Lens replacement**: either a permanent contact lens is inserted with the natural lens in place or an artificial lens replaces the natural one. Risks include possible damage to the retina, cataracts in the natural lens, or infections.

1. Name the two types of effector found in the human body, and explain how they respond to stimuli. [4 marks]

2. What is meant by 'homeostasis'? [1 mark]

3. What is a reflex action? [3 marks]

4. **a** Which stimulus is detected by the eye? [1 mark]
   b Which part of the eye contains the receptor cells? [1 mark]

5. How are impulses passed across a synapse? [2 marks]

6. Why is it important to maintain a constant body temperature? [4 marks]

7. Which region of the brain is concerned with:
   a memory? [1 mark] **b** coordinating muscle activity? [1 mark] **c** controlling the heartbeat? [1 mark]

8. Name the stages of the pathway involved in a reflex action, from stimulus to response. [5 marks]

9. Name the parts of the eye that refract the light. [3 marks]

10. **a** What is the scientific name for short sightedness? [1 mark]
    b What type of lens is used to correct short sightedness? [1 mark]

11. **H** Give two methods that scientists use to find out which part of the brain performs particular functions. [2 marks]

12. During a reflex action, the impulses pass from a relay neurone to a motor neurone via a synapse. Another neurone is also stimulated, at the same synapse, which links directly with the brain. Suggest the importance of this link. [2 marks]

13. **a** What is meant by the term 'accommodation' in the eye? [2 marks]
    b Explain how the ciliary muscles and suspensory ligaments bring about accommodation to view a close object. [4 marks]

14. **a** Explain why a person with hyperopia has blurred vision when reading. [3 marks]
    b What methods can be used to correct hyperopia? [5 marks]

Chapter checklist

Tick when you have:

reviewed it after your lesson ✓ ☐ ☐

revised once – some questions right ✓ ✓ ☐

revised twice – all questions right ✓ ✓ ✓

Move on to another topic when you have all three ticks

10.1 Principles of homeostasis ☐ ☐ ☐

10.2 The structure and function of the human nervous system ☐ ☐ ☐

10.3 Reflex actions ☐ ☐ ☐

10.4 The brain ☐ ☐ ☐

10.5 The eye ☐ ☐ ☐

10.6 Common problems of the eye ☐ ☐ ☐

11.1 Principles of hormonal control

Key points

- The endocrine system is composed of glands that secrete chemicals called hormones directly into the bloodstream. The blood carries the hormone to a target organ where it produces an effect.

- Compared with the nervous system, the effects of hormones are often slower but longer lasting.

- The pituitary gland is the master gland that secretes several hormones into the blood in response to body conditions. Some of these hormones act on other glands and stimulate them to release hormones to bring about specific effects.

- Key endocrine glands are the pituitary gland, thyroid gland, pancreas, adrenal glands, ovaries, and testes.

Synoptic links

There is more about the ovary and the testes and the effects of their hormones in Topics B11.6–B11.8, and about ADH and the kidney in Topic B12.3.

Study tip

Learn to label a diagram of the endocrine glands. Cover the labels on the diagram opposite and practise writing the names of the glands.

The endocrine system

- The **endocrine system** is made up of glands that secrete **hormones** directly into the bloodstream.

- The blood carries the hormone to the effector or target organ (or organs).

- There are receptors on the cell membranes of the effector organ. The receptors pick up the hormone molecules, triggering a response in the cell.

- Some hormones, such as **insulin** and **adrenaline**, can act very rapidly.

- Many hormones, such as growth hormones and sex hormones, are slow-acting but have long-term effects.

1 How does a hormone travel from the endocrine gland to the target organ?

The endocrine glands

- The endocrine glands secrete hormones to provide chemical coordination and control for the body.

- The **pituitary gland** in the brain acts as a master gland.

Some hormones from the pituitary gland target specific endocrine glands.

- **Follicle stimulating hormone** (**FSH**) stimulates the **ovaries** to secrete **oestrogen** (the female sex hormone).

- TSH stimulates the thyroid gland to secrete thyroxine.

Other pituitary hormones have a direct effect on the body.

- **ADH** affects the amount of urine produced by the kidney.

- Growth hormone controls the rate of growth in children.

2 Where is ADH produced?

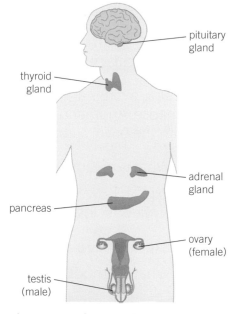

The main endocrine glands of the human body

Key words: endocrine system, hormones, insulin, adrenaline, pituitary gland, follicle stimulating hormone (FSH), ovaries, oestrogen, ADH.

Student Book
pages 162–163 **B11**

11.2 The control of blood glucose levels

- The pancreas monitors and controls the level of glucose in your blood. Receptors in the pancreas detect the level of blood glucose.

High levels of blood glucose

- If there is too much glucose in the blood, the pancreas produces the hormone **insulin**.
- Insulin causes glucose to move from the blood into the cells.
- In the liver and muscles, excess glucose is converted to glycogen for storage. When these stores are full, the glucose is stored as lipids, which can eventually make a person obese.

1 Which hormone reduces the level of glucose in the blood?

Low levels of blood glucose

- Insulin causes the blood glucose level to fall.
- If the level gets too low, receptors in the pancreas detect the low level.
- The pancreas releases **glucagon**, another hormone.
- The glucagon causes the glycogen in the liver to change into glucose.
- This glucose is released back into the blood.
- Glucagon interacts with insulin in a negative feedback cycle to control blood glucose levels.

Diabetes

- If the pancreas produces no insulin or too little insulin, the blood glucose level may become very high. This condition is known as **type 1 diabetes**.
- **Type 2 diabetes** develops when the body does not respond to its own insulin. Obesity is a significant factor in the development of type 2 diabetes.

2 Name one significant factor in the development of type 2 diabetes.

Higher

Key points

- Your blood glucose concentration is monitored and controlled by your pancreas.
- The pancreas produces the hormone insulin, which allows glucose to move from the blood into the cells and to be stored as glycogen in the liver and muscles.
- **H** The pancreas also produces glucagon, which allows glycogen to be converted back into glucose and released into the blood.
- **H** Glucagon interacts with insulin in a negative feedback cycle to control glucose levels.
- In type 1 diabetes, the blood glucose may rise to fatally high levels because the pancreas does not secrete enough insulin.
- In type 2 diabetes, the body stops responding to its own insulin.

Key words: insulin, glucagon, type 1 diabetes, type 2 diabetes

Study tips

Make sure you know the difference between the following terms:

- glucose – the sugar used in respiration
- glycogen – a storage carbohydrate found in the liver and muscles
- **H** glucagon – a hormone that stimulates the liver to break down glycogen to glucose.

Be sure to spell these words correctly.

Study tip

Remember: an increase of blood sugar causes a release of insulin. The insulin reduces blood sugar, which stops the release of more insulin. This is negative feedback.

Negative feedback control of blood glucose levels using insulin and glucagon

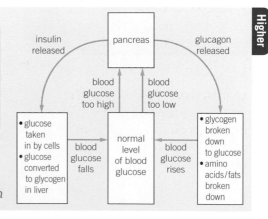

Higher

11.3 Treating diabetes

Key points

- Type 1 diabetes is normally controlled by injecting insulin to replace the hormone that is not made in the body.

- Type 2 diabetes is often treated by means of a carbohydrate-controlled diet and taking more exercise. If this does not work, drugs may be needed.

Synoptic links

There is more about stem cells in Topics B2.3 and B2.4.

For links between obesity and diseases such as type 2 diabetes, see Topic B7.4.

Study tip

Make sure you understand why type 1 diabetes and type 2 diabetes are different conditions.

On the up

If you can explain how type 2 diabetes can be treated with diet and exercise, you can achieve the top grades if you are also able to explain in detail how lifestyle choices affect the risk of developing type 2 diabetes.

Treating type 1 diabetes

- Type 1 diabetes is traditionally treated with human insulin produced by genetically engineered bacteria.

- A person with type 1 diabetes has to inject themselves with insulin before meals every day without fail.

- People who are very active and have diabetes need to match the amount of insulin injected with their diet and exercise.

- Some people use a pump attached to the body, which injects insulin. They can adjust the level of insulin injected by the pump.

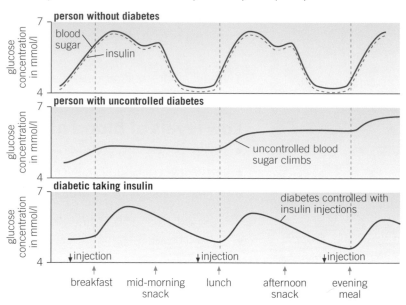

These graphs show the effect of insulin injections on people with type 1 diabetes. The injections keep the blood glucose level within safe limits

Doctors and other scientists are trying to develop new methods of treating and possibly curing type 1 diabetes. These include:

- pancreas transplants

- transplanting pancreatic cells

- using embryonic stem cells to produce insulin-producing cells

- using adult stem cells from people with diabetes

- genetically engineering pancreas cells to make them work properly.

> **1** What is the main treatment for type 1 diabetes?

Treating type 2 diabetes

- Type 2 diabetes can often be controlled by eating a balanced diet, exercising, and dieting if you are overweight. It is important for a person with type 2 diabetes to reduce the amount of carbohydrate in their diet.

- If controlling your diet, losing weight, and taking exercise do not work, doctors can prescribe drugs to treat type 2 diabetes. The drugs help insulin to work better, help the pancreas to make more insulin, or help to reduce the amount of glucose you absorb from your gut.

> **2** Explain how one drug to treat type 2 diabetes works in the body.

Student Book
pages 166–167

11.4 The role of negative feedback

Many hormones in your body are controlled as part of negative feedback systems.

Negative feedback
- Negative feedback systems work to maintain a steady state.
- If a factor in the internal environment increases, changes take place to reduce it and restore the original level.
- If a factor in the internal environment decreases, changes take place to increase it and restore the original level.
- Whatever the initial change, in negative feedback the response causes the opposite.
- Many hormones are involved in negative feedback systems, including insulin and glucagon, most female sex hormones, and thyroxine.

1   Why is negative feedback important?

Thyroxine
The hormone thyroxine:
- is produced by the thyroid gland in your neck.
- controls the basal metabolic rate (the rate at which substances are built up or broken down by chemical reactions in the body)
- controls how much oxygen is used by tissues
- controls how the brain of a growing child develops
- is important in growth and development.

Thyroxine and negative feedback
- In adults the level of thyroxine in the blood remains relatively stable due to negative feedback control. This involves thyroid stimulating hormone (TSH) produced by the pituitary gland.
- Falling levels of thyroxine in the blood are detected by sensors in the brain, causing an increase in the amount of TSH released from the pituitary gland.
- TSH stimulates thyroxine production by the thyroid gland.
- The rising level of thyroxine in the blood is detected by the sensors in the brain, and the level of TSH falls. This is negative feedback.

2   Where is TSH produced?

Adrenaline
- Adrenaline is produced by the adrenal glands above the kidneys.
- Adrenaline is called the 'fight or flight' hormone because it is released when you are stressed, frightened, or angry and prepares you to respond. The release of adrenaline is not controlled by negative feedback.

Adrenaline causes:
- your heart rate and breathing rate to increase
- stored glycogen in the liver to be converted to glucose for respiration
- your pupils to dilate to let in more light
- your mental awareness to increase
- an increase in the flow of blood containing extra glucose and oxygen to the limb muscles.

3   How does the action of adrenaline help you to escape from danger?

Key points
- Thyroxine from the thyroid gland stimulates the basal metabolic rate. It plays an important role in growth and development.
- Adrenaline is produced by the adrenal glands in times of fear or stress. It increases the heart rate and boosts the delivery of oxygen and glucose to the brain and muscles, preparing the body for 'fight or flight'.
- Thyroxine is controlled by negative feedback whereas adrenaline is not.

Study tips
Learn the sequence:
1. A decrease of thyroxine in the blood causes an increase in TSH release.
2. The TSH causes an increase in the thyroxine level.
3. Then the increased thyroxine level causes a decrease in TSH release.

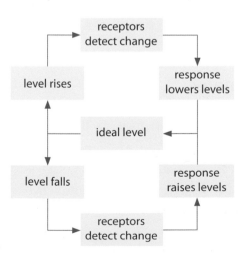

A negative feedback loop means values will vary around a normal level within a limited range

11.5 Human reproduction

Hormones play an important part in human reproduction at every stage.

Key points

- During puberty reproductive hormones cause secondary sexual characteristics to develop.

- Oestrogen is the main female reproductive hormone produced by the ovary. At puberty eggs begin to mature in the ovary and one is released approximately every 28 days at ovulation.

- Testosterone is the main male reproductive hormone produced by the testes. It stimulates sperm production.

- Hormones involved in the menstrual cycle of a woman include follicle stimulating hormone (FSH), luteinising hormone (LH), oestrogen, and progesterone.

Hormones and puberty

- Babies are born with primary sexual characteristics – ovaries in girls and testes in boys.

- At puberty the ovaries and testes produce sex hormones, which trigger the development of the secondary sexual characteristics.

Oestrogen and puberty in females

- The main female reproductive hormone is **oestrogen**, produced by the **ovaries**.

- These are the female secondary sexual characteristics: a growth spurt; growth of underarm and pubic hair; breast development; the external genitals grow and the skin darkens; body shape changes as fat is deposited on the hips, buttocks, and thighs; the brain changes and matures; mature ova start to form every month in the ovaries; the uterus grows and becomes active; menstruation begins.

The menstrual cycle

- Each month, eggs begin to mature in the ovary and the uterus produces a thickened lining ready for a pregnancy.

- Every 28 days a mature egg is released from the ovary. This is called **ovulation**.

- If the egg is not fertilised, the lining of the uterus, along with the egg, is shed around 14 days later.

Several hormones are involved in controlling the menstrual cycle.

- Follicle stimulating hormone (FSH) causes the eggs in the ovary to mature. (The follicle is a tissue of cells surrounding the maturing egg.)

- Luteinising hormone (LH) stimulates the release of the egg at ovulation.

- Oestrogen and progesterone stimulate the build-up and maintenance of the uterus lining.

---

1 What is ovulation?

---

fallopian tube (oviduct) – where the egg travels to the uterus and may be fertilised

ovary – eggs mature here

uterus (womb) – the fetus develops here

cervix – entrance to uterus

vagina – receives sperm during sexual intercourse

The female reproductive system

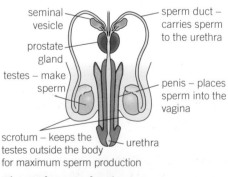

seminal vesicle

sperm duct – carries sperm to the urethra

prostate gland

testes – make sperm

penis – places sperm into the vagina

scrotum – keeps the testes outside the body for maximum sperm production

urethra

The male reproductive organs

Key words: oestrogen, ovaries, ovulation, testosterone

Testosterone and puberty in males

The main male reproductive hormone is **testosterone**, produced by the testes.

The male secondary sexual characteristics include: a growth spurt; growth of pubic hair, underarm hair, and facial hair; the larynx gets bigger and the voice breaks; the external genitalia grow and the skin darkens; the testes grow and become active, producing sperm throughout life; the shoulders and chest broaden as muscle develops; the brain matures.

---

2 Name the male sex hormone.

11.6 Hormones and the menstrual cycle

Key points

- The interactions of four hormones control the maturing and release of an egg from the ovary and the build-up of the lining of the uterus in the menstrual cycle.

- FSH from the pituitary stimulates eggs to mature in the follicles of the ovary, and the ovary to produce oestrogen.

- Oestrogen secreted by the ovaries stimulates the growth of the lining of the uterus and the release of LH, and inhibits FSH.

- LH stimulates ovulation.

- Progesterone is produced by the empty follicle after ovulation. It maintains the lining of the uterus for around 10 days and inhibits FSH and LH.

Control of the menstrual cycle

The complex events of the menstrual cycle are coordinated by the interactions of FSH, LH, oestrogen, and progesterone.

Follicle stimulating hormone (FSH):

- is secreted by the pituitary gland
- makes eggs mature in their follicles in the ovaries
- stimulates the ovaries to produce hormones including oestrogen.

Oestrogen:

- is made and secreted by the ovaries in response to FSH
- stimulates the lining of the uterus to grow again after menstruation in preparation for pregnancy
- inhibits the production of more FSH and stimulates the release of LH when oestrogen levels are high.

Luteinising hormone (LH):

- is secreted by the pituitary gland
- stimulates the release of a mature egg from the ovary
- levels fall again once ovulation has taken place.

Progesterone:

- is secreted by the empty egg follicle in the ovary after ovulation
- is one of the hormones that helps to maintain a pregnancy if the egg is fertilised .
- inhibits both FSH and LH
- maintains the lining of the uterus in the second half of the cycle, so it is ready to receive a developing embryo if the egg is fertilised.

As the oestrogen levels rise, the production of FSH is inhibited and the production of LH is stimulated. When LH levels reach a peak in the middle of the cycle, ovulation occurs.

FSH and LH are then inhibited by high levels of oestrogen and progesterone, which keep the uterus ready for pregnancy.

If the egg is not fertilised the levels of all the hormones then fall, and the lining of the uterus is lost from the body. FSH is no longer inhibited so its level rises and stimulates the ovaries to produce oestrogen again.

1   Name the two hormones produced by the pituitary gland that are involved in controlling the menstrual cycle.

2   Which hormone inhibits FSH?

The main events of the menstrual cycle

11.7 The artificial control of fertility

Key points

- Fertility can be controlled by a number of hormonal and non-hormonal methods of contraception.

- Contraceptive methods include oral contraceptives, hormonal injections, implants, and patches, barrier methods (e.g., condoms and diaphragms), intrauterine devices, spermicidal agents, abstinence, and surgical sterilisation.

Key word: contraception

Study tip

Make a table to show the advantages and disadvantages of each type of contraception.

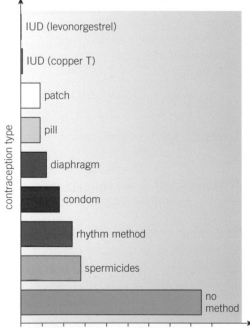

Failure rates for different methods of birth control based on data from the American Academy of Paediatrics

To prevent pregnancy, you need to prevent the egg and sperm meeting or prevent a fertilised egg from implanting in the uterus. This is known as **contraception**.

Fertility can be controlled by a variety of hormonal and non-hormonal methods of contraception. The different methods all have advantages and disadvantages.

Hormone-based contraception

- Oral contraceptives contain hormones to inhibit FSH production so that no eggs mature.

- The mixed pill contains low doses of oestrogen with some progesterone. Some pills contain only progesterone.

- The pill hormones:
  - inhibit FSH production so no eggs are released
  - stop the uterus lining developing, preventing implantation
  - make the mucus in the cervix thick to prevent sperm getting through

1 Name the two hormones found in contraceptive pills

Method	How it works	Advantages	Disadvantages
Oral contraceptive (pill)	Hormone-based	Easy to use, very effective	Person may forget, slight risk of raised blood pressure, thrombosis, breast cancer
Injections	Hormone-based	Easy to use, very effective. Long term	Slight risk of side effects as for pill
Patches	Hormone-based	Long term	Person may forget to change it. Slight risk of side effects as for pill
Spermicide	Chemical to kill sperm	Easy to obtain	Not very effective
Condom – thin latex sheath	Barrier method – prevents sperm entering vagina	No side effects. No need for medical advice. Protects against STDs	Can be damaged and sperm will pass into vagina
Diaphragm or cap	Barrier placed across cervix	No side effects. Works better with a spermicide	Must be fitted by a doctor and be positioned correctly
Intrauterine device	Inserted into uterus. May contain copper or progesterone. Prevents implantation	Very effective	Must be inserted by a doctor. Can cause period problems or infections
Abstinence	No intercourse	100% effective. Suitable for those with objections to using contraception	Unreliable if people only abstain around the time of ovulation
Vasectomy – male sterilisation	Operation to cut and tie the sperm ducts	Permanent – cannot forget to use contraception	Not usually reversible
Female sterilisation	Operation to cut and tie the oviducts so egg cannot reach uterus	Permanent	Woman needs a general anaesthetic

2 Use the bar chart to determine which is the most effective form of contraception.

11.8 Infertility treatments

There are many causes of infertility. Some infertility in women is caused by lack of female hormones, damage to the oviducts, obesity, or eating disorders. However, one of the most common causes is the age of the woman as couples leave it later to start trying for a family.

Lack of ovulation

- Some women do not make enough FSH to stimulate the maturation of the eggs in their ovaries. Artificial FSH can be used as a fertility drug. It stimulates the eggs in the ovary to mature and also triggers oestrogen production.

- Artificial LH can then be used to trigger ovulation.

- The woman may then get pregnant naturally.

- The doses of FSH and LH are carefully controlled to reduce the risk of multiple births.

In vitro fertilisation (IVF)

- IVF involves giving a mother FSH to stimulate the maturation of several eggs, followed by LH to stimulate the ovaries to the point of ovulation.

- The eggs are collected from the mother and fertilised by sperm from the father in the laboratory.

- The fertilised eggs develop into embryos in special solutions.

- At the stage when they are tiny balls of cells, the embryos are inspected using a microscope and healthy ones are selected.

- One or two embryos are inserted into the mother's uterus.

1 Why is FSH given to a woman who is infertile?

Advantages and disadvantages of fertility treatment

The obvious advantage of fertility treatment is that it gives infertile women the chance of having a baby.

There are some disadvantages:

- IVF is expensive, both for the NHS and for individuals. It requires a high level of skill to collect the eggs and to examine the embryos and return them to the uterus.

- IVF is not always successful, which is emotionally and physically stressful.

- It can result in multiple births, increasing the risk to mother and babies, and can lead to premature births. Premature babies need a lot of specialist care in hospitals, which is expensive.

- There are ethical issues if the mature eggs or embryos of a woman are stored for future use.

2 Suggest a possible medical reason why a doctor might advise a woman aged 45 that she is not suitable for IVF.

Key points

- FSH and LH can be used as a fertility drug to stimulate ovulation in women with low FSH levels.

- *In vitro* fertilisation (IVF) uses FSH and LH to stimulate ova to mature. They are collected, fertilised, allowed to start development, and replaced in the uterus.

- IVF is emotionally and physically stressful, often unsuccessful, and can lead to risky multiple births.

Study tip

Some people say IVF should not be available on the NHS. Make a list of the arguments for and against this viewpoint.

Data from 2010 showing the decreasing success rate of IVF as the mother gets older

Age of mother in years	IVF % success rate
under 35	32.2
35–37	27.7
38–39	20.8
40–42	13.6
43–44	5.0
over 44	1.9

11.9 Plant hormones and responses

Key points

- Plants are sensitive to light and gravity.
- Plant responses to light and gravity are brought about by the plant hormone auxin.
- The responses of roots and shoots to the stimuli of light and gravity are the result of the unequal distribution of auxin.
- Shoots grow towards light and against the force of gravity.
- Roots grow in the direction of the force of gravity.

- Plants are sensitive to light and gravity. Plant responses are called **tropisms**.
- Plant shoots grow towards light. This response is **phototropism**.
- Roots grow down towards gravity. This response is **gravitropism** (geotropism).
- **Auxin** is the hormone that controls phototropism and gravitropism.
- Unequal distribution of auxin causes unequal growth. This results in bending of the shoot or root.
- If the light is the same all around the shoot, the distribution of auxin is equal and all the cells grow at the same rate. The shoot grows straight up.
- If light falls on one side of the shoot, there is more auxin on the unlit side of the shoot. The auxin causes the cells on the unlit side to increase in length more than those on the lit side, so the shoot bends towards the light.

> **1** What causes shoots to bend towards light?

The effect of light and gravity on the growth of newly germinated seedlings

You can investigate the effect of light or gravity on the growth of newly germinated seedlings in many different ways. One of the simplest is to put cress seeds on damp cotton wool in a Petri dish inside a cardboard box with a hole cut in it. It is important to use newly germinated seedlings to see the effect of one-sided light as clearly as possible.

> **2** Will the shoots grow straight up, away from the hole, or towards the hole?

The response of shoots to light from one direction is the result of an uneven distribution of auxin. This causes uneven growth of the cells, resulting in a bend in the stem

Key words: tropisms, phototropism, gravitropism, auxin

Study tips

The action of auxin in gravitropism in shoots and roots is tricky! Make sure you can explain the effect of auxin on the growth of cells, and how this affects the direction of growth.

1. A normal young bean plant is laid on its side in the dark. Auxin is equally spread through the tissues.

2. In the root and the shoot, more auxin gathers on the lower side.

3. The root grows *more* on the side with *least* auxin, making it bend and grow down towards the force of gravity. When it has grown down, the auxin becomes evenly spread again.

The shoot grows *more* on the side with *most* auxin, making it bend and grow up away from the force of gravity. When it has grown up, the auxin becomes evenly spread again.

Gravitropism in shoots and roots. The uneven distribution of the hormone auxin causes unequal growth rates. The opposite response of roots and shoots to the presence of auxin causes the roots to grow down and the shoots to grow up

11.10 Using plant hormones

Auxins, **gibberellins**, and ethene are plant hormones. Plant hormones can be used by farmers (agriculture) and by gardeners (horticulture).

Key points

- Plant hormones are used in agriculture and horticulture.
- Auxins are used as weed killers, rooting powders, and in tissue culture.
- Ethene is used to control fruit ripening.
- Gibberellins can be used to increase fruit size, end seed dormancy, and promote flowering.

Auxins

- Auxins can be used both as weed killers and to stimulate root growth.
- Weed killers (herbicides) are used to kill unwanted plants on lawns. The broad-leaved weeds absorb more of the herbicide than the narrow-leaved grass. The weeds overgrow rapidly and die.
- When cuttings are taken from plants, auxins are used to encourage roots to grow before the cutting is planted.
- Auxins are also used in plant tissue cultures during the cloning process to produce many identical plants. The hormones stimulate growth and cell division.

1 Give two uses of auxins.

Synoptic link

For plant tissue culture and cloning, see Topic B2.2.

Gardeners and horticulturists rely on taking cuttings to produce lots of identical plants. Plant growth hormones are used as rooting powder. A little placed on the end of a cutting stimulates the growth of new roots and helps the cutting to grow into a new plant.

Auxin-based hormone rooting powder greatly increases the chances of growing successful cuttings

Key word: gibberellins

Gibberellins

Gibberellins are used:

- in the brewing industry to end seed dormancy, speeding up the germination of the barley seeds used to make malt
- to promote flowering throughout the year, especially in pot plants such as chrysanthemums and pelargoniums
- to increase the size of fruit, such as seedless grapes.

Study tip

Make sure you know the reasons why farmers and gardeners use each plant hormone.

Ethene

- Unripe fruit is firm and so easier to transport than ripe fruit. When needed, the fruit is exposed to ethene gas, which encourages it to ripen.

If plant hormones are used incorrectly they can cause damage to the environment. For example, weed killers may harm useful plants as well as weeds.

On the up

You can achieve the top grades if you are able to explain how the effects of plant hormones are useful in agriculture, horticulture, and the food industry.

2 Why is it important to use plant hormones correctly in agriculture?

1. Which endocrine gland produces:

   a FSH? [1 mark] b adrenaline? [1 mark] c oestrogen? [1 mark] d glucagon? [1 mark]

2. a What treatment is given to a person with type 1 diabetes? [1 mark]

   b Explain why this treatment is used. [2 marks]

3. Give three secondary sexual characteristics common to both boys and girls. [3 marks]

4. How do barrier methods of contraception work? [2 marks]

5. What is: a phototropism? [1 mark] b gravitropism? [1 mark]

6. Which of the following are controlled by hormones?
   Blinking, blood sugar concentration, growing, focusing on a book, breathing, menstrual cycle, swatting a fly, metabolic rate, sperm production, moving your hand from a hot surface. [5 marks]

7. Ⓗ Describe the sequence of events when glucagon controls blood glucose concentration. [6 marks]

8. Why is adrenaline called the 'fight or flight' hormone? [6 marks]

9. Ⓗ Name the stages in the process of *in vitro* fertilisation (IVF). [6 marks]

10. Ⓗ How are gibberellins used in: a brewing? [2 marks] b horticulture? [2 marks]

11. Explain how auxin causes shoots to bend towards light. [3 marks]

12. Ⓗ Describe the role of FSH, LH, oestrogen, and progesterone in controlling the menstrual cycle. Include how hormones interact to control the levels of other hormones in your description. [6 marks]

13. Ⓗ The availability of infertility treatment has been described as a 'postcode lottery' in that it may be available to some women but not others.
    Suggest reasons why such treatment is not readily available for all women in the UK. [6 marks]

Chapter checklist

Tick when you have:

reviewed it after your lesson ✓ ☐ ☐

revised once – some questions right ✓ ✓ ☐

revised twice – all questions right ✓ ✓ ✓

Move on to another topic when you have all three ticks

11.1 Principles of hormonal control ☐ ☐ ☐
11.2 The control of blood glucose levels ☐ ☐ ☐
11.3 Treating diabetes ☐ ☐ ☐
11.4 The role of negative feedback ☐ ☐ ☐
11.5 Human reproduction ☐ ☐ ☐
11.6 Hormones and the menstrual cycle ☐ ☐ ☐
11.7 The artificial control of fertility ☐ ☐ ☐
11.8 Infertility treatments ☐ ☐ ☐
11.9 Plant hormones and responses ☐ ☐ ☐
11.10 Using plant hormones ☐ ☐ ☐

B12

Student Book
pages 182–183

12.1 Controlling body temperature

Key points

- Your body temperature is monitored and controlled by the thermoregulatory centre in your brain. The thermoregulatory centre contains receptors sensitive to the temperature of the blood.

- The skin also contains temperature receptors and sends nerve impulses to the thermoregulatory centre.

- If the body temperature is too high, blood vessels dilate (vasodilation) and sweat is produced from the sweat glands. Both cause a transfer of energy from the skin to the environment.

- If the body temperature is too low, blood vessels constrict (vasoconstriction) and sweating stops, reducing the transfer of energy to the environment.

- Skeletal muscles contract (shiver) and the exothermic reactions of respiration needed for muscle contraction raise the temperature.

Synoptic link

For more on factors affecting enzyme action, see Topic B3.5.

Study tips

Do not say that capillaries dilate or constrict. They cannot do this as they have no muscle layer. It is the blood vessels supplying the capillaries that dilate or constrict.

Also, blood vessels never move. Either more blood flows in vessels near the skin surface, or more blood flows in the vessels lower down.

Human body temperature needs to be kept at about 37 °C so that the enzymes will work efficiently. The core body temperature, deep inside the body, must be kept stable.

- Body temperature is monitored and controlled by the **thermoregulatory centre** in the brain. This centre has receptors that detect the temperature of the blood flowing through the brain.
- Temperature receptors in the skin also send impulses to the brain to give information about the skin temperature.

> **1** Where is the blood temperature monitored in the body?

If the core body temperature rises:

- Blood vessels near the surface of the skin dilate (**vasodilation**) allowing more blood to flow through the skin capillaries. Energy is transferred by radiation to the environment and the skin cools. The skin looks red when you are hot due to increased blood flow.

- Sweat glands produce more sweat. Its water evaporates from the skin. The energy required for the water to evaporate comes from the skin, so you cool down. When it is hot, you need to drink more to balance this loss of water.

If the core body temperature falls:

- Blood vessels near the surface of the skin constrict (**vasoconstriction**) and less blood flows through the skin capillaries. Less energy is radiated to the environment.

- You shiver. Your muscles contract and relax quickly. This requires more respiration, and some of the energy transferred in the exothermic reactions warms the blood.

> **2** Explain why sweating cools the body.

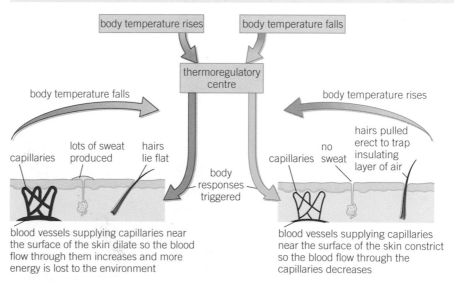

Changes in your core body temperature set off automatic responses to oppose these changes and maintain a steady internal environment

Key words: thermoregulatory centre, vasodilation, vasoconstriction

Student Book pages 184–185 **B12**

12.2 Removing waste products

Key points

- Water leaves the body via the lungs during exhalation.
- Water, mineral ions, and urea are lost through the skin in sweat.
- There is no control over water, mineral ion, or urea loss by the lungs or skin.
- Urea, along with excess water and mineral ions, is removed via the kidneys in the urine. The loss of water and mineral ions is carefully balanced by the body.
- If the body cells lose or gain too much water by osmosis, they do not function efficiently.

Synoptic links

There is more about the removal of carbon dioxide from the body in Topic B4.5.
For more on osmosis, see Topic B1.7. Topic B4.5 has more on the exhalation of air, and Topic B11.2 on controlling glucose levels. The role of the liver in the production of urea is covered Topic B9.4.

Study tip

Don't confuse *urea* and *urine*. Urea is a waste molecule made in the liver, carried to the kidneys in the blood, and excreted in the *urine*.

On the up

You should be able to describe how urea is formed and the differences between urea and urine. To achieve the top grades, you should also be able to explain the link between high levels of protein in the diet and an increase in the urea concentration in urine.

For your body to work properly, the conditions around the cells must be kept as constant as possible.

All the cell reactions produce waste products, which must be removed.

- Carbon dioxide, produced by respiration, is removed via the lungs when you breathe out.

1 How is carbon dioxide produced in the body?

- Urea, produced in the liver from the breakdown of excess amino acids, is excreted (removed) by the kidneys in the urine.
- In the liver, the amino group is removed from amino acids in the process of deamination. This forms ammonia, a toxic substance, which is then converted to urea. The urea passes in the blood to the kidneys to be excreted.

$$\text{amino acids} \xrightarrow[\text{in liver}]{\text{deamination}} \text{ammonia} \longrightarrow \text{urea} \xrightarrow[\text{to kidneys}]{\text{in blood}} \text{urine}$$

- Water and mineral ions enter the body when you eat and drink. If the water or ion content in the body is wrong, too much water may move into or out of the cells by osmosis. This could damage or destroy the cells.

2 Where is urea made?

Urea, water, and mineral ions are lost from the body in several ways. Some methods are not under the control of the body, others are.

- You cannot directly control the amount of urea, water, and mineral ions lost from the skin in sweat, or the amount of carbon dioxide and water lost from the lungs.
- Your kidneys control the amount of water, mineral ions, and urea your body excretes.

The regular production of urine is an important part of homeostasis – wherever you happen to be

12.3 The human kidney

The body has two kidneys. They filter the blood, excreting substances the body does not need in the urine, and keeping those substances that it does need in the blood.

A healthy kidney produces urine by:

- first filtering the blood
- reabsorbing all the glucose
- reabsorbing the dissolved mineral ions your body needs
- reabsorbing as much water as your body needs
- releasing urea, excess mineral ions, and water in the urine.

Because all the sugar and only some water, ions and urea are reabsorbed, this is called **selective reabsorption**.

The urine is temporarily stored in the bladder before being removed from the body.

1 What processes in the kidney form urine from the blood?

ADH and water balance

- If the water content of the blood is too low, the pituitary gland releases a hormone called **ADH** into the blood. This causes the kidneys to reabsorb more water, resulting in a more concentrated urine.
- ADH works by changing the permeability of the kidney tubules so that they reabsorb more water from the urine into the blood.
- If the water content of the blood is too high, less ADH is released into the blood. Less water is reabsorbed in the kidneys, resulting in a more dilute urine.
- Keeping the water balance is a negative feedback system. As the water level in the blood rises, it stops the production of more ADH.

The concentration of the blood, and the amount of urine you produce, is controlled by the hormone ADH

2 What is ADH and where is it produced?

Study tips

Remember that an increase in ADH leads to a reduction of water in the urine.

A rise in water level in the blood leads to a reduction in ADH being secreted from the pituitary gland. This is an example of negative feedback.

Higher

Key points

- The kidneys are important for excretion and homeostasis.
- A healthy kidney produces urine by filtering the blood. It then reabsorbs *all* of the glucose, plus any mineral ions and water needed by your body.
- Excess mineral ions and water, along with urea, are removed in the urine.
- **(H)** The water balance of the blood is maintained by the hormone ADH, which changes the amount of water reabsorbed by the kidney tubules.

Synoptic links

For information on diffusion, see Topic B1.6, and for active transport, see Topic B1.9.

Key words: selective reabsorption, ADH

Study tips

Make sure you understand that *all* small molecules are filtered out of the blood into the kidney tubules, but the useful ones, such as glucose, are reabsorbed.

Only large molecules, such as proteins, cannot be filtered out of the blood.

On the up

If you can describe the effect of ADH on the kidneys, you can achieve the top grades by being able to explain how the production of ADH will change in given situations.

12.4 Dialysis – an artificial kidney

Student Book
pages 188–189 **B12**

Key points

- People with kidney failure may be treated by regular sessions on a kidney dialysis machine or by having a kidney transplant.
- In a dialysis machine, the concentration of dissolved substances in the blood is restored to normal levels.
- The levels of useful substances in the blood are maintained, whilst urea and excess mineral ions pass from the blood into the dialysis fluid.

Synoptic link

For diffusion, see Topic B1.6.

Key word: dialysis

- If a person has kidney failure, they can be kept alive by **dialysis**. A dialysis machine carries out the same job as the kidneys. The blood flows between partially permeable membranes surrounded by dialysis fluid.
- The dialysis fluid contains the same concentration of useful substances, such as glucose and mineral ions, as the patient's blood. These substances therefore do not diffuse out of the blood, so they do not need to be reabsorbed as they do in the kidney.
- Urea diffuses out from the blood into the dialysis fluid.
- Dialysis restores the concentration of substances in the blood back to normal, but needs to be carried out at regular intervals.
- If a donor kidney becomes available, the patient may have a kidney transplant. If the transplant is successful, the person will not need further dialysis.

1 What is the purpose of dialysis?
2 What is the alternative treatment to dialysis?

Study tip

Look at as many different examples of dialysis diagrams as you can. Identify the membrane. Be clear about what diffuses through the membrane and what is in the original dialysis fluid.

12.5 Kidney transplants

Student Book
pages 190–191 **B12**

Key points

- In a kidney transplant, a healthy kidney from a donor replaces the function of the diseased or damaged kidney.
- To try and prevent rejection of the donor kidney, the tissue types of the donor and the recipient are matched as closely as possible. Immunosuppressant drugs are also used.

Synoptic links

For more on antigens, see Topics B5.9 and B6.1.

For information on stem cells, see Topics B2.3 and B2.4.

- For most patients a kidney transplant is a better option than dialysis. The diseased kidney is replaced with a healthy one from a donor in an operation.
- The donor kidney may be obtained from a victim of a fatal accident or sometimes from a living donor.
- The new kidney must be a very good tissue match to prevent rejection.
- There are proteins called antigens on the surface of cells. The recipient's antibodies may attack the antigens on the donor organ because they recognise them as being 'foreign'.
- Following the transplant, the recipient must take drugs to suppress the immune response to prevent rejection. These are called immunosuppressant drugs.
- Despite the advantages of a transplant, there are some risks from the operation. Treatment before and following the transplant involves suppressing the patient's immune system, which leaves them vulnerable to common infections.
- Future possible treatments include generating kidney tissue from embryonic stem cells.

1 What are antigens?
2 What is the main advantage of a kidney transplant compared with dialysis?

1. Where is the thermoregulatory centre? [1 mark]

2. Name three waste products that have to be removed from the body. [3 marks]

3. When blood passes through the kidney, substances pass from the blood into the kidney tubules.
   What is the name of this process? [1 mark]

4. Name the organ:
   a that controls the amount of water removed from the body [1 mark]
   b that removes carbon dioxide from the body [1 mark]
   c that produces sweat. [1 mark]

5. Use your own knowledge and the information in **Table 1** to evaluate the benefits of a kidney transplant rather than dialysis for a patient with kidney disease. [6 marks]

Table 1

Treatment	Advantages	Disadvantages
kidney transplant	recipient free from dependency on machines long-term costs less than dialysis: £5000 per year for drugs diet less restricted	risk of rejection so need immunosuppressant drugs costs about £17 000 per patient check-ups needed limited availability of donors
dialysis machine	patient can be kept alive whilst waiting for transplant suitable for patients with abdominal scars and wounds	regular visits to hospital holidays restricted to places that can provide kidney machines costs £35 000 per year possible infection from equipment dependent upon availability of machines and expert staff some dietary restrictions

6. Why do you pass more urine in the winter time than in the summer? [3 marks]

7. Why is it more difficult to transfer energy from your skin when you wear clothes? [1 mark]

8. Why does an athlete need to drink water during a long-distance race? [5 marks]

9. Explain how the endocrine system keeps the water concentration in the blood constant. Your answer should include reference to the negative feedback mechanism involved. [6 marks]

Chapter checklist

Tick when you have:

reviewed it after your lesson ✓ ☐ ☐

revised once – some questions right ✓ ✓ ☐

revised twice – all questions right ✓ ✓ ✓

Move on to another topic when you have all three ticks

12.1 Controlling body temperature ☐ ☐ ☐
12.2 Removing waste products ☐ ☐ ☐
12.3 The human kidney ☐ ☐ ☐
12.4 Dialysis – an artificial kidney ☐ ☐ ☐
12.5 Kidney transplants ☐ ☐ ☐

Practice questions

01.1 Which of the following are reflex actions?
Choose all the correct options from the list below. [3 marks]
- picking up a piece of paper from the floor
- pulling your hand away from a very hot plate
- blinking when a bright light is shone in your eyes
- choosing a cake from a plate
- coughing when a crumb enters your trachea

01.2 Give one example of a reflex action that occurs inside your body. [1 mark]

01.3 What is the main advantage of reflex actions? [1 mark]

01.4 Which part of the brain is concerned with intelligence and memory? [1 mark]

02 Following a meal your blood sugar rises. During the next few hours the blood sugar returns to normal levels.
Choose **one** option to answer each question.

02.1 The blood sugar rises because: [1 mark]
- glucose leaves the liver
- glucose enters the muscles
- glucose passes into the villi
- the muscles are exercising.

02.2 The rise in blood sugar is detected by receptors in the: [1 mark]
- brain
- liver
- pancreas
- intestine.

02.3 Ⓗ A response to the rise in blood sugar is a reduction in the production of: [1 mark]
- ADH
- glucagon
- insulin.

02.4 It is estimated that 415 million people in the world are living with type 2 diabetes, which is about 1 in 11 of the world's adult population. 46% of people with type 2 diabetes are undiagnosed. In Britain it is estimated that 1 in 16 people have type 2 diabetes, either diagnosed or undiagnosed.
Compared with the world figures, what is the order of magnitude of type 2 diabetes occurrence in the British figures?
Choose **one** option. [1 mark]
- a higher order of magnitude
- a lower order of magnitude
- the same order of magnitude

02.5 By 2040 the worldwide figure is expected to rise to 642 million.
Calculate the percentage increase in type 2 diabetes by 2040. [2 marks]

02.6 What is the main cause of type 2 diabetes? [1 mark]

03 Ⓗ **Figure 1** shows how the body controls the water levels in the blood.

Figure 1

03.1 Use **Figure 1** to explain the principle of negative feedback. [6 marks]

03.2 What would happen if at point 1, the person sat down and drank a litre of water? [5 marks]

04 **Figure 2** shows the female reproductive system.

Figure 2

Choose the letter from **Figure 2** that represents:

04.1 the place where eggs mature during the menstrual cycle. [1 mark]

04.2 the place where oestrogen is produced during the menstrual cycle. [1 mark]

04.3 the place where sperm are deposited during intercourse. [1 mark]

04.4 the place where the sperm may fuse with the egg after ovulation. [1 mark]

05 Hormones control human growth and development, as well as the menstrual cycle.

Give the name of the hormone that:

05.1 controls the basic metabolic rate. [1 mark]

05.2 starts the development of secondary sexual characteristics in boys. [1 mark]

05.3 is found in the contraceptive pill with oestrogen. [1 mark]

05.4 causes ovulation. [1 mark]

05.5 causes eggs to mature. [1 mark]

05.6 Ⓗ is suppressed by high levels of oestrogen in the second half of the menstrual cycle. [1 mark]

4 Genetics and evolution

When the science of genetics was first developed, people hadn't even seen a chromosome. Now, in the 21st century, scientists can analyse the entire genome of an organism in a day or two. You will learn how the information in your genetic code controls the way the chemicals that make up your cells, tissues, and organs are built up. You will also consider some of the new gene technologies that scientists are using.

The organisms alive today have evolved from ancestral organisms over millions of years. You will explore how this has occurred and study examples of evolution in progress today. You will also see how our increasing knowledge of genomes allows scientists to classify organisms in a different way, allowing us to make sense of global biodiversity.

I already know...

I will revise...

I already know...	I will revise...
about the nucleus of the cell and the chromosomes it contains.	that DNA makes up the chromosomes, the variants of the genes known as alleles, and how all the DNA of an organism can be analysed.
about mitosis and the cell cycle.	meiosis in cell division and the formation of gametes.
the process of reproduction.	how information is passed from one generation to another and how to use genetic diagrams, direct proportion, simple ratios, and probability to predict the outcome of a genetic cross.
how inheritance works.	the importance of selective breeding in the development of plants and animals and the increasing use of genetic engineering to introduce desirable characteristics.
how biological ideas develop.	how Charles Darwin built up the evidence for his theory of evolution by natural selection and some of the barriers to the acceptance of his ideas, as well as some of the modern evidence we have for evolution.
about the characteristics of eukaryotic and prokaryotic cells, and the differences between animal, bacterial, and plant cells.	new DNA-based systems for classifying organisms.

13.1 Types of reproduction

Key points

- In asexual reproduction, there is no fusion of gametes and only one parent. There is no mixing of genetic information, leading to genetically identical offspring (clones).

- Only mitosis is involved in asexual reproduction.

- Sexual reproduction involves the joining (fusion) of male and female gametes formed by meiosis. Meiosis leads to the formation of non-identical cells – sperm and egg cells in animals, and pollen and egg cells in flowering plants.

- In sexual reproduction there is a mixing of genetic information that leads to variation in the offspring.

- **Asexual reproduction** does not involve the fusion of gametes (sex cells). All of the genetic information comes from one parent. All of the offspring are genetically identical to the parent, so there is little variation.

- Identical copies produced by asexual reproduction are called clones.

- Clones are formed by mitosis.

1 Which type of cell division is used in asexual reproduction?

- **Sexual reproduction** involves the fusion of sex cells (gametes). There is a mixing of genetic information, so the offspring show variation.

- Gametes are formed by **meiosis**. Meiosis produces gametes in which the chromosome number is halved. When two gametes fuse to form a zygote, the full chromosome number is restored.

- In animals, the sex cells are egg cells and sperm.

- In plants, the sex cells are egg cells and pollen.

- Offspring produced by sexual reproduction are similar to both parents, but cannot be identical. This is because they have a combination of two sets of genes, leading to variation in the offspring.

2 Which type of reproduction leads to variation in the offspring?

Synoptic link

For chromosomes, genes, DNA, and mitosis, see Topic B2.1.

Key words: asexual reproduction, sexual reproduction, meiosis

Study tips

Remember that in humans, an egg and sperm each have 23 chromosomes, which is half the usual number. When they fuse at fertilisation, the zygote has 46 again.

Look for examples of the number of chromosomes in other organisms.

Write lists to compare asexual and sexual reproduction. Include the types of cell division and the names of gametes, and describe the offspring produced.

On the up

If you can describe the advantages and disadvantages of sexual and asexual reproduction, you can achieve the top grades by being able to explain in detail why meiosis is important for sexual reproduction.

13.2 Cell division in sexual reproduction

- Cells in the reproductive organs divide by meiosis to form the gametes (sex cells).

- Body cells have two sets of chromosomes, gametes have only one set.

- In meiosis, the genetic material is copied and then the cell divides twice to form four gametes, each with a single set of chromosomes.

- All gametes are genetically different from each other.

- Gametes join at fertilisation to restore the normal number of chromosomes. The new cell divides by mitosis. The number of cells increases and, as the embryo develops, the cells differentiate.

Synoptic link

Topic B2.1 covers mitosis.

Key word: meiosis

Study tips

Learn to spell mitosis and meiosis. Remember their meanings:

- **mit**osis – **m**aking **i**dentical **t**wo
- **mei**osis – **m**aking **e**ggs (and sperm).

- Cells in the reproductive organs divide by **meiosis** to form sex cells (gametes). In the human testes and ovaries, the gametes are the sperm and ova (egg cells).

- Body cells have pairs of chromosomes. One of each pair comes from each parent.

> **1** What type of cells are produced by meiosis?

Meiosis

- In meiosis, the genetic material is copied before cell division. Each chromosome forms two chromosomes.

- Then the cell divides twice.

- This forms four gametes, each with a single set of chromosomes. Every gamete has only one chromosome from each original pair.

- All of the gametes are genetically different from each other and from the parent cell.

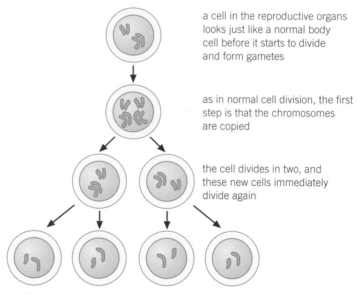

a cell in the reproductive organs looks just like a normal body cell before it starts to divide and form gametes

as in normal cell division, the first step is that the chromosomes are copied

the cell divides in two, and these new cells immediately divide again

this gives four sex cells, each with a single set of chromosomes – in this case two instead of the original four

The formation of sex cells in the ovaries and testes involves meiosis to halve the chromosome number. The original cell is shown with only two pairs of chromosomes to make it easier to follow what is happening

> **2** Explain how four gametes are formed from one cell.

- Sexual reproduction results in variation because the gametes from each parent fuse. So half the genetic information comes from the father and half from the mother.

- When gametes join at fertilisation, a single body cell with new pairs of chromosomes is formed (the zygote).

- A new individual then develops as this cell repeatedly divides by mitosis.

13.3 The best of both worlds

Asexual reproduction has the following advantages.

- Only one parent is needed.
- It is more time and energy efficient as individuals do not need to find a mate.
- It is faster than sexual reproduction.
- Many identical offspring can be produced by mitosis when conditions are favourable.

Disadvantages of asexual reproduction include the following.

- Offspring are clones so there is little variation.
- If environmental conditions change, all the offspring are affected.

1 Why is there little variation in offspring produced by asexual reproduction?

Sexual reproduction has the following advantages.

- It produces variation in the offspring.
- If the environment changes, variation gives a survival advantage by **natural selection**.
- Natural selection can be accelerated by humans in selective breeding to increase food production.

Disadvantages of sexual reproduction include the following.

- Two gametes are needed, which usually involves two parents.
- It takes time and energy to find a mate or to spread gametes.
- It is often slower than asexual reproduction.

Some organisms reproduce by both methods depending on the circumstances.

Malarial parasites have a life cycle that includes both asexual and sexual reproduction:

- asexual – in the human host
- sexual – in the mosquito.

Fungi:

- reproduce asexually by spores that are produced by mitosis
- reproduce sexually to give variation in adverse conditions.

Flowering plants reproduce both asexually and sexually:

- asexual – many plants produce offspring by mitosis, such as runners from strawberry plants and new bulbs from daffodils
- sexual – the pollen and egg cells are made by meiosis and fuse to form seeds.

2 What form of reproduction produces seeds in flowering plants?

Key points

- Sexual reproduction produces variation that helps survival through natural selection if the environment changes. Natural selection is accelerated by humans in selective breeding.
- Asexual reproduction needs only one parent, is time and energy efficient, is often faster than sexual reproduction, and many identical offspring are produced when conditions are favourable.
- Some organisms depend on both asexual and sexual reproduction depending on the circumstances.
- Malaria parasites reproduce sexually in mosquitoes and asexually in their human host.
- Many fungi reproduce asexually by spores but can also reproduce sexually to give variation.
- Many plants produce seeds sexually but also reproduce asexually, for example by runners or bulb division.

Key word: natural selection

Study tip

Make a table of organisms with tick boxes to show it they reproduce sexually, asexually, or using both methods. Add to the list when you come across new examples, such as onions or potatoes, and tick the correct boxes.

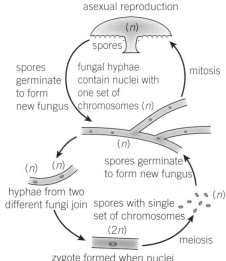

Fungi reproduce asexually using spores but in adverse conditions they may reproduce sexually to give variation and increase their chance of survival

13.4 DNA and the genome

Key points

- The genome of an organism is its entire genetic material.

- The whole human genome has now been studied and this will have great importance for medicine in the future.

- The genetic material in the nucleus of a cell is composed of DNA. DNA is a polymer made up of two strands forming a double helix.

- A gene is a small section of DNA on a chromosome. Each gene codes for a particular sequence of amino acids, to make a specific protein.

Study tip

Make sure you understand the difference between a *gene* (a section of a chromosome) and the *genome* (the entire genetic material).

DNA

- The genetic material is made of deoxyribonucleic acid (DNA).

- DNA is a polymer (a very long molecule) with two strands that are twisted into a double helix structure.

- The DNA is found in chromosomes. Each type of organism has a different number of chromosomes in its cells.

- A gene is a small section of DNA on the chromosome.

- Each gene has the code for a particular sequence of amino acids, to make a specific protein.

The DNA double helix

1 What is a gene?

Genome

- The **genome** of an organism is the entire genetic material of that organism.

- The whole human genome has now been studied.

- Knowing the human genome helps scientists and doctors in the following areas:

  - the search for genes linked to different types of disease

  - understanding and treating inherited disorders

  - tracing human migration patterns from the past.

2 What is meant by the term genome?

Key word: genome

13.5 DNA structure and protein synthesis

Key points

- The long strands of DNA consist of alternating sugar and phosphate sections. Attached to each sugar is one of four bases – A, C, G, or T. Each unit made up of a sugar, a phosphate, and a base is known as a nucleotide.

- A sequence of three bases is the code for a particular amino acid.

DNA structure

- The long strands of DNA are made of chains of alternating sugar and phosphate sections.

- One of four **bases** – A, C, G, or T – is attached to each sugar.

- Each unit containing a sugar, a phosphate, and a base is called a **nucleotide**.

1 Name the parts that make up a nucleotide molecule.

a section of three bases like this codes for one amino acid

DNA codes for the amino acids that make up the proteins, that make up the enzymes, that make each individual

Higher

- The order of bases controls the order in which amino acids are assembled to produce a particular protein.

- (H) In the complementary strands of DNA, a C is always linked to a G on the opposite strand, and a T to an A.

- (H) Proteins are synthesised according to a template. Carrier molecules bring specific amino acids to add to the growing protein chain in the correct order.

- (H) When the protein chain is complete it folds up to form a unique shape that enables the protein to carry out its function in the cell.

Synoptic links

For ribosomes, see Topic B1.2, and for the way amino acids are joined to form proteins, see Topic B3.3.

Key words: bases, nucleotide

Study tips

Three bases on DNA code for one amino acid. Amino acids are joined together to make a protein. It is the particular sequence of amino acids that gives each protein its specific shape and function.

- A sequence of three bases is the code for a particular amino acid.

- The order of bases controls the order in which amino acids are joined together to form a particular protein.

- A mutation is a change in the order of bases that causes the wrong protein to be made.

2 What controls the order in which amino acids are joined together in a protein?

DNA

- In the complementary strands of DNA, base C is always linked to base G, and base T is always linked to base A.

Protein synthesis

- A gene produces a template for a particular protein.

- The small template leaves the nucleus through a pore in the membrane.

- The template attaches to a ribosome in the cytoplasm.

- Carrier molecules in the cytoplasm each carry a specific amino acid.

- The carrier molecules attach themselves to the template in the order defined by the template.

- The amino acids they carry join together to form a protein chain.

- The complete protein chain detaches from the carrier molecules and folds into a specific shape.

- The carrier molecules return to the cytoplasm and pick up more amino acids.

The way the bases bind is vital to the structure of the DNA and the way it works

Protein synthesis takes place on the ribosomes in the cytoplasm of the cell but is controlled by the sequence of bases on the DNA in the nucleus

13.6 Gene expression and mutation

Key points

- Not all parts of the DNA code for proteins. Non-coding parts switch genes on or off, so variations in these areas of DNA can affect how genes are expressed.

- A change in the DNA structure may result in a change in the protein synthesised by the gene.

- Mutations occur continuously. Most do not alter the protein, or alter it so slightly that the function is not affected.

- A few mutations code for an altered protein with a different shape, affecting the function. This may be an advantage or a disadvantage.

Synoptic link

See Topic B3.4 for the importance of the shape of the active site of an enzyme, and Topic B7.2 for the role of mutations as a cause of cancer.

Key word: mutation

Study tip

Make a spider diagram with 'protein' as the body. Include functions, enzymes, amino acids, protein synthesis, and mutation as the 'legs' – then look for links between them.

Gene expression

- When a gene codes for a protein that is synthesised in the cell, the gene is said to be expressed.

- Most of the DNA does not actually code for proteins.

- The non-coding parts of the DNA are involved in switching genes, or parts of genes, on and off.

- Variations in the non-coding areas of our DNA may affect how our genes are expressed.

1   What is the importance of the non-coding sections of DNA?

Mutations

- New forms of genes result from changes in existing genes. The changes are called **mutations**.

- Mutations occur continuously. However, most changes are so slight that they do not alter the protein shape enough to alter its function.

- A few mutations result in an altered protein that folds to give a different shape. In this case the active site of an enzyme could be changed or a structural protein could have less strength.

- Mutations in the non-coding regions of the DNA may affect which genes are switched on or off.

- Some mutations are beneficial (e.g., a changed enzyme could be more efficient).

2   What could be the consequences if a mutation changes the shape of the active site of an enzyme?

Insects change dramatically as they grow. The DNA in the cells of a butterfly is the same as when it was a caterpillar. Different genes are switched on or off to produce very different bodies

Different genes will be expressed at different stages in the life of this elephant calf as it grows up and produces tusks

13.7 Inheritance in action

Key points

- Some characteristics are controlled by a single gene. Each gene may have different forms called alleles.

- The alleles present, or genotype, operate at a molecular level to develop characteristics that can be expressed as the phenotype.

- If the two alleles are the same, the individual is homozygous for that trait, but if the alleles are different they are heterozygous.

- A dominant allele is always expressed in the phenotype, even if only one copy is present. A recessive allele is only expressed if two copies are present.

- Most characteristics are the result of multiple genes interacting, rather than a single gene.

Key words: alleles, Punnett square, phenotype, genotype, homozygote, heterozygote, dominant, recessive

Study tips

Practise all the possible crosses and learn the genetic terms.

Practise constructing Punnett squares for different characteristics.

- Most of your characteristics, such as nose shape, are controlled by the interaction of several genes.

- Some characteristics are controlled by a single gene.

- Different forms of a gene are called **alleles**.

- Each allele codes for a different protein. The allele controls reactions at a molecular level.

- Genetic diagrams, including family trees and **Punnett squares**, illustrate how alleles and characteristics are inherited.

1 What is an allele?

Genetic terms

Genetic diagrams are biological models that can be used to predict and explain the inheritance of particular characteristics. Punnet squares are grids in which you can write symbols for the alleles.

It is important to use the correct terminology.

- **phenotype** – physical appearance of the characteristic, for example, dimples or no dimples.

- **genotype** – the genetic makeup, which is determined by which alleles the individual inherits, such as DD, Dd, or dd.

- **homozygote** – both alleles are the same, for example, DD or dd.

- **heterozygote** – the two alleles are different, for example, Dd.

- If an allele masks the effect of another it is said to be **dominant**. The allele whose effect is masked is said to be **recessive**.

- Dimples (D) is dominant. No dimples (d) is recessive. The genotype of a person with dimples could be DD or Dd, but the genotype of a person with no dimples must be dd.

- A genetic cross can predict the offspring of particular parents.

2 What is meant by the term heterozygous?

mother (no dimples) ♀ must be dd — allele for no dimples (recessive) — allele for dimples (dominant) — father (dimples) ♂ could be Dd or DD

Punnett square father (DD) possible alleles

♀\♂	D	D
d	Dd	Dd
d	Dd	Dd

mother (dd) possible alleles

possible offspring – all have dimples, all Dd

Punnett square father (Dd) possible alleles

♀\♂	D	d
d	Dd	dd
d	Dd	dd

mother (dd) possible alleles

possible offspring – 1/2, or 50% chance of dimples (Dd) 1/2, or 50% chance of no dimples (dd)

The different forms of genes, known as alleles, can result in the development of quite different characteristics. Genetic diagrams such as these Punnett squares help you explain what is happening and predict what the possible offspring might be like

B13

13.8 More about genetics

Key points

- Direct proportion and ratios can be used to express the outcome of a genetic cross.
- Use Punnett squares and family trees to understand genetic inheritance.
- (H) Construct a Punnett square diagram to predict the outcome of a monohybrid cross.
- Ordinary human body cells contain 23 pairs of chromosomes; 22 control general body characteristics only but the sex chromosomes carry the genes that determine sex.
- In human females the sex chromosomes are the same (XX) whilst in males the sex chromosomes are different (XY).

On the up

If you can use direct proportion and simple ratios to express the outcome of a genetic cross, you can achieve the top grades by being able to explain why you only get the expected ratios in a genetic cross if there are large numbers of offspring.

Study tip

Make sure you remember that the human sex chromosomes are XX in females and XY in males.

Key word: sex chromosomes

Direct proportion and simple ratios

When you look at genetic crosses using Punnett squares, you can work out the proportion of the offspring that would be expected to have a particular genotype or phenotype and the ratios of one genotype or phenotype to another.

The diagrams below show two Punnett squares for genetic crosses between mice. B is the dominant allele for black fur and b is the recessive allele for brown fur. Cross 1 shows a cross between two heterozygous black mice, and Cross 2 between a homozygous recessive brown mouse and a heterozygous black mouse.

Cross 1: bb × BB

Gametes	B	B
b	Bb	Bb
b	Bb	Bb

Cross 2: bb × Bb

Gametes	B	b
b	Bb	bb
b	Bb	bb

In cross 1 you can look at the genotypes and the phenotypes of the offspring, and work out the proportions and ratios of the different possible genetic combinations.

Genotypes: the proportions of the genotypes are:

1/4 or 25%	2/4 or 50%	1/4 or 25%
homozygous dominant (BB)	heterozygous (Bb)	homozygous recessive (bb)

The possible genotypes appear in a ratio of 1 : 2 : 1 homozygous dominant : heterozygous : homozygous recessive.

Phenotypes: the proportions of the phenotypes are:

$\frac{3}{4}$ or 75% dominant (black) $\frac{1}{4}$ or 25% recessive (brown)

The possible phenotypes appear in a ratio of 3 : 1 dominant : recessive.

The proportions and ratios of the possible offspring will be the same for every heterozygous cross you look at.

1 What are the proportions and ratios of the genotypes and phenotypes in cross 2?

Sex determination

- Humans have 23 pairs of chromosomes, one pair being the **sex chromosomes**.
- Human females have two X chromosomes (XX). Males have an X chromosome and a Y chromosome (XY).
- When cells divide by meiosis to make gametes, all the resulting egg cells will contain an X chromosome. Half the sperm will contain an X chromosome but the other half will contain a Y chromosome.
- The chances of having a boy or girl at each fertilisation are $\frac{1}{2}$ or 50 : 50 (1 : 1).

2 Which chromosomes determine that a child is born a boy?

B13

13.9 Inherited disorders

Key points

- Some disorders are inherited.
- Polydactyly is a dominant phenotype caused by a dominant allele that can be inherited from either or both parents.
- Cystic fibrosis is a recessive phenotype and is caused by recessive alleles that must be inherited from both parents.

Synoptic link

There is more about how scientists can change the genes of an organism in Topic B14.4.

Key words: polydactyly, cystic fibrosis, carrier, genetic engineering

Study tips

Before attempting to answer a genetics question, always determine whether an allele is dominant or recessive. To show a characteristic caused by a recessive allele, the person must have two copies of the allele.

male with polydactyly
female with polydactyly
unaffected male
unaffected female

Polydactyly is passed through a family tree by a dominant allele

- **Polydactyly** is a genetic condition in which a baby is born with extra fingers or toes. It is caused by a dominant allele. This inherited disorder can be passed on by one parent who has the allele.

- **Cystic fibrosis** is caused by a recessive allele. It affects cell membranes and causes the production of thick, sticky mucus. The mucus can affect several organs, including the lungs and pancreas.

- A child must inherit a recessive allele from both parents to develop cystic fibrosis. The disorder can be passed on from two parents who have the allele but do not have cystic fibrosis themselves. The parents are described as **carriers** of the allele.

- By using genetic diagrams it is possible to see how a disorder (or allele) has been inherited, and to predict whether future offspring will inherit it.

1 Name a genetic disorder that is controlled by a dominant allele.

- If one parent is heterozygous for polydactyly, each child has a 50% chance of inheriting the disorder.

- If both parents are heterozygous for cystic fibrosis, each child has a 25% chance of inheriting the disorder.

- The outcomes of genetic crosses can be shown on a Punnett square.

both parents are carriers, so Cc

	P	p
p	Pp	pp
p	Pp	pp

50% chance polydactyly, PP or Pp, 50% chance normal pp

	C	c
C	CC	Cc
c	Cc	cc

genotype:
25% normal (CC)
50% carriers (Cc)
25% affected by cystic fibrosis (cc)

phenotype:
3/4, or 75% chance normal
1/4, or 25% chance cystic fibrosis

Pp = Parent with polydactyly
pp = Normal parent

A genetic diagram (Punnett square) for polydactyly

A genetic diagram (Punnett square) for cystic fibrosis

2 What are the chances of a child having cystic fibrosis if one parent has the disorder and the other parent is heterozygous?

- It is hoped that in the future some genetic disorders can be cured by **genetic engineering** techniques.

Family trees

Family trees show males and females in a family. They can be used to:

- track inherited diseases
- show family likenesses
- show the different alleles that organisms have inherited.

13.10 Screening for genetic disorders

Key points

- Cells from embryos and fetuses can be screened for the alleles that cause many genetic disorders.
- Embryonic and fetal cells are used to identify genetic disorders but screening raises economic, social, and ethical issues.

chorionic villus sampling – transcervical method

- ultrasound device
- placenta
- catheter

chorionic villus sampling – transabdominal method

- needle
- placenta

amniocentesis

- needle
- amniotic fluid

Amniocentesis and chorionic villus sampling enable doctors to take cells from a developing fetus. The cells can then be screened for genetic diseases

Synoptic links

Monoclonal antibodies are used to test for genetic disorders – see Topic B6.5.

For more about gene therapy and ethical issues, see Topics B14.4 and B14.7.

Screening embryos

- Embryo screening involves tests to diagnose genetic disorders before the baby is born.
- Cells from developing fetuses are collected by amniocentesis or chorionic villus sampling during pregnancy.
  - In amniocentesis, a sample of fluid from around the developing fetus is tested.
  - In chorionic villus sampling, a sample of the placenta is tested.
- To screen an embryo during IVF, a single cell is taken from the embryo before implantation.
- Whatever the potential genetic problem, the screening process involves isolating the DNA from embryo cells and testing it.
- The results of the test may give the parents choices. Sometimes the parents decide to terminate the pregnancy. Other parents decide this is not ethical but can prepare for having an affected baby.
- In IVF, only healthy embryos are implanted into the mother. Embryos carrying faulty genes are destroyed and some people think this is unethical.

1 What part of the cell is tested following the collection of embryo cells for genetic screening?

There are some concerns about embryo screening.

- There is a risk of miscarriage. Healthy fetuses could be lost due to the tests.
- Information from the screening process may not be reliable. A false negative result could lead to a baby with the disorder being born. A false positive may lead to a healthy pregnancy being terminated.
- Decisions about terminating a pregnancy are hard to take. It can be very emotional and some people have religious and ethical objections to terminating a pregnancy.
- There are economic issues because screening is expensive. However, it is also expensive to look after a child with a disability who may need a lot of support from medical and social care.
- There are ethical issues involved with destroying living embryos.

2 Suggest why every woman is not offered embryo screening for every pregnancy.

Study tip

Write lists of the pros and cons of embryo screening. Always look at both sides of the argument and write a balanced account. Your conclusion should be based on the argument you have given.

1 What is the molecule in chromosomes that carries the genes? [1 mark]

2 What is the difference between a gene and a genome? [2 marks]

3 What are alleles? [1 mark]

4 What is the main advantage of sexual reproduction? [1 mark]

5 Which sort of cell division is involved in:
 a asexual reproduction? [1 mark] **b** sexual reproduction? [1 mark]

6 Explain why offspring produced by asexual reproduction are genetically identical. [2 marks]

7 How many sets of chromosomes are found in:
 a the cells of fungal hyphae? [1 mark] **c** pollen? [1 mark]
 b human body cells? [1 mark] **d** sperm? [1 mark]

8 Explain why two parents without cystic fibrosis can have a child with the condition. [4 marks]

9 What is a nucleotide? [3 marks]

10 Compare mitosis and meiosis. [4 marks]

11 When environmental conditions change, what are the disadvantages to plants that reproduce by asexual reproduction? [3 marks]

12 Ⓗ Describe the process of protein synthesis in the cell. [6 marks]

13 Ⓗ Explain the possible consequences for a protein's shape if a mutation occurs in the gene that codes for the protein. [4 marks]

Chapter checklist

Tick when you have:

reviewed it after your lesson	✓	☐	☐
revised once – some questions right	✓	✓	☐
revised twice – all questions right	✓	✓	✓

Move on to another topic when you have all three ticks

13.1 Types of reproduction	☐	☐	☐
13.2 Cell division in sexual reproduction	☐	☐	☐
13.3 The best of both worlds	☐	☐	☐
13.4 DNA and the genome	☐	☐	☐
13.5 DNA structure and protein synthesis	☐	☐	☐
13.6 Gene expression and mutation	☐	☐	☐
13.7 Inheritance in action	☐	☐	☐
13.8 More about genetics	☐	☐	☐
13.9 Inherited disorders	☐	☐	☐
13.10 Screening for genetic disorders	☐	☐	☐

14.1 Variation

Key points

- Variation is the differences in the characteristics of individuals in a population.
- Variation may be due to differences in the genes inherited (genetic causes), the conditions in which organisms develop (environmental causes), or a combination of both genes and the environment.

Synoptic link

For the effect of alcohol on a fetus, see Topic B7.5.

The puppies in this litter have the same parents. The puppies have many similarities but mixing of their parents' genes has led to variations in their appearance. Can you guess what the parents may have looked like?

- Differences in the characteristics of individuals of the same kind (same species) may be due to:
    - differences in the genes they have inherited
    - the conditions in which they have developed
    - a combination of both genetic and environmental causes.

1 What are the two factors that influence some of our characteristics?

- Genes are the most important factor in controlling the appearance of an individual.

Environmental variation

- Plants may be affected by lack of light, nutrients, or space to grow. If deprived of nutrients, a plant cannot grow as well as other plants with the same genes grown in better conditions.
- Human development may be affected during pregnancy. If the mother smokes or drinks a lot of alcohol, the baby may have a low birthweight.
- Once animals are born, too much or too little food can alter their characteristics. For example, genes may determine if a person has the potential to be a good athlete. However, training to develop muscles and eating the correct diet will also alter the athlete's body.

2 Which environmental factors can change a plant's appearance?

Study tips

Genes control the development of characteristics.

Characteristics may be changed by the environment.

Look at photos of organisms and work out which features are controlled by genes and which are altered by diet or surroundings.

14.2 Evolution by natural selection

Key points

- The theory of evolution by natural selection states that all species of living things have evolved from simple life forms that first developed over 3 billion years ago.

- Mutations occur continuously. Very rarely, a mutation leads to a new phenotype. If the new phenotype is suited to an environmental change it can lead to a relatively rapid change in the species.

- If two populations of a species become so different that they can no longer interbreed to form fertile offspring, they have formed two new species.

Synoptic links

See Topic B13.2 for more about meiosis and sexual reproduction.

For more about Darwin's theory of evolution and how it was developed, see Chapter B15, and for more about competition between plants and animals in the natural world, see Topics B16.4 and B16.5.

Topic B13.5 has more about genes.

For more about evolution and natural selection, see Chapter B15.

Key words: mutation, natural selection

Study tips

Remember the key steps in natural selection:

mutation of gene → advantage to survival → breed → pass on genes

Look for these stages in the introduction to a question.

- Most organisms produce large numbers of offspring.

- Individual organisms will show a wide range of variation because of differences in their genes.

- All the organisms in the population will compete for food, shelter from predators, and mates.

- The organisms with the characteristics most suited to the environment will survive. For example, they may have the best camouflage, the best eyesight to find food, the most strength to build a burrow, or they may be the quickest to run from a predator or the best suited to the climate. The 'fittest' organisms survive.

1   Why do organisms show a wide range of variation?

- The organisms that survive are more likely to breed successfully.

- The genes that have enabled these organisms to survive are then passed on to their offspring.

- Sometimes a gene changes and becomes a new form of the gene. These changes are called **mutations**. If the mutated gene controls a characteristic that makes the organism better adapted to the environment, then the new gene will be passed on to the offspring.

- Mutations may be particularly important in **natural selection** if the environment changes. For example, the rabbit disease myxomatosis killed most of the rabbits in the UK. A few rabbits had a mutated gene that gave them immunity. The rabbits with the mutated gene survived to breed and the rabbit population became immune to the disease.

- A new species may evolve if one population of a species changes so much that they can no longer breed with another population to produce fertile offspring. This can take millions of years.

- The evolution of a population can sometimes occur in a relatively short time. For example, if a bacterium has a mutation that makes it resistant to antibiotics, then this mutation can spread rapidly through the population until all the bacteria are resistant.

2   Why did some rabbits survive myxomatosis?

Only the best-adapted predators capture prey and survive to breed – and only the best-adapted prey animals escape to breed

14.3 Selective breeding

Key points

- Selective breeding is a process where humans breed plants and animals for desired characteristics.

- Desired characteristics include disease resistance, increased food production in animals and plants, domestic dogs with a gentle nature, and heavily scented flowers.

- Problems can occur with selective breeding, including defects in some animals due to lack of variation.

Key word: selective breeding

Study tip

Make sure you understand how selective breeding leads to lack of variation in offspring. Remember that alleles control characteristics.

On the up

You should be able to explain the process of selective breeding and why humans use the process, as well as being able to explain why inbreeding is a problem when breeding dogs.

To achieve the top grades, you should also be able to explain in detail how the variation of alleles in a population is reduced by selective breeding and why the reduction of variation in a population through selective breeding is a problem.

- Farmers and breeders select animals or plants with desired characteristics, for example:

  - Cows that produce the most milk are selected to breed the next generation of dairy cattle.

  - High-yielding cows may be crossed with bulls of a mild temperament.

  - Seeds are selected from the plants with the biggest grains to grow the next crop.

- This is called **selective breeding** and it has been responsible for much of the progress in agriculture.

- Selective breeding is used to select for a wide range of features. Examples include:

  - disease resistance in food crops or garden plants

  - animals that produce more meat or milk

  - domestic dogs and farm animals with a gentle nature

  - large, unusual, brightly coloured or heavily scented flowers.

parents:

good milk yield   good temperament   +

possible offspring:

good milk yield, average temperament

good milk yield, good temperament

average milk yield, average temperament

average milk yield, good temperament

this is the cow that will be selected for further breeding

Sometimes an animal or plant with one desirable trait will be cross-bred with an organism showing another desirable trait. Only the offspring showing both of the favoured features will be used for further breeding

1 Why do farmers select particular cows for breeding?

Limitations of selective breeding

- Selective breeding greatly reduces the number of alleles in the population.

- There is less variation between individuals in the population.

- A new disease or climate change could destroy a whole population.

- Inbreeding of related organisms, such as breeds of dogs, has led to inherited defects.

2 What is the main genetic problem resulting from selective breeding?

14.4 Genetic engineering

Higher

- Genetic engineering involves changing the genetic make-up of an organism.
- Genes can be transferred to the cells of animals, plants, or microorganisms at an early stage in their development. This gives them a desired characteristic such as resistance to a disease.

Key points

- Genes can be transferred to the cells of animals and plants at an early stage of their development so they develop desired characteristics. This is genetic engineering.

- **(H)** In genetic engineering, genes from the chromosomes of humans and other organisms can be 'cut out' using enzymes and transferred to the cells of bacteria and other organisms using a vector, which is usually a bacterial plasmid or a virus.

- Crops that have had their genes modified are known as genetically modified (GM) crops. GM crops often have improved resistance to insect attack or herbicides and generally produce a higher yield.

Principles of genetic engineering

- A gene for a desired characteristic is 'cut out' of the chromosome of an organism using an enzyme.

- The gene is then inserted into the chromosome of another organism. A vector (carrier) such as a plasmid or virus may be used to transfer the gene.

- In genetic engineering, the new gene is often inserted into an organism of the same species to give it a 'desired' characteristic.

- Sometimes genes are inserted into a different species such as a bacterium. For example, the human gene to produce insulin can be placed in bacteria. Then the bacteria can produce large quantities of insulin to treat diabetes.

insulin gene cut out of DNA by an enzyme

human cell with insulin gene in its DNA

plasmid with insulin gene in it taken up by bacterium

bacterium with ring of DNA called a plasmid

insulin gene inserted into plasmid by another enzyme

bacterium multiplies many times

plasmid taken out of bacterium and split open by an enzyme

the insulin gene is switched on and the insulin is harvested

insulin

The principles of genetic engineering. A bacterial cell receives a human gene so it makes a human protein – in this case, the hormone insulin

Synoptic links

For the use of insulin to treat diabetes, see Topics B11.2 and B11.3, and for the possibility of using genetic engineering to treat inherited problems such as cystic fibrosis, see Topic B13.9.

Study tip

H

The basic principles of genetic engineering are always the same, so do not be put off by an unfamiliar example. Identify the vector and any enzymes used in the process.

1   What is used to cut genes out of chromosomes?

- New genes can be transferred to crop plants.
- Crops with changed genes are called genetically modified (GM) crop plants.
- GM crops may make their own pesticide, or be herbicide-resistant, and usually have increased yields.

2   What features might GM crops have that make them give higher yields than traditional crops?

B14

14.5 Cloning

Key points

- Tissue culture is a modern technique for cloning plants. Small groups of cells are taken from part of a plant to grow identical new plants. It is important for preserving rare plant species in nurseries as well as for commercial use.

- Taking cuttings is an older and simpler method of producing many identical new plants from a parent plant. It is widely used by gardeners.

- Transplanting cloned embryos involves splitting apart cells from a developing animal embryo before they become specialised and then transplanting the identical embryos into host mothers.

Synoptic link

For more on plant cuttings, see Topic B11.10.

Key word: tissue culture

Study tips

Remember that clones have identical genetic information to each other and to the single parent.

Make lists of the benefits and disadvantages of cloning.

- Individuals that are genetically identical to their parents are known as clones.

- It is much more difficult to clone animals than plants.

- Cloning is used to produce new individuals that are useful in farming and agriculture.

- In plants, the process of cloning can be cheap and effective. Plants can be cloned by taking cuttings and growing them.

- **Tissue culture** is the process of taking small groups of cells from part of a plant and growing them under special conditions. A mass of identical plant cells forms, called a callus. Each callus cell can be grown into a new plant.

- Tissue culture can be used to reproduce large numbers of a rare or top-quality plant. It is a more expensive process than taking cuttings.

small tissue sample taken from parent plant

tissue grown in agar with combination of nutrients and plant hormones to form big mass of tissue

different mixture of hormones and nutrients results in many tiny identical plantlets

plantlet clones grown on

Tissue culture makes it possible to produce thousands of identical plants quickly and easily from one small tissue sample

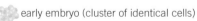
1   Name a quick, cheap way of cloning plants.

- Embryo transplants are used to clone animals. In this process an embryo with unspecialised cells is split into smaller groups of cells. Each group of genetically identical cells is transplanted into a host animal and allowed to develop into a new individual.

- Sometimes animals or plants are genetically modified to produce useful substances before they are cloned.

2   Suggest why it is more difficult to successfully clone animals than plants.

early embryo (cluster of identical cells)

1. Divide each embryo into several individual cells.

2. Each cell grows into an identical embryo in the lab.

3. Transfer embryos into their host mothers, which have been given hormones to get them ready for pregnancy.

4. Identical cloned calves are born. They are not biologically related to their host mothers.

Cloning cattle embryos

14.6 Adult cell cloning

- In adult cell cloning the nucleus of an adult cell, such as a skin cell, replaces the nucleus of an egg cell.

- First the nucleus is removed from an unfertilised egg cell. The nucleus is taken from the skin cell and placed inside the 'empty' egg cell.

- The new cell is given an electric shock that causes it to start to divide. The ball of cells is called an embryo.

- The embryo is genetically identical to the adult skin cell.

- Once the embryo has developed into a ball of cells, it is inserted into the womb of a host mother.

- Dolly the sheep was produced by adult cell cloning in 1997.

Key points

- In adult cell cloning:
  - the nucleus is removed from an unfertilised egg cell
  - the nucleus from an adult body cell, such as a skin cell, is inserted into the empty egg cell
  - a small electric shock stimulates the egg cell to divide to form an embryo
  - the embryo develops into a ball of cells
  - it is inserted into the womb of an adult female to continue its development.

- The cells of the embryo contain the same genetic information as the adult skin cell.

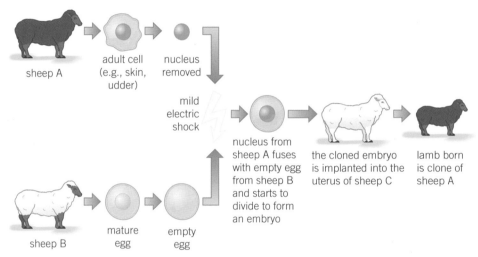

sheep A — adult cell (e.g., skin, udder) — nucleus removed — mild electric shock — nucleus from sheep A fuses with empty egg from sheep B and starts to divide to form an embryo — the cloned embryo is implanted into the uterus of sheep C — lamb born is clone of sheep A

sheep B — mature egg — empty egg

Adult cell cloning remains a very difficult technique, but scientists hope it may bring benefits in the future

1 Name the two cells needed in adult cell cloning.

Benefits

- Using this technique, cloned animals have been developed that have been genetically engineered to produce valuable proteins in their milk. These have uses in medicine.

- Cloning can save animals from extinction.

Risks

- Many people have concerns about the ethics of cloning.

- Cloning limits the variation in a population (it limits the gene pool). This can be a problem for natural selection if the environment changes.

- There are concerns about using the technique to clone humans in the future.

2 Give one benefit of adult cell cloning.

Study tips

Plants can be cloned by tissue culture.

An animal can be cloned by dividing an embryo or by cloning an adult cell.

Draw flow diagrams to illustrate these processes.

Student Book
pages 230–231

B14

14.7 Ethics of genetic technologies

There are many benefits, but also concerns, with using genetic engineering in medicine and agriculture.

Key points

- Modern medical research is exploring the possibility of genetic modification to overcome some inherited disorders.
- There are benefits and risks associated with genetic engineering in agriculture and medicine.
- Some people have ethical objections to genetic engineering.

On the up

If you can outline the potential risks and benefits of genetic engineering, you can achieve the top grades by being able to evaluate the risks and benefits.

Synoptic link

Find out more about genetic diseases in Topics B13.9 and B13.10.

Study tip

Higher

Cloning and genetic engineering are different – although cloned plants and animals may also be genetically modified! Learn the techniques for both processes.

Benefits

- If a person has a faulty gene they may have a genetic disorder. If the correct gene can be transferred to the person they could be cured.
- Several medical drugs have been produced by genetic engineering, such as insulin, human growth hormone, and antibodies.
- GM crops have been developed that are resistant to herbicides or to insects. Farmers can then spray the crops with herbicides or insecticides without damaging them.
- Other GM crops can grow well in dry, hot, or cold parts of the world.
- Genetic technology can improve the growth rate of plants and animals.

1 Suggest why farmers grow GM crops.

- GM crops have a bigger yield, but farmers have to buy new GM seed every year because the crops are infertile.
- Some people are concerned about accidentally introducing genes into wild flower populations.
- Insects that are not pests may be affected by GM crops.
- In the long term, insects could become resistant to pesticides.
- Many people worry about the effect of eating GM crops on human health.
- Many people argue about whether or not cloning and genetic engineering are ethical.
  - What will be the long-term effects?
  - Might we create new organisms that we know nothing about?
  - Are these processes ethically acceptable?

2 Look at the photograph. What would be the benefit of golden rice to children with a form of blindness caused by vitamin A deficiency?

Varieties of GM rice called golden rice have been developed to help solve the problem of blindness in children who lack vitamin A in their diet. Yellow beta carotene is needed to make vitamin A in the body. The amount of beta carotene in golden rice and golden rice 2 is reflected in the depth of colour of the rice

1. Which two factors cause variation between organisms of the same type? [2 marks]

2. What is a clone? [2 marks]

3. In adult cell cloning, which cell provides the nucleus for the clone? [1 mark]

4. How are new genes formed? [1 mark]

5. In the genetic engineering of bacteria to produce insulin, where does the gene for insulin production originate from? [1 mark]

6. What class of chemicals is used to stimulate the cells in tissue culture? [1 mark]

7. Give an example of how selective breeding has been used in horticulture. [1 mark]

8. In 1915 the oyster population in Malpeque Bay, Canada, was almost completely destroyed by disease. Explain how the population increased, slowly at first, and then recovered. [6 marks]

9. Describe the process of adult cell cloning. [6 marks]

10. Explain why it is more difficult to successfully clone animals than plants. [5 marks]

11. Explain how, in the long term, insect pests could become resistant to pesticides when they have a diet of insect-resistant crops. [4 marks]

12. Ⓗ Describe the stages in the production of insulin by genetic engineering. [6 marks]

Chapter checklist

Tick when you have:

reviewed it after your lesson ✓ ☐ ☐

revised once – some questions right ✓ ✓ ☐

revised twice – all questions right ✓ ✓ ✓

Move on to another topic when you have all three ticks

14.1 Variation ☐ ☐ ☐

14.2 Evolution by natural selection ☐ ☐ ☐

14.3 Selective breeding ☐ ☐ ☐

14.4 Genetic engineering ☐ ☐ ☐

14.5 Cloning ☐ ☐ ☐

14.6 Adult cell cloning ☐ ☐ ☐

14.7 Ethics of genetic technologies ☐ ☐ ☐

Student Book
pages 234–235

B15

15.1 The history of genetics

Key points

- In the mid-19th century, Gregor Mendel carried out breeding experiments on plants. One of his observations was that the inheritance of each characteristic is determined by 'units' that are passed on unchanged to descendents.

- In the late 19th century, the behaviour of chromosomes during cell division was observed.

- In the early 20th century, it was observed that chromosomes and Mendel's 'units' behaved in similar ways. This led to the idea that the units, now called genes, were located on the chromosomes.

- In the mid-20th century, the structure of DNA was determined and the mechanism of gene function was worked out.

- This work by many scientists led to the gene theory being developed.

Synoptic links

For genetics and simple crosses, see Topics B13.7, B13.8, and B13.9. Topics B13.4 and B13.5 give the structure of DNA.

On the up

If you can explain why the importance of Mendel's work was not recognised until after his death, you can achieve the top grades by being able to use a Punnett square to draw conclusions from the results of Mendel's experiments.

Gregor Mendel

- Gregor Mendel carried out breeding experiments using pea plants in the mid-19th century.

- He observed clear patterns of inheritance in pea plants. He did this work before anyone had discovered chromosomes.

- Mendel counted the number of plants with a particular characteristic and recorded his findings carefully.

- He realised that there are separate units of inheritance that are passed on unchanged.

- He realised that some characteristics are dominant. Smooth peas are dominant over wrinkled peas, and green peas are dominant over yellow peas.

- He used mathematical models to describe patterns of monohybrid inheritance – the inheritance of single characteristics involving pairs of units.

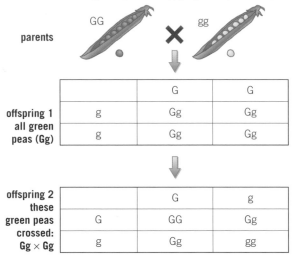

genotype – 1 GG:2 Gg:1 gg
phenotype – 3 green peas:1 yellow pea

Gregor Mendel was the father of modern genetics. His work with peas was not recognised in his own lifetime, but now we know that his ideas were correct

After Mendel

- Chromosomes were observed during cell division in the late 19th century.

- In the early 20th century, scientists realised that Mendel's 'units' and chromosomes behave in a similar way. This led to the idea that the 'units' are genes on chromosomes.

1 What do we now call Mendel's units of inheritance?

- In the 1950s the combined work of Watson and Crick and of Franklin and Wilkins resulted in their working out the structure of DNA.

- As a consequence, the mechanism of gene function was established.

- The modern gene theory – that genes code for the production of proteins – was then developed and the research moved forward very quickly.

2 What is the modern gene theory?

15.2 Theories of evolution

- Scientists have estimated that life began on Earth about 3 billion years ago.

- Before the 18th century there were few scientific ideas about how evolution works.

- Jean-Baptiste Lamarck suggested a theory called 'the inheritance of acquired characteristics'. Lamarck's theory stated that characteristics that develop during an organism's lifetime can be passed on to the next generation. People found this difficult to believe. For example, if two parents were to build up their muscles in the gym, Lamarck's theory would predict that this characteristic would be passed on to their offspring.

- We now know that in the great majority of cases this type of inheritance cannot occur.

In Lamarck's model of evolution, giraffes have long necks because each generation stretched up to reach the highest leaves. So each new generation had a slightly longer neck

1 What is meant by acquired characteristics?

- Charles Darwin suggested the theory of natural selection after he had made a journey to the Galápagos Islands. He recorded many observations of life on the islands.

- He noticed that organisms of a particular species show a wide range of variation for a particular characteristic.

- He also observed that reproduction always gives more offspring than the environment can support.

- He concluded that those that are the 'fittest' are more likely to survive and breed (natural selection).

- Darwin's theory stated that small changes in organisms took place over a very long time. Those that are best adapted breed and pass on their characteristics.

- Darwin did not know about genes. We can now say that the best-adapted organisms survive to breed. They are the ones that pass on their genes to the next generation.

2 Who suggested the theory of evolution by natural selection?

Key points

- Earlier theories of evolution, including that of Jean-Baptiste Lamarck, are based mainly on the idea that changes that occur in an organism during its lifetime can be inherited. We now know that in the vast majority of cases this type of inheritance cannot occur.

- Charles Darwin proposed his theory of evolution by natural selection largely as a result of observations made on a round-the-world expedition.

- The individual organisms in a particular species tend to show a wide range of variation for each characteristic.

- Reproduction always gives more offspring than the environment can support. The organisms that have inherited the characteristics most suited to their environment – the 'fittest' – are more likely to survive and breed successfully.

- When they breed, they pass on the characteristics that have enabled them to survive to the next generation.

Synoptic link

See Topic B14.2 for the basic process of natural selection.

Study tip

Make sure you know why we still accept Darwin's theory but not Lamarck's. Make a list of the key points of the theory of natural selection.

15.3 Accepting Darwin's ideas

Darwin's theory of evolution by natural selection was only gradually accepted for several reasons.

- The theory of natural selection challenged the idea that God made all the animals and plants that live on Earth.

- Many scientists were not convinced because they still did not think there was sufficient evidence for the theory.

1   What name is given to Darwin's theory of evolution?

- Darwin could not explain why there was variety in organisms, or how inheritance worked. Scientists did not know about genes and genetics until about 50 years later.

- Darwin had tried to show that birds, such as finches on the Galápagos Islands, could change over time if they lived under different environmental conditions. During his lifetime he could not explain, in terms of genes, why the offspring inherited the useful adaptations.

2   Which birds did Darwin observe to find evidence for evolution?

Key points

- Darwin's theory of evolution by natural selection was only gradually accepted for a number of reasons.

- These include:
  - conflict with the widely held belief that God made all the animals and plants on Earth
  - insufficient evidence
  - no mechanism for explaining variety and inheritance (genetics were not understood for another 50 years).

Study tips

Remember the difference between evolution and natural selection:

- Evolution is the theory that all species have evolved from simple life forms that developed more than 3 billion years ago.

- Natural selection is the process by which evolution comes about.

On the up

If you can explain how finches on different islands evolved different-shaped beaks by natural selection, you can achieve the top grades by being able to explain how the finch species on the different Galápagos Islands are evidence for evolution by natural selection.

This gaudy tree frog has evolved to fill a specific niche in the Costa Rican rainforests

15.4 Evolution and speciation

Key points

- Alfred Russel Wallace independently proposed the theory of evolution by natural selection. He published joint writings with Darwin in 1858, which prompted Darwin to publish *The Origin of Species* the following year (1859).

- Wallace worked worldwide gathering evidence for evolutionary theory. He is best known for his work on warning coloration in animals and his theory of speciation.

- A build-up of evidence over time has led to our current understanding of the theory of speciation. New species arise as a result of:

    - isolation: where two populations of a species become separated

    - genetic variation between the populations

    - natural selection that operates differently on the two populations

    - speciation: where the populations become so different that successful interbreeding is no longer possible.

Key word: speciation

1 How can populations become isolated?

2 What is meant by genetic variation?

- Alfred Russel Wallace also proposed a theory of evolution by natural selection at the same time as Darwin (1858). This prompted Darwin to publish *The Origin of Species* in 1859.

- Wallace worked worldwide to gather evidence for his theory. He is best known for his work on warning coloration in animals and his theory of **speciation**.

- New species can arise from existing species if a group becomes isolated from the rest.

    - Geographical isolation could occur if an island separates from the mainland or if a new river separates two areas. Mountain ranges and old craters can also isolate organisms.

    - Organisms of a species in one area may be exposed to different environmental conditions (environmental isolation).

- If the environment, food supply, and predators are different for each separated population, they will evolve differently.

Darwin's finches became isolated on different islands. The conditions, particularly the type of food present, varied on each island. The finches developed differently due to the alleles that were selected in natural selection

- Each population has a wide range of alleles that control their characteristics. This is genetic variation.

- Natural selection will occur in both areas, but different characteristics will be beneficial in the two populations. The alleles for characteristics that help the organisms to survive in their particular area are selected. The organisms with these alleles will survive and breed.

- If the populations are later brought together and cannot interbreed, we say that they belong to two separate species and speciation has occurred.

Study tips

When answering questions on speciation, ask yourself:

- how did the groups become separated? (e.g., by a river)

- which factor is being selected for or against? (e.g., the ability to find food or escape predation)

- how does each group change? (e.g., some have better adapted beaks or can run faster).

15.5 Evidence for evolution

Key points

- Fossils are the remains of organisms from millions of years ago that can be found in rocks, ice, and other places.

- Fossils may be formed in different ways including the absence of decay, parts replaced by other materials as they decay, and as preserved traces of organisms.

- Fossils give us information about organisms that lived millions of years ago.

- It is very difficult for scientists to know exactly how life on Earth began because there is little valid evidence. Early forms of life were soft-bodied so left few traces behind and many traces of early life have been destroyed by geological activity.

Using timescales

Timescales for the evolution of life are big:

a thousand years is 10^3 years

a million years is 10^6 years

a billion years is 10^9 years.

Study tip

Make a list of the different types of fossil evidence.

- Scientists believe that the Earth is about 4500 million years old and that life began about 3500 million years ago.

- There is some debate as to whether the first life developed due to the conditions on Earth, or whether simple life forms arrived from another planet.

- We can date rocks. Fossils are found in rocks, so we can date when different organisms existed.

- Fossils may be formed in various ways:

  - from the hard parts of animals that do not decay easily, such as bones, teeth, shells, claws

  - from parts of organisms that have not decayed because some of the conditions for decay are absent, for example, fossils of animals preserved in ice

  - parts of the organism being replaced by other materials, such as minerals, as they decay

  - as preserved traces of organisms, such as footprints, burrows, and rootlet traces.

- Most organisms that died did not leave a fossil because the exact conditions for fossil formation were not present.

1 Name a hard part of an animal that will not decay easily.

- Many early life forms had soft bodies so few traces were left behind.

- Traces that were left are likely to have been destroyed by geological activity such as earthquakes.

- Fossils give us evidence about organisms that lived millions of years ago.

2 Why is the fossil record incomplete?

1. The reptile dies and falls to the ground.

2. The flesh rots, leaving the skeleton to be covered in sand or soil and clay before it is damaged.

3. Protected, over millions of years, the skeleton becomes mineralised and turns to rock. The rocks shift in the earth with the fossil trapped inside.

4. Eventually, the fossil emerges as the rocks move and erosion takes place.

It takes a very long time for fossils to form, but they provide us with invaluable evidence of how life on Earth has developed

15.6 Fossils and extinction

Key points

- You can learn from fossils how much or how little organisms have changed as life has developed on Earth.
- Extinction may be caused by a number of factors including new predators, new diseases, or new, more successful competitors.

Key word: extinction

Study tip

Always mention a *change* when you give possible reasons for the extinction of a species.

- The fossil record is incomplete, but we can learn a lot from fossils that exist. Some organisms have changed a lot over time. Others have changed very little, while some have become extinct.

whole animal	forefeet	
modern horse (*Equus*) from 2 million years ago — 1.6 m		The modern horse is a fast runner on hard ground with only one toe forming the hoof.
pliohippus from 5 million years ago — 1.0 m		With a single toe forming the hoof, this looks more like a modern horse.
merychippus from 25 million years ago — 1.0 m		Bigger again, walking mainly on one enlarged toe for speed.
mesohippus from 37 million years ago — 0.6 m		Bigger, only three toes on the ground for moving fast on drier ground.
hyracotherium from 55 million years ago — 0.4 m		Small, swamp-dwelling with four well-spread toes for walking on soft ground.

The evolutionary history of the horse based on the fossil record

- **Extinction** means that a species that once existed has completely died out.
- Extinction can be caused by a number of factors, but always involves a change in circumstances:
  - A new disease may kill all members of a species.
  - The environment changes over geological time.
  - New diseases may be introduced.
  - A new predator may evolve or be introduced to an area that kills and eats all of a species.
  - A new competitor may evolve or be introduced into an area. The original species may be left with too little to eat.
  - A single catastrophic event may occur that destroys the habitat (e.g., a massive volcanic eruption).
  - Natural changes in species occur over time.

1 How can a new predator cause the extinction of a species?
2 Name a catastrophic event that could destroy a large number of habitats.

15.7 More about extinction

Key points

- Extinction can be caused by a variety of factors including changes to the environment over geological time and single catastrophic events such as massive volcanic eruptions or collisions with asteroids.

- The biggest influences on the survival of species are changes in the environment.

- Climate change is an important influence in determining which species survive. A species that is very well adapted to a hot climate may become extinct in an Ice Age. It could be that there is insufficient food or it is too cold to breed.

- Climate change may make it too cold or hot, or too wet or dry, for a species and reduce its food supply.

| **1** | Why might a species die out if the climate changes? |

- Fossil evidence shows that there have been mass extinctions on a global scale.

- Many of the species died out over a period of several million years – a short time in geological terms.

  - The habitat the species lives in may be destroyed by catastrophic events such as a major volcanic eruption.

  - The environment can change dramatically following a collision between a giant asteroid and Earth.

- Why the dinosaurs became extinct has puzzled many scientists. Different ideas have been suggested.

  - The collision of a giant asteroid caused huge fires, earthquakes, landslides, and tsunamis. The dust that rose masked the Sun, causing darkness and lower temperatures. Plants could not grow.

  - The extinction was a slower process due to sea ice melting and cooling the sea temperature by about 9 °C. This meant there was less plankton, so less food was available.

| **2** | Suggest another factor that could have caused the dinosaurs to die out. |

Timeline (diagram)

	approx. time years ago
NOW	
50–70% species lost / dinosaurs died out	65 million
50% marine invertebrates lost	205 million
80% land quadrupeds lost	
80–95% marine species lost	251 million
70% species lost	360–75 million
60% species lost	440 million
ORIGINS OF LIFE	3500 million years ago

The five main extinction events so far in the evolutionary history of the Earth

Study tips

Remember that the timescales in forming new species and mass extinctions are huge.

Try to develop an understanding of time in millions and billions of years.

15.8 Antibiotic-resistant bacteria

Key points

- Bacteria can evolve rapidly because they reproduce at a fast rate.

- Mutations of bacterial pathogens produce new strains.

- Some strains might be resistant to antibiotics and so are not killed. They survive and reproduce, so the population of the resistant strain increases by natural selection. The resistant strain will then spread because people are not immune to it and there is no effective treatment.

- The bacterium MRSA is resistant to many antibiotics.

- To reduce the rate of development of antibiotic-resistant strains, it is important that doctors do not prescribe antibiotics inappropriately, patients use the correct antibiotics prescribed, and patients complete each course of antibiotics.

- The development of new antibiotics is costly and slow and is unlikely to keep up with the emergence of new resistant strains.

Some pathogens, particularly viruses, can mutate (change) resulting in a new form called a mutation.

The changed pathogen can spread rapidly because:

- people are not immune to it
- there is no effective treatment.

1 Why do some new pathogens spread rapidly?

Antibiotic-resistant bacteria

- Mutations of pathogens produce new strains; some are resistant to antibiotics.

- Antibiotics kill the individual pathogens that have not developed resistance.

- The resistant pathogens survive and reproduce, and a whole population of a resistant strain develops. This is an example of natural selection.

- Methicillin-resistant *Staphylococcus aureus* (MRSA) is a bacterium that has evolved through natural selection. MRSA and other bacteria have become resistant to commonly used antibiotics.

- In order to slow down the rate of development of resistant strains, antibiotics should not be used for mild infections, the correct antibiotics must be prescribed, and patients should always complete each course of antibiotics.

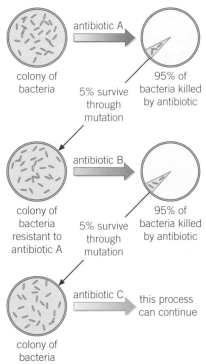

colony of bacteria

antibiotic A

95% of bacteria killed by antibiotic

5% survive through mutation

colony of bacteria resistant to antibiotic A

antibiotic B

95% of bacteria killed by antibiotic

5% survive through mutation

colony of bacteria resistant to antibiotics A and B

antibiotic C

this process can continue

Bacteria can develop resistance to many different antibiotics in a process of natural selection, as this simple model shows

Synoptic link

For more about bacteria, see Chapter B5.

Study tip

Remember that the development of antibiotic resistance is a good example of natural selection in action.

2 How does natural selection cause resistant populations of bacteria to develop?

- The development of new antibiotics is a costly and slow process.

15.9 Classification

Key points

- Traditionally, living things have been classified into groups depending on their structures and characteristics in a system described by Carl Linnaeus.
- Linnaeus classified organisms into kingdom, phylum, class, order, family, genus, and species.
- Organisms are named by the binomial system of genus and species.
- As evidence of the internal structures of organisms became more developed due to improvements in microscopes, and the understanding of biochemical processes progressed, new models of classification were proposed.

- There are millions of different types of living organism. By putting organisms into groups we can make more sense of how closely they are related. Grouping organisms is called **classification**. Biologists study the similarities and differences between organisms in order to classify them. The system traditionally used was described by Carl Linnaeus and is called the natural classification system.
- The easiest system to understand is one that starts with large groups and splits these up gradually into smaller ones. Linnaeus classified organisms into kingdom, phylum, class, order, family, genus, and species. The largest groups are the kingdoms and Linnaeus had only two – animals and plants.
- The smallest group in the classification system is the **species**. Members of a species are very similar and can breed together to produce fertile offspring.

1 What is meant by the term 'species'?

- To avoid confusion, all living organisms are given a Latin name that all biologists use. The name has two parts – the genus name followed by the species name. This is called the binomial system. Modern man is called *Homo sapiens*.
- Due to evidence from improved microscopy and a better knowledge of biochemical processes, new models of classification have been proposed.
- Currently three domains are divided into six kingdoms.

Key words: classification, species

15.10 New systems of classification

Key points

- Studying the similarities and differences between organisms allows us to classify them into archaea, bacteria, and eukaryota.
- Classification also helps us to understand evolutionary and ecological relationships.
- Models such as evolutionary trees allow us to suggest relationships between organisms.

Synoptic link

For more about prokaryotic and eukaryotic cells, see Topic B1.3.

The three-domain system

- Carl Woese and others introduced the idea of a higher level of classification called a **domain**. They used evidence from the biochemistry of ribosomes and the way cells divide. The three domains are called the **archaea**, bacteria, and eukaryota.
- Archaea are primitive forms of bacteria, including extremophiles that can live in extreme conditions. The domain has one kingdom – the archaebacteria.
- The domain bacteria contains the true bacteria as well as the cyanobacteria, which can photosynthesise. The domain has one kingdom – the eubacteria.
- The eukaryota all have cells that contain a nucleus enclosing the genetic material. The domain has four kingdoms – protista, fungi, plants, and animals.

1 What are the three domains?

- **Evolutionary trees** are models that can be drawn to show the relationships between different groups of organisms. When new evidence is found, biologists may modify these evolutionary relationships. Ecological relationships tell us how species have evolved together in an environment.

Key words: domain, archaea, evolutionary trees

2 Why is it useful to draw evolutionary trees?

1 **a** Who was the 'father of genetics'? [1 mark]

   b Who built the first model of DNA? [1 mark]

2 Why are there no fossils of early life forms? [2 marks]

3 The Earth is 4.5 billion years old. What is the shortest way to express 4.5 billion in numbers? [1 mark]

4 How might a new competitor lead to the extinction of a species? [1 mark]

5 **a** What are the two main ideas put forward for the extinction of the dinosaurs? [2 marks]

   b Suggest another possible cause of the extinction. [1 mark]

   c Why is the cause not likely to be a new predator? [1 mark]

6 Why is there variation between members of the same species? [4 marks]

7 MRSA is a bacterium that is resistant to many antibiotics.
Describe and explain how the spread of MRSA can be reduced in hospitals. [5 marks]

8 Suggest three factors that could change in a habitat area, causing problems for the organisms living there. [3 marks]

9 What is the main difference between Lamarck's theory of evolution and Darwin's theory? [6 marks]

10 Why do biologists draw evolutionary trees? [2 marks]

11 What is meant by 'geographical isolation'? [3 marks]

12 What are the stages of speciation? [5 marks]

Chapter checklist

Tick when you have:

reviewed it after your lesson ✔ ☐ ☐

revised once – some questions right ✔ ✔ ☐

revised twice – all questions right ✔ ✔ ✔

Move on to another topic when you have all three ticks

15.1 The history of genetics ☐ ☐ ☐

15.2 Theories of evolution ☐ ☐ ☐

15.3 Accepting Darwin's ideas ☐ ☐ ☐

15.4 Evolution and speciation ☐ ☐ ☐

15.5 Evidence for evolution ☐ ☐ ☐

15.6 Fossils and extinction ☐ ☐ ☐

15.7 More about extinction ☐ ☐ ☐

15.8 Antibiotic-resistant bacteria ☐ ☐ ☐

15.9 Classification ☐ ☐ ☐

15.10 New systems of classification ☐ ☐ ☐

01   **Figure 1** is a genetic diagram that shows a cross between a plant that produces red flowers and one of the same species that produces white flowers.

Figure 1

Study tips

Genetics questions often look difficult at first. However, keep calm and remember that there are only three combinations of alleles: AA, Aa, and aa. Read the information given and decide which combination applies to each parent or offspring. Remember an offspring with genotype aa must have inherited an a allele from each parent.

Use **Figure 1** to answer the questions.

Write the correct number for each of the following:

01.1	the dominant characteristic	[1 mark]
01.2	a gamete with a recessive allele	[1 mark]
01.3	an embryo.	[1 mark]

Write the correct letter to identify each process:

01.4	mitosis	[1 mark]
01.5	meiosis	[1 mark]
01.6	fertilisation.	[1 mark]

01.7 Choose the correct **bold** word from the list below to copy and complete the sentence.

The letters R and r are symbols to represent _____.   [1 mark]

   alleles   chromosomes   genes

Figure 2 shows another process.

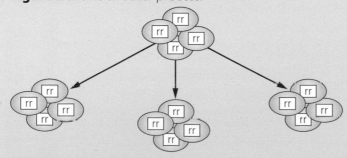

Figure 2

Use the correct **bold** words from the lists to copy and complete the sentences.

01.8 The process shown in the second diagram is _____.   [1 mark]

   asexual reproduction   fertilisation   sexual reproduction

01.9 The flowers produced by these plants will be _____ . [1 mark]

red   **pink**   **white**

02 Many organisms have become extinct whilst others have evolved into new forms.

02.1 Dinosaurs became extinct millions of years ago.
How do we know dinosaurs existed? [1 mark]

02.2 Many scientists think that the dinosaurs became extinct in a mass extinction when an asteroid collided with Earth. A dust cloud rose as a result of the collision.
Explain why this event might have caused the extinction of the dinosaurs. [3 marks]

02.3 Mass extinctions are relatively rare.
Give **two** reasons why a single species may become extinct. [2 marks]

02.4 Describe how a new species may develop as a result of geographic isolation. [6 marks]

03 About 25% of the world's food crops are destroyed every year through insect attack.
The corn borer is an insect that eats corn.
Genetic modification has been used to make a variety of corn that is resistant to the corn borer insect.
The GM corn has a gene from a bacterium that causes it to produce a low level of a bacterial protein.
This protein is poisonous to the corn borer. The insect is killed when it eats the maize.

03.1 **(H)** Explain how the non-GM corn is modified and how it then produces the bacterial protein. [6 marks]

03.2 Use the information about the GM corn and your own knowledge to evaluate the use of the GM corn compared with non-GM corn. [4 marks]

04 Glycogen is an important storage compound found in humans.

04.1 Where is glycogen stored? [1 mark]

04.2 Glycogen can be converted into glucose.
Name the type of chemical that converts glycogen to glucose. [1 mark]

04.3 There are several genetic diseases that cause problems with glycogen storage. These diseases are caused by recessive alleles (g).
In one type of glycogen storage disease, glycogen is not converted to glucose.
The dominant allele (G) allows glycogen to be converted to glucose.
(H) Construct a genetic diagram to show how two parents without the disease can have a child with glycogen storage disease. [4 marks]

04.4 The gender (sex) of humans is determined by the X and Y chromosomes.
Give the combinations of these chromosomes for a male human and for a female human. [2 marks]

04.5 In another type of glycogen storage disease the recessive allele is found on the X chromosome. This disease is usually restricted to males, being rarely found in females. Suggest why. [3 marks]

Study tip

For question **03**, you need to tell the whole story and use scientific terms that are not in the question. You must explain how the gene is transferred into the corn and then describe how the DNA code in the gene determines the order of amino acids in the protein.

Study tips

When you see the word 'evaluate', you must look for two sides of an argument, or the pros and cons of a process. In this case you should look for the advantages and disadvantages of GM corn versus non-GM corn.

Always give a conclusion with a reason for your decision.

5 Ecology

Ecology is the study of organisms and their relationships with the living and non-living environment in which they live. We are discovering the importance of the balance of nature in maintaining the health of Earth. You will be looking at the way organisms are adapted to their environment and how they compete for mates and resources such as light and food.

Life on Earth as we know it depends on the sugar made by plants using energy from the Sun. You will be learning about the feeding relationships and material cycles that maintain the diversity of life. You will also consider the impact of the human population on the Earth.

I already know...

I will revise...

I already know...	I will revise...
that plants and animals have different requirements from their environments.	how to investigate and measure the distribution and abundance of species in a system.
Darwin's theory and about natural selection.	the competition between organisms for scarce resources, and the adaptations of organisms that result from natural selection and enable them to compete successfully in specific environments.
that plants need mineral ions and water from the soil, carbon dioxide from the air, and light to make the chemicals they need.	the material cycles in nature that return chemicals from the bodies of organisms to the soil, water, and air.
factors that affect the growth of bacterial populations.	the importance of decomposition and the factors that affect the rate of decay and of compost formation.
how people reproduce.	the reasons for the human population explosion and its impact in terms of pollution of the land, water, and air.
the types of food people need to keep them healthy and the impact of poor diet on non-communicable diseases.	what is meant by food security and the measures that can be taken to make food production both more efficient and sustainable.

Student Book
pages 258–259

B16

16.1 The importance of communities

Key points

- An ecosystem is the interaction of a community of living organisms with the non-living (abiotic) parts of their environment.

- Organisms require materials from their surroundings and other living organisms to survive and reproduce.

- Within a community, each species depends on other species for food, shelter, pollination, seed dispersal, etc. If one species is removed it can affect the whole community. This is called interdependence.

- A stable community is one in which all the species and environmental factors are in balance so that population sizes remain fairly constant.

Synoptic link

There is more about the role of microorganisms such as bacteria, protista, and fungi in Topics B17.4, B17.5, and B17.6.

Key words: community, interdependence

On the up

If you can describe what is meant by a stable community, you can achieve the top grades by being able to use evidence to write hypotheses about why populations have changed in a community.

- Organisms require materials from their surroundings and from other living organisms to survive and reproduce.

- Organisms live in complex **communities** containing populations of different species from all the kingdoms.

- An ecosystem is the interaction of a community of living organisms (biotic factors) with the non-living (abiotic) elements of their environment.

- The Sun is the source of energy for an ecosystem.

- Carbon, nitrogen, and water are recycled through an ecosystem.

- Animals and plants are interdependent. For example, plants produce food, animals eat plants and other animals, animals pollinate plants and disperse seeds, animals use plant material for nests and shelters, and plants use animal waste to obtain nutrients.

- Organisms compete for resources both within their species and with populations of other species.

1 Give an example of a resource for which animals compete in a community.

- If one species is removed from a community, it can affect the whole community. This is called **interdependence**.

- A stable community is one in which all the species and environmental factors are in balance so that population sizes remain fairly constant.

- Tropical rainforests, mature oak woodlands, and mature coral reefs are stable communities.

Without insects, birds, and mammals, many plants would not be able to reproduce

2 What is a stable community?

Study tip

Look for examples of communities in the world around you. Even a stone wall may house a community of animals and plants.

16.2 Organisms in their environment

Key points

- Abiotic factors that may affect communities of organisms include:
  - light intensity
  - temperature
  - moisture levels
  - soil pH and mineral content
  - wind intensity and direction
  - carbon dioxide levels for plants
  - the availability of oxygen for aquatic animals.
- Biotic factors that may affect communities of organisms include:
  - the availability of food
  - new predators arriving
  - new pathogens
  - new competitors.

Study tip

Make sure you know the difference between abiotic and biotic factors.

Snow leopards are one of the rarest big cats. They live in cold, high-altitude environments where there is very little prey for them to hunt

Living organisms form communities. Biologists study the relationships within and between these communities. These relationships can be influenced by external factors.

Abiotic factors

- Amount of light – few plants live on a forest floor because the light is blocked out by the trees. Shaded plants often have broader leaves or more chlorophyll.

- Temperature – for example, Arctic plants are small, which limits the number of herbivores that can survive in the area.

- Availability of water – water is important for all organisms, so few can survive in a desert. If it rains in the desert then plants grow and produce flowers and seeds very quickly. This provides food for animals.

- Availability of mineral ions – most plants struggle to grow where mineral ions such as nitrates are in short supply, so few animals can live in that area.

- The pH of the soil has a major effect on what can grow in it and on the rate of decay. This in turn affects the release of mineral ions back into the soil. A low (acidic) pH inhibits decay.

- Wind intensity and direction can affect plants, influencing the shapes of trees and the rate of transpiration, for example.

- Availability of carbon dioxide – lack of carbon dioxide will limit plant growth and consequently the food available for animals.

- Availability of oxygen – water animals can be affected by lack of oxygen in the water. Some invertebrates can live at very low oxygen levels, but most fish need high levels of oxygen dissolved in water.

- Availability of nesting sites, shelter, and appropriate habitats – to feed and breed successfully organisms need a suitable place to live. Loss of nesting sites causes a decrease in bird populations.

1 Give three examples of abiotic factors that affect plants.

Biotic factors

- Availability of food – organisms are more likely to breed successfully when there is plenty of food.

- If new predators arrive, prey organisms with no defence may easily be caught and their population will quickly be depleted.

- New pathogens or parasites – if organisms do not have resistance to the disease the whole population can be wiped out.

- New competitors – if a new species enters the community it may compete for the same food source as one of the native species, resulting in a drop in numbers of the native species.

2 Why are new pathogens a threat to a community?

16.3 Distribution and abundance

Key points

- A range of experimental methods using transects and quadrats is used by ecologists to determine the distribution and abundance of species in an ecosystem.

← 0.5 m length →

For plants partly covered by the quadrat, decide whether they are in or out of the quadrat, and stick to this decision. In this quadrat, you have 6 or 7 plants per 0.25 m² (that's 24 or 28 plants per m²)

Study tips

Remember – you sample quadrats along a transect to see a change in species distribution in a line from A to B.

You sample quadrats on coordinates from a random number generator to count the number of a species in an area.

Investigating the population size of daisies in a field

You need to plan the data you will collect before you start:

- What size of quadrat will you use?

- How will you make your sampling random?

- How many samples will you take?

Quantitative data can be used to describe how physical factors might be affecting where organisms live in an environment (their **distribution**) and how many organisms live there (their **abundance**).

Quantitative data can be obtained by random **quantitative sampling** using a **quadrat** or sampling along a **transect**.

A quadrat is a square frame made of metal or wood, which may be subdivided into a grid. If several quadrats are placed randomly in a field the investigator can count the number of a particular type of plant or animal in each quadrat. This can be used to estimate the number of, for example, daisies in the whole field.

- **Sample size** is important. In a large field enough random quadrats must be placed to be sure the sample is representative of the whole field.

- An estimate of the number of, for example, daisies is usually given as a mean per square metre.

A transect is not random. A line is marked between two points (e.g., from the top of a rocky shore down to the sea). You can place a quadrat every five metres along the line and count the organisms inside. Physical factors could also be measured at each quadrat point. This method supplies a lot of information about the habitat and the organisms in it.

| 1 | What is a quadrat? | 2 | What is a transect? |

Finding the range, the mean, the median, and the mode

You need to understand the terms **range**, **mean**, **median**, and **mode** when recording quantitative data.

The following readings are the numbers of daisies counted in 11 random 1 m² quadrats:

10 11 20 15 11 10 18 20 10 13 5

The **range** is the difference between the minimum and maximum readings. In this case the range of the numbers of daisies is 20 − 5 = 15 daisies per m².

The **mean** is the sum of the readings divided by the number of readings taken. In this case the mean is 143/11 = 13 daisies per m².

The **median** is the middle value of the readings when written in order:

5 10 10 10 11 11 13 15 18 20 20

In this case it is the 6th value out of the 11 readings, so the median is 11 daisies per m².

The **mode** is the reading that appears the most frequently. In this case the mode is 10 daisies per m².

Key words: distribution, abundance, quantitative sampling, quadrat, transect, sample size, range, mean, median, mode

Student Book
pages 264–265

B16

16.4 Competition in animals

Key points

- Animals compete with each other for food, territories, and mates.
- Animals have adaptations that make them successful competitors.

Key word: competition

Study tip

Learn to look at an animal and spot the adaptations that make it a successful competitor.

- Animals are in **competition** with each other for water, food, space, a mate, and breeding sites.
- An animal's territory must be large enough for it to find water and food, and have space for breeding.
- Predators compete with each other for prey, as they want to eat them.
- Predators and prey may be camouflaged, so that they are less easy to see.
- Prey animals compete with each other to escape from predators, and to find food for themselves.
- Some animals, such as caterpillars, may be poisonous and have warning colours so that they are not eaten.

1 Why do animals need a territory?

2 Some caterpillars are not poisonous but predators avoid them. Suggest why.

Student Book
pages 266–267

B16

16.5 Competition in plants

Key points

- Plants often compete with each other for light, space, water, and mineral ions from the soil.
- Plants have many adaptations that make them good competitors.

1 Why do plants try to spread their seeds as far as possible?

Study tip

Make memory cards of factors that organisms compete for. Sort them into piles for animals and plants.

Plants compete for space, light, water, and mineral ions.

Animals compete for food, mates, and territory.

- All plants compete for light, water, mineral ions, and space. For example, in woodland some smaller plants (e.g., snowdrops) flower before the trees are in leaf. This ensures that they get enough light, space, water, and mineral ions.
- Plants have many adaptations that make them good competitors.
- Plants that grow deep roots can reach underground water better than those with shallow roots.
- Some plants spread their seeds over a wide area so that they do not compete with themselves.
  - Some of these plants use animals to spread their fruits and seeds.
  - Some plants use the wind (e.g., sycamore) or mini-explosions (e.g., broom) to spread their seeds.

Investigating competition in plants

Set up two trays of cress seeds – one crowded and one spread out. Keep all other conditions identical. After a few days record the differences in the growth of the seedlings.

crowded

spread out

Competition in cress seeds

2 Suggest the factors the seedlings compete for.

B16 # 16.6 Adapt and survive

Key points

- To survive and reproduce, organisms need a supply of materials from their surroundings and from the other living organisms in their habitat.

- Organisms, including microorganisms, have features (adaptations) that enable them to survive in the conditions in which they normally live.

- Extremophiles have adaptations that enable them to live in environments with extreme conditions of salt, temperature, or pressure.

Key words: adaptations, extremophiles

- To survive and reproduce, organisms require materials from their surroundings and from the other organisms living there.

- Plants need light, carbon dioxide, water, oxygen, and mineral ions from the soil.

- Animals need food from other organisms, water, and oxygen.

- Different microorganisms need different materials. Some microorganisms are like plants, others are like animals, and some do not need oxygen or light to survive.

- Special features of organisms are called **adaptations**.

- Adaptations allow organisms to survive in a particular habitat, even when the conditions are extreme, such as extremely hot, very salty, or at high pressure.

1 What is meant by an adaptation?

- Plants are adapted to obtain light and other materials efficiently in order to make food by photosynthesis.

- Animals may be plant-eating (herbivores) or they may eat other animals (carnivores). Their mouthparts are adapted to their diet.

- Most organisms live in temperatures below 40 °C so their enzymes can work.

- **Extremophiles** are organisms, usually microorganisms, that are adapted to live in conditions where most enzymes do not work because they would denature.

2 What are extremophiles?

B16 # 16.7 Adaptation in animals

Key points

- Organisms, including animals, have features (adaptations) that enable them to survive in the conditions in which they normally live. These adaptations may be structural, behavioural, or functional.

Synoptic link

For surface area : volume ratios, see Topic B1.10.

- If animals were not adapted to survive in the areas they live in, they would die.

- Adaptations may be structural, such as the shape or colour of an organism; behavioural, such as migration; or functional, such as antifreeze in cells.

- Animals in cold climates (e.g., in the Arctic) have thick fur and fat under the skin (blubber) to keep them warm.

- Some animals in the Arctic (e.g., Arctic fox, Arctic hare) are white in the winter and brown in the summer. This means that they are camouflaged so they are not easily seen. Both predators and prey may be camouflaged.

- Bigger animals have a lower surface area : volume ratio than smaller animals. This means that bigger animals can conserve energy more easily, but it is more difficult for them to cool down.

1 Why do large animals find it difficult to cool down?

- In the hot, dry conditions found in a desert, animals are adapted to conserve water and to stop them getting too hot. Animals in the desert may hunt or feed at night so that they remain cool during the day.

2 Why do some desert animals shelter during the day?

16.8 Adaptations in plants

- Plants need light, water, space, and mineral ions to survive.
- Plant adaptations may be structural, behavioural, or functional.
- Plants need to collect and conserve water. They lose water as water vapour through stomata in the leaves.
- An extensive root system allows the plant to collect water in a dry environment.
- Water can be conserved if a plant has very small or waxy leaves. A plant might have a swollen stem to store water.
- In dry conditions, such as in deserts, some plants (such as cacti) have become very well adapted to conserve water. Others (such as the mesquite tree) have adapted to collect water using extensive root systems.
- Plants are eaten by animals. Some plants have developed thorns, poisonous chemicals, and warning colours to put animals off.

Key points

- Organisms, including plants, have features (adaptations) that enable them to survive in the conditions in which they normally live. These adaptations may be structural, behavioural, or functional.

Synoptic link

Topics B4.8 and B4.9 cover transport and transpiration in plants.

Study tip

Remember that plants need their stomata open to exchange gases for photosynthesis and respiration. However, this leads to loss of water by evaporation, so desert plants have adaptations to conserve water.

On the up

You should be able to explain how a plant's adaptation allows it to survive in its habitat. To achieve the top grades, you should be able to explain how an unfamiliar plant is adapted and give reasons for its adaptations.

Cacti are well adapted to conserve water and to stop animals eating them

1 Name the ways a plant can conserve water.
2 Give one way in which plants may be protected from being eaten by animals.

1 What is meant by the term 'community'? [2 marks]

2 What is the difference between a mean and a median? [2 marks]

3 Give three abiotic factors that affect the distribution of animals. [3 marks]

4 How does cutting down trees affect birds? [3 marks]

5 Why are there few animals living in very cold regions, such as the Arctic? [4 marks]

6 Describe and explain the effect of new predators on a community. [6 marks]

7 How can you use a quadrat to make a line transect? [3 marks]

8 Why are adaptations important? [2 marks]

9 Describe adaptations in plants that allow them to prevent water loss if the conditions become warmer and more windy. [6 marks]

10 On sandy beaches, at low tide, it is possible to see worm casts produced by lugworms, *Arenicola marina*. Describe a valid investigation to determine the abundance of lugworms on a sandy beach that has an area of about 1000 m². [6 marks]

11 Some students investigated the numbers of lugworms on a beach and had the following results for each count of casts per m².

10	11	20	15	5	13	10	20	18	10	11

   a What is the range? [1 mark]

   b What is the mean? [1 mark]

   c What is the median? [1 mark]

   d What is the mode? [1 mark]

   e What is the abundance if the area of the beach is 1000 m²? [1 mark]

Chapter checklist ✓

Tick when you have:

reviewed it after your lesson ✓ ☐ ☐

revised once – some questions right ✓ ✓ ☐

revised twice – all questions right ✓ ✓ ✓

Move on to another topic when you have all three ticks

16.1 The importance of communities ☐ ☐ ☐

16.2 Organisms in their environment ☐ ☐ ☐

16.3 Distribution and abundance ☐ ☐ ☐

16.4 Competition in animals ☐ ☐ ☐

16.5 Competition in plants ☐ ☐ ☐

16.6 Adapt and survive ☐ ☐ ☐

16.7 Adaptation in animals ☐ ☐ ☐

16.8 Adaptations in plants ☐ ☐ ☐

17.1 Feeding relationships

Key points

- Photosynthetic organisms are the producers of biomass for life on Earth.
- Feeding relationships within a community can be represented by food chains. All food chains begin with a producer, which synthesises new molecules. On land this is usually a green plant that makes glucose by photosynthesis.
- Producers are eaten by primary consumers, which in turn may be eaten by secondary consumers and then tertiary consumers.
- Consumers that eat other animals are often predators and those that are eaten are prey. In a stable community the numbers of predators and prey rise and fall in cycles.

Synoptic links

See Topics B8.1 and B8.3 for photosynthesis and how the products of photosynthesis are used in cells.

For more on feeding relationships, food chains, and pyramids of biomass, see Topics B18.8, B18.9, and B18.11.

Key words: biomass, producers, primary consumers, secondary consumers

- Sunlight is the source of energy for green plants and algae to photosynthesise.
- The glucose from photosynthesis is synthesised into other compounds to make plant cells.
- The new material adds to the **biomass** of the organism.
- Therefore plants are **producers** of biomass and start a food chain.
- Producers are eaten by primary consumers, for example herbivores such as sheep, or fish that eat phytoplankton.
- **Primary consumers** are eaten by animals called **secondary consumers** – carnivores such as lions or seals.
- The secondary consumers may be eaten by tertiary consumers.
- Food chains are simple models of the feeding relationships in a community.

producer → primary consumer → secondary consumer → tertiary consumer

phytoplankton → fish → seal → killer whale

Food chains can be used to represent feeding relationships within a community

1 Give an example of a producer and an example of a primary consumer.

Predators and prey

- Primary consumers eat plants or algae. Cellulose is difficult to digest so they have to eat a lot of plant material to gain enough nutrients. However, plants stay in one place so primary consumers do not have to expend energy chasing them.
- Secondary and tertiary consumers have to catch their food. They are called predators.
- The animals that are eaten by consumers are called prey.
- In a stable community, the numbers of predators and prey rise and fall in cycles.

2 What is a predator?

17.2 Materials cycling

Key points

- Material in the living world is recycled to provide the building blocks for future organisms.
- Decay of dead animals and plants by microorganisms returns carbon to the atmosphere as carbon dioxide and mineral ions to the soil.
- Carbon dioxide in the atmosphere is used by plants in photosynthesis.
- The water cycle provides fresh water for plants and animals on land before draining into the seas. Water is continuously evaporated, condensed, and precipitated.

Synoptic links

For the main chemicals that make up cells, see Topic B3.3, and for the chemistry of respiration, see Topic B9.1

Transpiration is covered in Topics B4.8 and B4.9.

Key word: decomposers

Study tips

The main stages of the water cycle are: condensation, precipitation, evaporation, transpiration, respiration.

2 What is meant by 'precipitation of water'?

- Many materials cycle through both the abiotic and biotic components of the ecosystem.
- For example, carbon in carbon dioxide in the air (abiotic) is taken in by plants and converted to glucose (biotic). Plants take mineral ions from the soil (abiotic) and these, with glucose, enter animals when the plants are eaten (biotic).
- Materials must be returned to the environment for use by future organisms.
- Leaves shed leaves, animals produce droppings, and eventually all organisms die.
- Bacteria and fungi known as **decomposers** break down the waste material and dead organisms.
- Detritus feeders, or detritivores, such as maggots and some worms and beetles, may start the process of decay by eating the waste or dead organisms.
- The decomposers then digest the dead animals, plants, and detritus feeders (and their waste) returning carbon dioxide, water, and mineral ions to the environment.

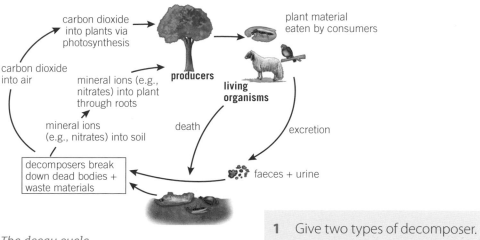

The decay cycle

1 Give two types of decomposer.

Water is vital for life. **The water cycle** provides fresh water for animals and plants on land before draining into the seas and oceans.

- Water evaporates constantly from the land surface, rivers, and the sea.
- As water rises into cooler air it condenses, forming clouds, and is then precipitated back to the surface of the Earth as rain, snow, hail, or sleet.
- Water passes through the bodies of animals and plants. It is released during respiration and decay.
- Animals also release water in urine, faeces, and sweat (in mammals).
- Plants release water into the atmosphere during transpiration (evaporation).

The water cycle in nature

17.3 The carbon cycle

Key points

- The carbon cycle returns carbon from organisms to the atmosphere as carbon dioxide, which is used by plants in photosynthesis.
- The decay of dead plants and animals by microorganisms returns carbon to the atmosphere as carbon dioxide.

Synoptic link

For carbon dioxide and climate change, see Topics B18.1, B18.4, and B18.5.

Study tip

Make sure you can label the processes in a diagram of the carbon cycle.

Key word: carbon cycle

On the up

If you can describe the main events in the carbon cycle, you can achieve the top grades by being able to explain the links between photosynthesis, respiration, and combustion.

- The **carbon cycle** involves both photosynthesis and respiration.
- Photosynthesis removes carbon dioxide from the atmosphere. The carbon dioxide is used to make organic molecules (carbohydrates, fats, and proteins).
- Green plants and algae, as well as animals, respire. This returns carbon dioxide to the atmosphere.
- When humans cut down and burn trees (combustion), carbon dioxide is released into the atmosphere.
- Animals eat green plants and build the carbon into their bodies.
- When plants, algae, or animals die (or produce waste), microorganisms release the carbon in their bodies back into the atmosphere as carbon dioxide, through respiration. Mineral nutrients are returned to the soil.
- The combustion of wood and fossil fuels also releases carbon dioxide into the atmosphere.
- A stable community recycles all of the nutrients it takes up.

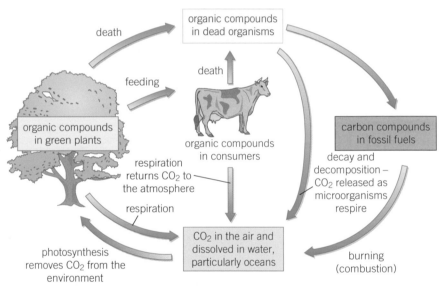

The carbon cycle in nature

1 Which process takes carbon dioxide out of the atmosphere?

2 Which two processes return carbon dioxide to the atmosphere?

17.4 Rates of decomposition

Key points

- Factors that affect the rate of decay of organic matter are temperature, oxygen availability, and moisture levels.
- Gardeners and farmers try to provide optimum conditions for the rapid decay of waste organic matter. The compost produced is used as a natural fertiliser.
- Anaerobic decay produces methane gas. Biogas generators can be used to produce methane gas as a fuel.

Study tip

Decomposing microorganisms recycle all the molecules of life. They return carbon to the atmosphere as carbon dioxide and mineral ions to the soil where they are used again by growing plants.

A year's worth of grass clippings and kitchen waste can be reduced to useful compost in a bin like this

On the up

You should be able to choose a suitable dependent variable and plan a way to measure it accurately. To achieve the top grades, you should also be able to calculate percentage change and rate of decay.

Factors that affect the rate of decay by decomposers

- Temperature – the enzymes controlling the decay reactions (digestion and respiration) are affected by temperature. If it is very cold the enzymes work slowly. If it is too hot they are denatured.
- Moisture – most microorganisms grow faster in moist conditions.
- Decay – this is faster if it is warm and wet. Many decomposers also need oxygen.
- Oxygen – some microorganisms are anaerobic but many need a supply of oxygen for aerobic respiration.

1 What are the two optimum conditions needed by all decomposers?

- Gardeners and farmers try to provide optimum conditions for the rapid decay of waste material.
- Compost produced by the decay of waste organic material is used as natural fertiliser.
- Anaerobic decay produces methane. Conditions are controlled in biogas generators to produce methane gas for use as a fuel.

2 Suggest what conditions must be controlled in a biogas generator.

Investigating the effect of temperature on the rate of decay of fresh milk by measuring pH change

There are a number of things to consider when planning this investigation.

- How will you change the temperature of your milk samples?
- How will you measure the pH of your milk?
- How will you record what you do and the data you collect?
- What are the limitations of your investigation?
- How might you display your data?

3 Suggest how you could measure the rate of decay at each temperature chosen in the investigation.

1. Why are green plants referred to as producers? [2 marks]

2. Give three examples of gases that are cycled in nature. [3 marks]

3. What is biomass? [1 mark]

4. What factor can you measure to determine the level of decay in milk? [1 mark]

5. What other name is given to primary consumers? [1 mark]

6. What are the ideal environmental conditions for decay by aerobic bacteria? [3 marks]

7. How is carbon dioxide returned to the environment from plants? [3 marks]

8. Describe how water is returned to the environment by human bodily functions. [3 marks]

9. What is the importance of the decay cycle in nature? [3 marks]

10. In a stable community, the numbers of predators and prey rise and fall in cycles. If there is a large number of prey animals, there will be a large number of predators.
Explain why the numbers of predators will eventually fall and the effect this will have on the prey. [4 marks]

11. Food chains are simple models. In what way do they not illustrate the complete picture of feeding relationships in a stable community? [4 marks]

12. Nitrates are recycled in nature. Describe what could happen to a nitrate ion from the time it is absorbed by a plant until it re-enters the environment. [6 marks]

Chapter checklist

Tick when you have:

reviewed it after your lesson ✓ ☐ ☐

revised once – some questions right ✓ ✓ ☐

revised twice – all questions right ✓ ✓ ✓

Move on to another topic when you have all three ticks

17.1 Feeding relationships ☐ ☐ ☐

17.2 Materials cycling ☐ ☐ ☐

17.3 The carbon cycle ☐ ☐ ☐

17.4 Rates of decomposition ☐ ☐ ☐

18.1 The human population explosion

Key points

- Biodiversity is the variety of all the different species of organisms on Earth, or within an ecosystem.

- High biodiversity helps to ensure the stability of ecosystems by reducing the dependence of one species on another for food, shelter, and the maintenance of the physical environment.

- Humans reduce the amount of land available for other animals and plants by building, quarrying, farming, and dumping waste.

- The future of the human species on Earth relies on us maintaining a good level of biodiversity. Many human activities are reducing biodiversity and only recently have measures been taken to address the problem.

- Rapid growth in the human population and an increase in the standard of living mean that ever more resources are used and more waste is produced.

Synoptic link

For more information on communities, see Topic B16.1.

Key word: biodiversity

- **Biodiversity** is a measure of the variety of all the different species of organisms on Earth, or within a particular ecosystem.

- High biodiversity helps to ensure the stability of ecosystems. It reduces the dependence of one species on another for food, shelter, and the maintenance of the physical environment.

- There are increasing numbers of people on our planet. Currently the world population is about 7 billion, and it is growing.

- Many people want and demand a better standard of living.

- We are using up raw materials and those that are non-renewable cannot be replaced.

- When goods are produced there is a lot of industrial waste.

- We are producing more and more waste and pollution.

- Humans reduce the amount of land available for animals and plants by building, quarrying, farming, and dumping waste.

- The continuing increase in the human population is affecting the ecology of the Earth.

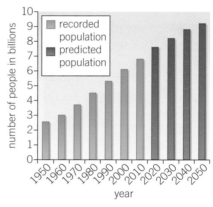

Human population growth. Current UN predictions suggest that the world population could soar to over 16 billion by 2150

1 How does building houses for humans affect animals and plants?

- Humans pollute:
  - waterways with sewage, fertiliser, and toxic chemicals
  - air with smoke and gases such as sulfur dioxide, which contributes to acid rain
  - land with toxic chemicals such as pesticides and herbicides, which can then be washed into the water.

- The future of the human species on Earth relies on our maintaining a good level of biodiversity. Many human activities are reducing biodiversity and only recently have measures been taken to address the problem.

2 What is biodiversity?

18.2 Land and water pollution

Key points

- Unless waste and chemical materials are properly handled, more pollution will be caused.

- Pollution can occur on land, from landfill, and from toxic chemicals, such as pesticides and herbicides, which may also be washed from land to water.

- Pollution can occur in water from sewage, fertilisers, or toxic chemicals.

- Pollution kills plants and animals, which can reduce biodiversity.

This pond may look green and healthy, but all the animal life it once supported is dead as a result of increased competition for light and oxygen

On the up

You should be able to describe how sewage, fertilisers, pesticides, and herbicides pollute the land and water. To achieve the top grades, you should be able to explain in detail how pollution affects biodiversity and explain how pesticides in water can kill top predators in food chains.

Polluting the land

- Sewage contains human body waste and waste water from homes. Sewage must be treated properly to remove gut parasites and toxic chemicals or these can get onto the land.

- Farming methods can pollute the land.

- Herbicides (weedkillers) and pesticides (which kill insects) are also poisons. The poisons sprayed onto crops can get into the soil and into the food chain. The poisons may kill top predators by accumulating in the food chain. Eventually many of these chemicals are washed into rivers and streams.

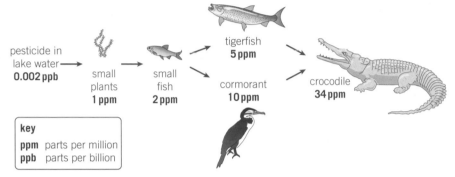

pesticide in lake water → 0.002 ppb

small plants 1 ppm

small fish 2 ppm

tigerfish 5 ppm

cormorant 10 ppm

crocodile 34 ppm

key
ppm parts per million
ppb parts per billion

The feeding relationships between different organisms can lead to dangerous levels of toxins building up in the top predators. This is called bioaccumulation

- Toxic chemicals from landfill also leak into the waterways and pollute the water, killing organisms such as fish.

- Farmers also use chemical fertilisers on the land, to keep the soil fertile, and these can be washed into rivers.

1 Why must sewage be treated?

Polluting the water

- Fertilisers and untreated sewage can cause a high level of nitrates in the water, which leads to the death of the organisms in the river:

1. High levels of mineral ions such as nitrates stimulate the rapid growth of algae and other water plants.

2. Competition for light increases and many plants die because they cannot photosynthesise.

3. Microorganisms feed on the dead plants so the microorganism population increases rapidly.

4. Respiration by the microorganisms depletes the oxygen concentration in the water.

5. Most of the aerobic organisms, such as fish, die due to lack of oxygen, so there is even more decay by microorganisms. Lack of oxygen eventually means the water cannot sustain living organisms.

2 How can pollution by nitrates eventually lead to the death of all the organisms in the river?

Student Book
pages 290–291

B18

18.3 Air pollution

- Burning fossil fuels can produce sulfur dioxide and other acidic gases. These emissions and smog can be reduced by burning biofuels instead. Power stations and cars also release acidic gases.

- The sulfur dioxide dissolves in water in the air, forming acidic solutions. The solutions then fall as acid rain – sometimes a long way from where the gases were produced.

- Acid rain kills organisms, which can reduce biodiversity.

- Acid rain can change the soil's pH, which damages roots and may release toxic minerals (e.g., aluminium ions), which damage organisms in soil and waterways.

- The enzymes that control reactions in organisms are very sensitive to pH (acidity or alkalinity).

- Trees can be damaged if the leaves are soaked in acid rain for long periods. When trees are damaged, food and habitats for many other organisms are lost.

- Smoke pollution from burning fossil fuels is caused by tiny solid particles called particulates in the air.

- The particulates can damage the lungs when breathed in. They also reduce the light that reaches the Earth's surface, resulting in a dimming and cooling effect.

Key points

- Pollution can occur in the air from smoke and from acidic gases.
- Air pollution kills plants and animals, which can reduce biodiversity.

Study tips

Make a list of the problems caused by acid rain.

1 Which gas is the main cause of acid rain?
2 Explain how birds are affected by acid rain.

Student Book
pages 292–293

B18

18.4 Deforestation and peat destruction

Deforestation means that many trees are cut down. Large-scale deforestation is happening in tropical areas to provide timber and land for agriculture.

- Deforestation has:
  - increased the release of carbon dioxide into the atmosphere due to burning of the trees or decay of the wood by microorganisms
  - reduced the rate at which carbon dioxide is removed from the atmosphere by photosynthesis
  - reduced **biodiversity** due to loss of food and habitats.

- Deforestation has occurred so that:
  - crops can be grown to produce ethanol-based biofuels
  - more cattle and rice can be produced for food.

- Rearing cattle and growing rice produces methane, which has led to an increase of methane in the atmosphere.

The destruction of **peat bogs**, and other areas of peat, also results in the release of carbon dioxide into the atmosphere. This occurs because:

- the peat is removed from the bogs and used in compost for gardens, where it is decayed by microorganisms, releasing carbon dioxide through respiration

- some peat is burned as a fuel, also releasing carbon dioxide.

If gardeners use peat-free composts, the peat bogs will not be destroyed.

Key points

- Large-scale deforestation in tropical areas has occurred to provide land for cattle and for rice fields, as well as to grow crops for biofuels.

- The destruction of peat bogs and other areas of peat to produce garden compost reduces the area of this habitat and thus the biodiversity associated with it.

- The decay or burning of peat releases carbon dioxide into the atmosphere.

Study tip

Remember that trees, plants in peat bogs, and algae in the sea all use carbon dioxide for photosynthesis. Carbon compounds are then 'locked up' in these plants.

Key word: biodiversity

1 Which process removes carbon dioxide from the air?
2 Which processes cause the release of carbon dioxide from peat?

18.5 Global warming

Key points

- Levels of carbon dioxide and methane in the atmosphere are increasing, and contribute to global warming.

- Biological consequences of global warming include loss of habitat when low-lying areas are flooded by rising sea levels, changes in the distribution patterns of species in areas where temperature or rainfall has changed, and changes to the migration patterns of animals.

- In the normal balance of nature, carbon dioxide is released into the air by respiration and removed by plants and algae in photosynthesis.

- Carbon dioxide also dissolves in oceans, rivers, lakes, and ponds.

- We say that the carbon dioxide is stored in carbon sinks by plants and water.

1   What is a carbon sink?

Levels of carbon dioxide and methane are increasing in the atmosphere. These gases are greenhouse gases and cause the greenhouse effect. Most scientists think that an increase in greenhouse gases contributes to global warming.

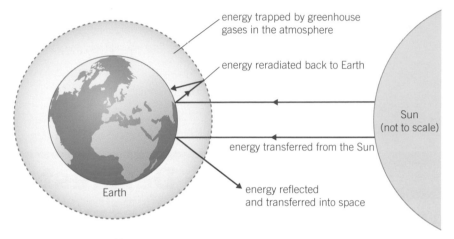

energy trapped by greenhouse gases in the atmosphere

energy reradiated back to Earth

Sun (not to scale)

energy transferred from the Sun

energy reflected and transferred into space

Earth

The greenhouse effect is vital for life on Earth

- An increase in the Earth's temperature of only a few degrees Celsius may:

  - cause big changes in the Earth's climate

  - cause a rise in sea level due to melting of ice caps and glaciers

  - cause changes in migration patterns (e.g., of birds)

  - result in changes in the distribution of species

  - reduce biodiversity.

2   Why might sea levels rise in the future?

Synoptic links

For information on how plants use carbon dioxide to make food, see Topic B8.1.

For more about changes in the distribution of organisms, see Topic B16.8.

Study tips

Remember which gases cause which problems:

- Carbon dioxide and methane increase causes global warming.

- Sulfur dioxide and nitrogen oxides cause acid rain.

Higher tier

18.6 The impact of change

Key points

- Environmental changes such as the availability of water, temperature, and the composition of the

- Animals and plants are affected by their environment. If the environment changes, the organisms may not be able to live there any longer.

- Factors that might change include: temperature, rainfall, light, and levels of atmospheric gases.

- The changes may be seasonal, geographic, or caused by human interaction.

- Animals and plants are adapted to their particular environmental conditions.

atmosphere affect the distribution of species in an ecosystem.

- These changes may be seasonal, geographic, or caused by human interaction.

Synoptic link

For more about the distribution of organisms in the environment, see Chapter B16.

- The distribution of organisms in a particular habitat can change with the seasons. Animals migrate in and out of areas when the temperature or food availability changes.

- Different geographic regions may have varying temperatures, soil structure and pH, altitude, availability and saltiness of water, or prevailing winds, which will influence which organisms can live there.

- Many environmental changes are the result of human activities. These include global warming, climate change, the effect of acid rain, deforestation, and pollution. These activities can all cause damage to the environment.

- To combat climate change we can maintain rainforests, reduce water pollution and monitor water pH, protect sites of special scientific interest, and introduce conservation measures such as replanting woodlands and hedges, which help to increase biodiversity and reduce the impact of damage to the environment.

1 Name three environmental factors that may change with the seasons.
2 Why is it important to replant woodlands and hedges?

Student Book
pages 298–299 **B18**

18.7 Maintaining biodiversity

Scientists and concerned citizens have put programmes in place to reduce the negative effects of humans on ecosystems and biodiversity. People can help maintain biodiversity in many ways.

- **Breeding programmes** are carried out to restore endangered species to a sustainable population.

- There may be difficulties because:
  - many rare animals and plants do not reproduce easily or fast
  - artificial breeding programmes must avoid inbreeding
  - the habitat that the organism needs to survive may have been lost.

- If a **rare habitat** is protected or regenerated, this protects the biodiversity, which may increase again. Examples include coral reefs, mangroves, and heathlands.

- By replanting hedgerows and allowing wild plants to grow on the edges of fields, farmers are helping to increase biodiversity.

- Governments in regions such as Costa Rica have introduced laws to protect rainforests and other habitats. They also buy land and replace forests that have been cut down.

- Many governments are working with transport and electricity industries to reduce carbon dioxide emissions.

- Waste placed in landfill sites affects biodiversity by using land and producing pollution. Taxing landfill has reduced waste. Most countries now recycle glass, paper, plastics, and metal. Organic waste can be used as compost or in methane generators.

1 Why are farmers encouraged to keep areas of their fields free of crops?
2 How have governments controlled the amount of waste that goes into landfill?

Key point

- Scientists and concerned citizens have put programmes in place to reduce the negative effects of humans on ecosystems and biodiversity.

Synoptic link

For some problems that can result from inbreeding, see Topic B14.3.

On the up

You should be able to describe programmes to reduce negative effects on ecosystems and explain how they work. You should also be able to use information to explain the conflicting pressures on maintaining biodiversity. To achieve the top grades, you should be able to evaluate the conflicting pressures on maintaining biodiversity in some habitats.

18.8 Trophic levels and biomass

Key points

- Trophic levels can be represented by numbers, starting at level 1 with plants and algae. Further trophic levels are numbered according to how far the organism is along the food chain.

- Level 1 – producers (plants and algae); level 2 – primary consumers (herbivores); level 3 – secondary consumers (carnivores that eat herbivores); level 4 – tertiary consumers (carnivores that eat secondary consumers). Apex predators are carnivores with no predators.

- Decomposers break down dead plant and animal matter by secreting enzymes into the environment. Small, soluble molecules then diffuse into the microorganism.

- Pyramids of biomass can be constructed to represent the relative amount of biomass at each level of a food chain. Trophic level 1 is always at the bottom of the pyramid.

- Biomass is the mass of living material in plants and animals.

- **Trophic levels** represent an organism's position in a food chain. Producers (plants and algae) are at level 1, primary consumers (herbivores) are at level 2, secondary consumers (carnivores) are at level 3, and tertiary consumers (carnivores that eat carnivores) are at level 4. Apex predators are carnivores with no predators, found at the top of a food chain.

- Decomposers break down dead plant and animal matter by secreting enzymes into the environment. Small, soluble molecules then diffuse into the microorganism.

- A pyramid of biomass represents the relative amount of biomass at each level of a food chain. Trophic level 1 is always at the bottom.

- A pyramid of biomass may represent the biomass in the trophic levels of a food chain more accurately than a pyramid of numbers. For example, one bush may have many insects feeding on it, but the mass of the bush is far greater than the mass of the insects.

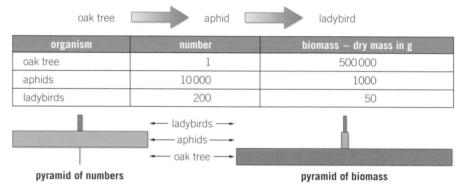

organism	number	biomass – dry mass in g
oak tree	1	500 000
aphids	10 000	1000
ladybirds	200	50

A pyramid of biomass is drawn to scale to represent the biomass of the organisms at each level of a food chain

1 Why are plants always at the base of the pyramid of biomass?

- Plants grow as a result of photosynthesis and the subsequent production of material such as cellulose and protein. So trophic level 1 has the largest amount of biomass. Level 2 has less biomass because the herbivore does not eat all of the plant material at level 1, and it cannot digest some of what it eats, so this is lost in the faeces. Carnivores at level 3 can eat only parts of the herbivore, so even less biomass is transferred to level 3.

- Most of the biomass at each level is used in respiration to transfer energy within the organism for processes such as movement. So respiration also reduces the amount of biomass transferred to the next level.

2 Which organisms transfer energy to the environment from dead and waste material?

Study tip

Data in questions may be given as tables, graphs, charts, or unusual diagrams, as well as in text. To gain maximum marks, read the stem of the question carefully, and check you know what information is given in all the illustrations. If you have not used the data in your answer you may have missed the point of the question.

Key word: trophic levels

Synoptic link

For more about how different organisms interdepend, see Topic B17.1.

Student Book
pages 302–303

B18

18.9 Biomass transfers

- Producers transfer only about 1% of the **incident energy** from light in photosynthesis. Most light does not fall on plants.

- There is energy loss from a food chain between each stage of the chain. Therefore not all of the energy taken in by an organism results in the growth of that organism. Only about 10% of the biomass from each trophic level is transferred to the level above it.

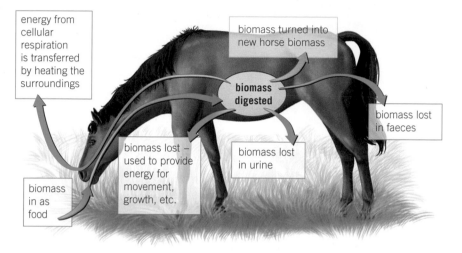

Only between 2% and 10% of the biomass eaten by an animal such as this horse will get turned into new cells, that is, transferred to the next trophic level. The rest will be used for movement, inadvertently heating the surroundings, or lost in waste materials

- An animal cannot digest all of the biomass (food) it eats, so some energy is stored in waste materials – in faeces or in the urea found in urine.

- Some of the biomass is used for respiration, which transfers energy needed for living processes. This includes movement, so the more an animal moves, the more energy it transfers and the less is available for growth.

- In animals that need to keep a constant temperature, energy transferred from the previous level of the food chain is needed to keep the animal at its normal body temperature.

- Much of the energy transferred from glucose, in respiration, is eventually dissipated (spread out) in the surroundings, warming them up.

---

1 Which process in cells transfers energy from food material?

Investigating the use of biomass in cellular respiration

Plants transfer energy by heating their surroundings during cellular respiration. You can investigate this by germinating peas in a vacuum flask.

2 What would be the best way to monitor the temperature continuously?

Key points

- Most producers are plants and algae that transfer about 1% of the incident energy from light for photosynthesis.

- Only approximately 10% of the biomass from each trophic level is transferred to the level above it.

- Losses of biomass occur because not all the ingested material is absorbed – some is egested as faeces, some absorbed material is lost as waste products, such as carbon dioxide and water in respiration and water and urea in urine, and large amounts of glucose are used in respiration.

Key word: incident energy

Study tip

Make sure that you can explain the different ways in which biomass is lost between the levels of a food chain.

18.10 Factors affecting food security

Food security is having enough food to feed a population. Factors affecting food security include the following.

- Increasing birth rates – this may particularly affect some less developed countries, countries where large families are respected, or if contraception is not used for religious reasons.
- Changing diets in developed countries – as a result of these changes, particular desired foods are transported across the world from where they are produced. This reduces food security because people rely on buying food rather than growing it.
- New pests and pathogens – global travel, the movement of seed and animals from one part of the world to another, and climate change have led to an increase in new pests and pathogens spreading from one place to another.
- Environmental changes – scientists think that the increase in both droughts and flooding is caused by global warming.
- The cost of agricultural inputs – GM seeds, irrigation systems, fertilisers, and pesticides all add to the cost of food production, reducing food security.
- Conflicts usually lead to food insecurity due to difficulty accessing food and water.

Key points

- Food security is having enough food to feed a population.
- Factors affecting food security include:
  - increasing birth rates
  - changing diets in developed countries resulting in scarce food resources being transported around the world
  - new pests and pathogens affecting farming
  - environmental changes affecting food production
  - the cost of agricultural inputs
  - conflicts affecting access to water or food.

1 What is meant by 'food security'?

2 How has global warming contributed to food insecurity?

18.11 Making food production efficient

- The shorter the food chain, the less energy will be wasted. It is therefore more efficient for us to eat plants than it is to eat animals.
- We can produce meat more efficiently by:
  - preventing the animal from moving so it does not waste energy on movement; but this is seen as cruel by many people and is controversial
  - keeping the animal in a warm shed so it does not need as much energy from food to maintain its body temperature.
- Fish in fish farms are fed high-protein food to encourage rapid growth. The fish are kept in big cages to restrict their movement.

Key points

- The efficiency of food production can be improved by restricting energy transfer from food animals to the environment. This can be done by limiting their movement and by controlling the temperature of their surroundings.
- Some animals are fed high-protein foods to increase growth.

1 Animals reared for meat are sometimes kept in warm sheds. Explain why.

2 Give an example of an ethical consideration when farming animals for efficient food production.

Study tip

Make a list of the ways in which the efficiency of food production can be improved. Note one advantage and one disadvantage of each method you have listed.

18.12 Sustainable food production

Key points

- Fish stocks in the oceans are declining. It is important to maintain fish stocks at a level where breeding continues, or certain species may disappear altogether.

- Control of net size and the introduction of fishing quotas play important roles in conserving fish stocks at a sustainable level.

- Modern biotechnology techniques enable large quantities of microorganisms to be cultured for food.

- The fungus *Fusarium* is useful for producing mycoprotein, a protein-rich food suitable for vegetarians. The fungus is grown on glucose syrup, in aerobic conditions, and the biomass is harvested and purified.

- Genetically modified bacteria produce drugs such as insulin on an industrial scale.

- Genetically modified crops could provide more food or food with an improved nutritional value.

Synoptic links

For genetic engineering and the production of human insulin by microorganisms, see Topic B14.4.

For more about the production of genetically modified crops, see Topic B14.7.

Study tip

Learn what can be done to conserve fish stocks so that we will have fish in the future.

The human population is increasing rapidly and food resources are at risk of running out.

Sustainable food production involves managing resources, and finding new types of food such as mycoprotein. This ensures that there is enough food for the current population and in the future.

- Fish stocks in the oceans are declining.

- To maintain fish stocks, fishermen:

  - can only remove a strict allocation of fish (a quota) per year so the numbers of fishing trips are reduced

  - must use certain-sized nets to avoid catching small, young fish so they can grow to full size and breed.

- If these measures are not implemented some species of fish could become extinct.

1 Why are fishermen not allowed to remove small, young fish?

The role of biotechnology

- Genetically modified crops could provide more food or food with improved nutritional value.

- Fermenters can be used to produce drugs, such as insulin, on an industrial scale from genetically modified bacteria. The conditions in the fermenters are controlled to maximise the growth rate of the bacterial population.

- The fungus *Fusarium* is grown in fermenters to produce mycoprotein. This is a protein-rich food suitable for vegetarians. *Fusarium* is grown aerobically on cheap glucose syrup made from waste starch. The biomass of the mycoprotein is harvested and purified. Developing foods such as mycoprotein could help to solve the problem of world food shortages.

2 What is grown to produce mycoprotein?

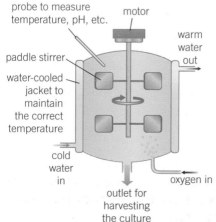

probe to measure temperature, pH, etc.
motor
warm water out
paddle stirrer
water-cooled jacket to maintain the correct temperature
cold water in
oxygen in
outlet for harvesting the culture

Conditions inside the fermenters used to culture microorganisms, such as Fusarium, *are kept as stable as possible*

1 What does the word 'biomass' mean?   [1 mark]

2 Give three ways in which humans reduce the land available for plants and animals.   [3 marks]

3 What is meant by 'organic waste'?   [2 marks]

4 Name three pollutants that can pass from land to rivers and streams.   [3 marks]

5 What type of organism is at the bottom of a pyramid of biomass?   [1 mark]

6 Why does deforestation cause a reduction in biodiversity?   [2 marks]

7 How can energy wastage be reduced in a food chain involving humans?   [2 marks]

8 Describe the effect of acid rain on biodiversity.   [4 marks]

9 a Why is food security important?   [1 mark]

   b Give three factors that can reduce food security.   [3 marks]

10 When trees are cut down, carbon dioxide is released into the atmosphere. Explain how. [3 marks]

11 Humans throw waste garden material into a compost heap. The heap gets hot. Explain why. [4 marks]

12 Why do we more commonly eat herbivores than carnivores?   [3 marks]

13 When a calf eats grass, only about 30% of the material in the grass is turned into new material in the growth of the calf. What happens to the other 70%?   [5 marks]

14 Ⓗ What would be the consequences affecting living organisms if the Earth's temperature rose a few degrees?   [4 marks]

15 Why are gardeners encouraged to buy peat-free compost?   [5 marks]

16 Using named examples, describe the role of biotechnology in sustainable food production.   [6 marks]

Chapter checklist

Tick when you have:

reviewed it after your lesson	✓	☐	☐
revised once – some questions right	✓	✓	☐
revised twice – all questions right	✓	✓	✓

Move on to another topic when you have all three ticks

18.1 The human population explosion ☐ ☐ ☐
18.2 Land and water pollution ☐ ☐ ☐
18.3 Air pollution ☐ ☐ ☐
18.4 Deforestation and peat destruction ☐ ☐ ☐
18.5 Global warming ☐ ☐ ☐
18.6 The impact of change ☐ ☐ ☐
18.7 Maintaining biodiversity ☐ ☐ ☐
18.8 Trophic levels and biomass ☐ ☐ ☐
18.9 Biomass transfers ☐ ☐ ☐
18.10 Factors affecting food security ☐ ☐ ☐
18.11 Making food production efficient ☐ ☐ ☐
18.12 Sustainable food production ☐ ☐ ☐

01.1 Calculate the surface area : volume ratio for the two cubes **A** and **B** in **Figure 1**. [4 marks]

Study tip

Remember that the larger the animal, the smaller the surface area compared with its volume. Small organisms transfer energy to the environment much faster than larger ones.

cube **B**

cube **A**

2 cm   4 cm

Figure 1

01.2 Some organisms have the same volume as cube **B**, but a much larger surface area. Describe how the body shape of these organisms is adapted to increase the surface area. [1 mark]

01.3 Scientists have been monitoring populations of organisms in the Antarctic. The water is getting warmer due to climate change. Scientists observed that the smaller organisms in some populations survive better than larger organisms.
In terms of surface area : volume ratio, explain why this is. [2 marks]

01.4 As the water gets warmer, less oxygen is dissolved in it. This affects the growth of the organisms.
Explain why. [2 marks]

01.5 The increasing temperature of the Antarctic could affect the evolution of a population of fish.
Explain how. [4 marks]

02 **Figure 2** shows a food web that shows the relationships between organisms in a stable community.

Study tip

Do not be put off by an unfamiliar diagram such as **Figure 2**. It will be based on something you have learnt. In this case the food web shows how food chains are not isolated but how one organism can form part of two (or more) chains. Use your knowledge of food chains to answer the question.

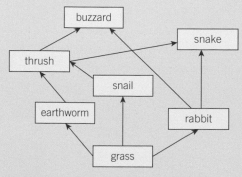

Figure 2

02.1 Which organism is a producer? [1 mark]
02.2 Give the names of two primary consumers in the food web. [2 marks]
02.3 Which organism is both a predator and a prey animal? [1 mark]
02.4 What is the difference between a food web and a food chain? [3 marks]
02.5 What is meant by a stable community? [1 mark]
02.6 A drought killed off all the adult snails.
Give **one** reason why the population of earthworms could decrease. [2 marks]
02.7 Explain the effect on the community if the grass died in the drought. [3 marks]

02.8 **Figure 3** shows a food chain of seawater organisms. The numbers show the accumulation of a toxin that was dumped in the sea by a ship, in μm per kg of organism.

| phytoplankton 100 μg/kg | → | shrimps 150 μg/kg | → | small fish 500 μg/kg | → | large fish 1500 μg/kg |

Figure 3

Use the information in **Figure 3** to explain why the phytoplankton, shrimps, and small fish did not die of poisoning, but many of the large fish died.   [5 marks]

03 The levels of carbon dioxide and methane in the atmosphere are increasing. Many scientists believe this increase may contribute to global warming.

03.1 Describe **two** consequences of an increase of only a few degrees in the Earth's temperature.   [2 marks]

03.2 Describe the human activities that may have contributed to an increase in atmospheric carbon dioxide and methane.   [6 marks]

04 Some organisms live in environments that are very extreme, containing high levels of salt, high temperatures, or high pressures. These organisms are called extremophiles.
Some extremophile bacteria can survive in very salty conditions.

04.1 Explain why most bacteria cannot survive in very salty conditions.   [3 marks]

04.2 Suggest what would happen to the extremophiles if they were placed in river water.   [1 mark]

04.3 Scientists were surprised to find extremophiles living at temperatures between 80 °C and 105 °C.
Explain why the scientists did not expect to find bacteria at such high temperatures.   [2 marks]

01 In fish and chip shops, potatoes are cut into chips several hours before they are needed.

The mass of the chips must be kept constant during this time.

To keep the mass constant, the chips are kept in a solution of sodium chloride.

Figure 1 shows some apparatus and materials.

test tubes with labels

test-tube rack

potatoes

cutting board

scalpel

electric scales

forceps

Figure 1

01.1 Describe how you would use apparatus and materials including those shown in **Figure 1** to find the concentration of sodium chloride solution that keeps the mass of the chips constant.

You should include:
- the measurements you would make
- how you would make the investigation a fair test.   [6 marks]

I would make up a range of sodium chloride solutions by diluting 1 mol/dm³ sodium chloride with distilled water. The range would be 0.2, 0.4, 0.6, and 0.8 mol/dm³.
I would also use distilled water, which is 0.0 mol/dm³, and the 1 mol/dm³ solution.
I would put the same volume of each solution into separate test tubes and label them. Then I would cut 6 chips with the scalpel and make sure they are the same length and thickness by using a ruler. I would then dab a chip dry with a paper towel, weigh it, record the mass in a table, and place it in one of the test tubes.
I would do the same for the other chips so that there are six tubes, each with one chip. I would leave the test-tube rack in a safe place for about 24 hours, then I would take each chip out of its solution with the forceps, dab it dry, and then reweigh it. I would record the new masses in the table and calculate the change in mass.

It would be a fair test if the chips are all from the same potato and are all the same size. Also, the volumes of the solutions in the test tubes should be the same. The time should also be the same.

Introduction

This is an example of a question focusing on practical skills. The student answers are marked and include comments to help you answer this type of question as effectively as possible.

This answer would gain 6 marks. The student has described a method that is clear and detailed and will enable valid results to be collected. The measurements to be made are stated and how to make the investigation a fair test is clear.

This answer would gain 2 marks. The student has realised that when cutting with a cork borer all the cylinders will be exactly the same size. The answer demonstrates knowledge of risks linked to investigations.

The student has realised that the skin will not allow osmosis to take place, so the answer would gain 1 mark for recognising that the skin is impermeable and a second mark for recognising the principle of a fair test.

01.2 In a similar investigation, a student used a cork borer to cut cylinders of potato.

The student

* cut six cylinders from a potato, making sure they were all the same length
* trimmed the skin off the ends of the cylinders.

Give **two** advantages of using a cork borer rather than a scalpel to cut potato chips. [2 marks]

The diameter of all the cylinders would be the same and it is then only necessary to cut them to the same length. It is safer than cutting with a scalpel.

01.3 Explain why it is important to remove the skin from the ends of the cylinders. [2 marks]

The skin is impermeable, so if some cylinders had skin on, the water could not go in equally.

The student investigated the effect of different concentrations of sodium chloride solutions on the cylinders.

Table 1 shows the student's results.

Table 1

	Concentration of sodium chloride solution in mol/dm^3					
	0	0.2	0.4	0.6	0.8	1.0
Change in length of cylinders in mm	+4.1	+1.5	−1.4	−3.6	−4.6	−5.2

01.4 Use the graph paper to draw a graph to display the student's results.

You should:
* add a suitable scale and label to the *y*-axis
* plot the student's results
* draw a line of best fit. [4 marks]

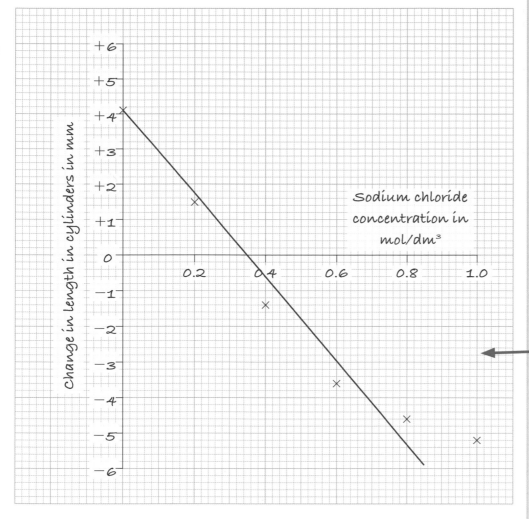

The student would gain 3 marks, 1 for correct scale and label on the *y*-axis, and 2 for correct plots. However, the line of best fit is not close enough, as it should show a smooth curve.

01.5 In which concentration of sodium chloride would the mass of the chips **not** change? [1 mark]

Concentration 0.35 mol/dm³

This answer would gain 1 mark as it is correct for the line shown in the student's graph.

01.6 Explain the changes in length of the potato cylinders that were placed in the 1.0 mol/dm³ sodium chloride solution. [3 marks]

The cylinders shrank by 5.2 mm. This is because the liquid outside the cells had a higher concentration of salt than the liquid inside the cells and so water moved out of the cells by osmosis. This made the cells and the cylinders shrink in length.

The student would gain 2 marks for correctly identifying the concentration gradient and for knowing that therefore water moved out of the cells into the liquid outside. However, they would not gain the final available mark by explaining that this happened because the cell membranes are partially permeable.

02 Some students wanted to find out if germinating peas respire.

The teacher provided the students with some dried peas that had been soaked in water for one day. Dried peas are inactive, but soaked peas become active again.

The students used the soaked peas to set up the apparatus shown in **Figure 2**. When the pump is turned on, air is sucked through the apparatus.

Figure 2

Remember that answers to questions asking you to 'explain why' should always contain 'because' or 'so'. This answer would gain 2 marks as the student has not indicated that the carbon dioxide must be removed because the investigation seeks to find out if carbon dioxide is produced in respiration.

02.1 Soda lime and potassium hydroxide absorb carbon dioxide. Explain why these chemicals are necessary in this investigation. [3 marks]

Air contains carbon dioxide, which must be removed.

Always be precise with answers. A better answer would say that the limewater turned cloudy or milky. This answer would not gain a mark.

02.2 What is the purpose of the limewater in flask **1**? [1 mark]

It checks to see if there is no carbon dioxide left before air goes into flask 2.

02.3 If the peas respire, what will happen to the lime water in flask **3**? [1 mark]

The limewater will change colour.

Many students think temperature is an important control in all experiments. Better students read all of the information. A good answer to this question needs to be clear about 'the control' and 'controlling variables'. Here, the control is 'use dried peas instead of soaked peas' in flask 2. This answer would not gain a mark.

02.4 Describe a suitable control for this experiment. [1 mark]

Make sure the temperature stays the same.

02.5 Explain why pea seeds are used in this experiment rather than cress seedlings. [2 marks]

The cress would photosynthesise.

This answer would gain 1 mark. The student has recognised that cress would photosynthesise, but has not explained why this would be a problem (the cress would use up the carbon dioxide / only oxygen would be released).

Practical questions

01 A group of students were investigating the knee jerk reflex. The students wanted to find out how the speed of the hammer affected the distance the lower leg moved.

Figure 1 shows how the experiment was set up.

experimenter

subject

metre rule

5 cm grid

Figure 1

Each trial was recorded on video. A frame was taken every 33 milliseconds. The video was then played using single-frame advance. The number of frames for the hammer to move to the knee was found. The smaller the number of frames, the faster the speed of the hammer. The video was also used to find the distance moved by the toe.

In each trial, the experimenter held the hammer 20 cm from the subject's knee and then hit the subject's tendon. For each trial the experimenter used the hammer at a different speed.

Table 1 shows some of the results.

Table 1

Trial number	1	2	3	4	5	6	7	8	9	10
Distance hammer moved to knee in cm	20	20	20	20	20	20	20	20	20	20
Number of frames it took the hammer to move to the knee	15	14	12	10	9	8	7	6	2	2
Distance moved by toe in cm	0	0	5	5	4	10	10	10	10	10

01.1 Using **Table 1**, identify the independent variable, the dependent variable, and a control variable. [3 marks]

01.2 Give **two** advantages of using a video to make the measurements. [2 marks]

01.3 Suggest how the accuracy of this experiment could have been improved. [1 mark]

01.4 Draw a conclusion from the results of the experiment. [2 marks]

02 Gardeners buy packets of dry seeds. Before planting, the dry seeds must be soaked in water. When the soaked seeds are planted, they will germinate (sprout) and eventually grow into plants.

Some students wanted to investigate the process of respiration in pea seeds. The students predicted that some of the energy released in respiration will heat the surroundings.

One group of students set up two thermos flasks as shown in **Figure 2**.

The students used thermometers with a temperature range of 0 °C to 100 °C. They decided to record the temperature every 6 hours.

02.1 The temperature readings are likely to be inaccurate. Explain why. [2 marks]

02.2 Suggest how the students could monitor the temperature more accurately. [2 marks]

02.3 A second group of students decided to turn the flasks upside down and hold them in a clamp. To stop the thermometers falling out, they used rubber bungs with a hole for the thermometer. They set up the flasks as shown in **Figure 3**.

What is the advantage of inverting the flasks? [2 marks]

02.4 What is the disadvantage of using rubber bungs instead of cotton wool? [1 mark]

02.5 A third group of students decided it would be an improvement to use boiled, soaked peas as a control. After four days, they noticed that the temperature in the control flask was higher than in the experimental flask with soaked peas that had not been boiled.

Explain the reason for this result. [3 marks]

02.6 How could the third group improve the design of their experiment? [2 marks]

Figure 2

Figure 3

Study tip

Question **02** is about designing an investigation. Do not be put off if you have not done this experiment – all the information you need is in the question. The key fact here is that the students are measuring the temperature. Remember that the mercury level will change if you move the thermometer. The design in **Figure 3** is better because you can read the thermometer while it is surrounded by the peas.

Make sure you understand the biological processes involved. Peas need water to be active and oxygen for respiration. Boiled peas are dead but will be decayed by microorganisms. Disinfectant will kill the microorganisms.

Summary of 'Working scientifically'

A minimum of 15% of the total marks in your exam will be based on 'Working scientifically'. Questions could ask about the methods and techniques you have practised during the Required practicals (see the Practice questions on pages 159–160). You will also be asked to apply the principles of scientific enquiry in general, as outlined below.

WS1 Development of scientific thinking

- Understand how scientific methods and theories develop over time.
- Use a variety of models to solve problems, make predictions, and to develop scientific explanations and understanding of familiar and unfamiliar facts.
- Appreciate the power and limitations of science and consider any ethical issues that may arise.
- Explain everyday and technological applications of science. This will include evaluating their personal, social, economic, and environmental implications. You may also be asked to make decisions based on the evaluation of evidence and arguments.
- Evaluate risks both in practical science and in wider contexts, including perception of risk in relation to data and consequences.
- Recognise the importance of peer review of results and of communicating results to a range of audiences.

WS2 Experimental skills and strategies

- Use scientific theories and explanations to develop hypotheses.
- Plan experiments or devise procedures to make observations, produce or characterise a substance, test hypotheses, check data, or explore phenomena.
- Apply knowledge of a range of techniques, instruments, apparatus, and materials to select those appropriate to the experiment.
- Carry out experiments, handling apparatus correctly and taking into account the accuracy of measurements, as well as any health and safety considerations.
- Recognise when to apply knowledge of sampling techniques to make sure that any samples collected are representative.
- Make and record observations and measurements using a range of apparatus and methods.
- Evaluate methods and suggest possible improvements and further investigations.

WS3 Analysis and evaluation

- Present observations and other data using appropriate methods.
- Translate data from one form to another.
- Carry out and represent mathematical and statistical analysis.
- Represent distributions of results and make estimates of uncertainty.
- Interpret observations and other data, including identifying patterns and trends, making inferences, and drawing conclusions.
- Present reasoned explanations, including relating data to hypotheses.
- Be objective; evaluating data in terms of accuracy, precision, repeatability, and reproducibility; and identifying potential sources of random and systematic error.
- Communicate the reasoning for investigations, the methods used, the findings, and reasoned conclusions through paper-based and electronic reports, as well as using other forms of presentation.

WS4 Scientific vocabulary, quantities, units, symbols, and nomenclature

- Use scientific vocabulary, terminology, and definitions.
- Recognise the importance of scientific quantities and understand how they are determined.
- Use SI units (e.g., kg, g, mg; km, m, mm; kJ, J) and IUPAC chemical names, whenever appropriate.
- Use prefixes and powers of ten for orders of magnitude (e.g., tera, giga, mega, kilo, centi, milli, micro, and nano).
- Interconvert units.
- Use an appropriate number of significant figures in calculation. Quote your answer to the same number of significant figures as the data provided in the question, to the least number of significant figures.

Essential 'Working scientifically' terms

Your knowledge of what it means to 'work scientifically' will be tested in your exams. In order to understand the nature of science and experimentation, you will need to know some technical terms that scientists use. You should be able to recognise and use the terms below:

accurate a measurement is considered accurate if it is judged to be close to the true value

anomalies/anomalous results results that do not match the pattern seen in the other data collected or that are well outside the range of other repeat readings (outliers)

categoric variable has values that are labels (described in words), for example, types of material

control variable a variable that may, in addition to the variable under investigation (the independent variable – see below), affect the outcome of an investigation and therefore has to be kept constant, or at least has to be monitored as carefully as possible

data information, either qualitative (descriptive) or quantitative (measured), that has been collected

dependent variable the variable for which the value is measured for each and every change in the variable under investigation (called the independent variable – see below)

directly proportional a relationship that, when drawn on a line graph, shows a positive linear relationship (a straight line) that crosses through the origin

fair test a test in which only the independent variable has been allowed to affect the dependent variable

gradient (of a straight line graph) change of the quantity plotted on the y-axis divided by the change of the quantity plotted on the x-axis

hazards anything that can cause harm, for example, an object, a property of a substance, or an activity

hypothesis a proposal intended to explain certain facts or observations

independent variable the variable under investigation, for which values are changed or selected by the investigator

line graph used when both variables (x and y) plotted on a graph are continuous. The line should normally be a line of best fit, and may be straight or a smooth curve

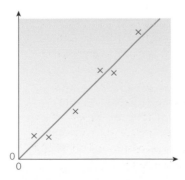

When a straight line of best fit goes through the origin (0, 0) the relationship between the variables is directly proportional

peer review evaluation of scientific research before its publication by others working in the same field

precise a precise measurement is one in which there is very little spread about the mean value. Precision depends only on the extent of random errors – it gives no indication of how close results are to the true (accurate) value

precision a measure of how precise a measurement is

prediction a forecast or statement about the way in which something will happen in the future, which is often quantitative and based on a theory or model

random error an error in measurement caused by factors that vary from one measurement to another

range the maximum and minimum values for the independent or dependent variables – this is important in ensuring that any patterns are detected and are valid

relationship the link between the variables (the independent and dependent variables, x and y) that were investigated

repeatable a measurement is repeatable if the original experimenter repeats the investigation using the same method and equipment and obtains the same results or results that show close agreement

reproducible a measurement is reproducible if the investigation is repeated by another person using different equipment and the same results are obtained

resolution this is the smallest change in the quantity being measured by a measuring instrument that gives a perceptible change in the reading

risk depends on both the likelihood of exposure to a hazard and the seriousness of any resulting harm

systematic error error that causes readings to be spread about some value other than the true value, due to results differing from the true value by a consistent amount each time a measurement is made. Sources of systematic error can include the environment, methods of observation, or instruments used. Systematic errors cannot be dealt with by simple repeats. If a systematic error is suspected, the data collection should be repeated using a different technique or a different set of equipment, and the results compared

tangent a straight line drawn to touch a point on a curve so that it has the same gradient as the curve at that point

validity the suitability of the investigative procedure to answer the question being asked

uncertainty the degree of variability that can be expected in a measurement. A reasonable estimate of the uncertainty in a mean value calculated from a set of repeat readings would be half of the range of the repeats. In an individual measurement, its uncertainty can be taken as half the smallest scale division marked on the measuring instrument or half the last figure shown on the display on a digital measuring instrument

variables physical, chemical, or biological quantities or characteristics

Glossary

Abundance A measure of how common or rare a particular type of organism is in a given environment.

Active site The site on an enzyme where the reactants bind.

Active transport The movement of substances from a dilute solution to a more concentrated solution against a concentration gradient, requiring energy from respiration.

Adaptations Special features that make an organism particularly well suited to the environment where it lives.

ADH Anti-diuretic hormone helps control the water balance of the body and affects the amount of urine produced by the kidney.

Adrenaline A hormone that prepares the body for flight or fight.

Adult stem cells Stem cells that are found in adults that can differentiate and form a limited number of cells.

Aerobic respiration An exothermic reaction in which glucose is broken down using oxygen to produce carbon dioxide and water and release energy for the cell.

Agar gel Widely used solid (gel) culture medium used for growing microorganisms.

Algae Simple aquatic organisms (protista) that make their own food by photosynthesis.

Alleles Different forms of the same gene, sometimes referred to as variants.

Alveoli Tiny air sacs in the lungs that increase the surface area for gaseous exchange.

Amino acids Molecules made up of carbon, hydrogen, oxygen, and nitrogen that are the building blocks of proteins.

Amylase An enzyme that speeds up the digestion of starch into sugars.

Anaerobic respiration An exothermic reaction in which glucose is broken down in the absence of oxygen to produce lactic acid in animals, and ethanol and carbon dioxide in plants and yeast. A small amount of energy is transferred for the cell.

Aorta The artery that leaves the heart from the left ventricle and carries oxygenated blood to the body.

Aphids Insects that penetrate the plant phloem and feed on the dissolved food. They act as plant pathogens and are also vectors that carry pathogenic viruses, bacteria, and fungi into healthy plant tissue.

Archaea One of the three domains, containing primitive forms of bacteria that can live in many of the extreme environments of the world.

Arteries Blood vessels that carry blood away from the heart. They usually carry oxygenated blood and have a pulse.

Asexual reproduction Involves only one individual and the offspring is identical to the parent. There is no fusion of gametes or mixing of genetic information.

Atria The upper chambers of the heart.

Auxin A plant hormone that controls the responses of plants to light (geotropism) and gravity (gravitropism).

Bacteria Single-celled prokaryotic organisms.

Bases (DNA) Nitrogenous compounds that make up part of the structure of DNA and RNA. They are represented by the letters A, T, C, and G.

Benign tumour A growth of abnormal cells that are contained in one area, usually within a membrane, and that do not invade other tissues.

Bile Neutralises stomach acid to give a high pH for the enzymes from the pancreas and small intestine to work well. It is not an enzyme.

Biodiversity A measure of the variety of all the different species of organisms on earth.

Binary fission Reproduction by simple cell division, for example, in bacteria.

Biomass The amount of biological material in an organism.

Cancer The common name for a malignant tumour, formed as a result of changes in cells that lead to uncontrolled growth and division.

Capillaries The smallest blood vessels. They run between individual cells and have a wall that is only one cell thick.

Carbohydrase An enzyme that speeds up the breakdown of carbohydrates into simple sugars.

Carbohydrates Molecules that contain only carbon, hydrogen, and oxygen. They provide the energy for metabolism and are found in foods such as rice, potatoes, and bread.

Carbon cycle The cycling of carbon through the living and non-living world.

Carcinogens Agents that cause cancer or significantly increase the risk of developing cancer.

Carriers Individuals who are heterozygous for a recessive allele linked to a genetic disorder. Because carriers have one healthy allele they are not affected themselves but they can pass on the affected allele to their offspring.

Catalyst A substance that speeds up the rate of another reaction but is not used up or changed itself.

Causal mechanism Something that explains how one factor influences another.

Cell cycle The three-stage process of cell division in a body cell that involves mitosis and results in the formation of two identical daughter cells.

Cell membrane The membrane around the contents of a cell that controls what moves in and out of the cell.

Cell wall The rigid structure around plant and algal cells. It is made of cellulose and strengthens the cell.

Cellulose The complex carbohydrate that makes up plant and algal cell walls and gives them strength.

Central nervous system (CNS) The part of the nervous system where information is processed. It is made up of the brain and spinal cord.

Cerebral cortex The region of the brain associated with consciousness, memory, and language.

Cerebellum The region of the brain concerned with coordinating muscular activity and balance.

Chlorophyll The green pigment contained in the chloroplasts.

Chloroplasts The organelles in which photosynthesis takes place.

Chlorosis The yellowing seen on the leaves of plants when they cannot make chlorophyll due to lack of magnesium ions.

Ciliary muscles Muscles that contract and relax to change the shape of the lens of the eye.

Clinical trials Testing of potential new drugs on healthy and patient volunteers.

Classification The organisation of living organisms into groups according to their similarities.

Cloning The production of identical offspring by asexual reproduction.

Communicable (infectious) diseases Diseases caused by pathogens that can be passed from one organism to another.

Community A group of interdependent living organisms in an ecosystem.

Competition The process by which living organisms compete with each other for limited resources such as food, light, or reproductive partners.

Contraception Methods of preventing pregnancy that usually involve preventing the sperm and egg from meeting. Contraception can involve hormones, chemicals that kill sperm, artificial barriers, intrauterine devices, abstinence, and surgery.

Coordination centres Areas that receive and process information from receptors.

Coronary arteries The blood vessels that supply oxygenated blood to the heart muscle.

Correlation An apparent link or relationship between two factors.

Culture medium A liquid or gel used to support the growth of microorganisms or other cultures, often containing specific nutrients.

Cystic fibrosis An inherited disorder that affects the lungs, digestive system, and reproductive system and is inherited through a recessive allele.

Cytoplasm The water-based gel in which the organelles of all living cells are suspended and in which most of the chemical reactions of life take place.

Decomposers Microorganisms that break down waste products and dead bodies.

Denatured The breakdown of the molecular structure of a protein so it no longer functions.

Dialysis The process of cleansing the blood through a dialysis machine when the kidneys fail.

Differentiate The process where cells become specialised for a particular function.

Diffusion The spreading out of the particles of any substance in a solution, or the particles in a gas, resulting in a net movement of particles from an area of higher concentration to an area of lower concentration down a concentration gradient.

Digestive system Organ system where food is digested and absorbed.

Distribution Where particular types of organisms are found within an environment.

Domain The highest level of classification. There are three domains: archaea, bacteria, and eukaryota.

Dominant (allele) The phenotype will be apparent in the offspring even if only one of the alleles is inherited.

Double circulatory system The circulation of blood from the heart to the lungs is separate from the circulation of blood from the heart to the rest of the body.

Effectors Areas (usually muscles or glands) that bring about responses in the body.

Embryonic stem cells Stem cells from an early embryo that can differentiate to form the specialised cells of the body.

Endocrine system The glands that produce the hormones that control many aspects of the development and metabolism of the body, and the hormones they produce.

Endothermic reaction A reaction that requires a transfer of energy from the environment.

Enzymes Biological catalysts, usually proteins.

Epidermal The name given to cells that make up the epidermis or outer layer of an organism.

Eukaryotic cells Cells from eukaryotes that have a cell membrane, cytoplasm, and genetic material enclosed in a nucleus.

Evolutionary trees Models used to explain the evolutionary links between groups of organisms.

Exothermic reaction A reaction that transfers energy to the environment.

Extinction The permanent loss of all members of a species from an area or from the world.

Extremophile An organism that can survive and reproduce in extreme conditions.

Fatty acids Part of the structure of a lipid molecule.

Follicle stimulating hormone (FSH) Causes the eggs to mature in the ovary.

Genetic engineering The process by which scientists can manipulate and change the genotype of an organism.

Genome The entire genetic material of an organism.

Genotype The genetic makeup of an individual for a particular characteristic, for example, hair or eye colour.

Gibberellins Plant hormones that are important in initiating seed germination.

Glucagon Hormone involved in the control of blood sugar levels.

Glucose A simple sugar.

Glycerol Part of the structure of a lipid molecule.

Glycogen Carbohydrate store in animals.

Gravitropism The response of a plant to gravity.

Guard cells Cells that surround the stomata in the leaves of plants and control their opening and closing.

Haemoglobin The red pigment that carries oxygen around the body in the red blood cells.

Heterozygote An individual with different alleles for a characteristic.

Homeostasis The regulation of the internal conditions of a cell or organism to maintain optimum conditions for function, in response to internal and external changes.

Homozygote An individual with two identical alleles for a characteristic.

Hormones Chemicals produced in one area of the body of an organism that have an effect on the functioning of another area of the body. In animals, hormones are produced in glands.

Hybridoma A cell created during the production of monoclonal antibodies by the fusion of an antibody-specific lymphocyte and a tumour cell.

Hyperopia Long sightedness, where the rays of light from distant objects can be focused clearly on the retina but the rays of light from close objects are not focused and the objects appear blurred.

Hypertonic (osmosis) A solution that is more concentrated than the cell contents.

Hypotonic (osmosis) A solution that is less concentrated than the cell contents.

Incident energy Light from the Sun arriving at the surface of the Earth.

Inoculation Introducing microorganisms to a culture medium, or introducing modified microorganisms into an individual to protect them against disease.

Insulin Hormone involved in the control of blood sugar levels.

Interdependence The network of relationships between different organisms within a community, for example, each species depends on other species for food, shelter, pollination, seed dispersal, etc.

Ionising radiation Radiation that is damaging to living organisms as it can cause mutations in the DNA, which can lead to cancer.

Isotonic (osmosis) A solution that is the same concentration as the cell contents.

Lactic acid The end product of anaerobic respiration in animal cells.

Limiting factor Something that limits the rate of a reaction, for example, photosynthesis.

Lipase Enzymes that speed up the breakdown of lipids into fatty acids and glycerol.

Lipids Include fats and oils and are found in foods such as butter, olive oil, and crisps. They are made of carbon, hydrogen, and oxygen.

Malignant tumour A growth of cells that invade neighbouring tissues and spread to different parts of the body in the blood where they form secondary tumours. Also known as a cancer.

Mean The arithmetical average of a series of numbers.

Median The middle value in a list of numbers.

Medulla The region of the brain concerned with unconscious activities, such as controlling the heart rate and breathing rate.

Meiosis Two-stage process of cell division that reduces the chromosome number of daughter cells. It is Involved in making gametes for sexual reproduction.

Metabolism The sum of all the reactions taking place in a cell or the body of an organism.

Mitochondria The site of aerobic cellular respiration in a cell.

Mitosis Part of the cell cycle where one set of new chromosomes is pulled to each end of the cell, forming two identical nuclei during cell division.

Mode The number that occurs most often in a set of data.

Motor neurones Carry impulses from the central nervous system to the effector organs.

Mutation A change in the genetic material of an organism.

Myopia Short sightedness, where the rays of light from close objects are brought into focus on the retina but distant objects appear blurred as the light is focused in front of the retina.

Natural selection The process by which evolution takes place. Organisms produce more offspring than the environment can support. Only those that are most suited to their environment will survive to breed and pass on their useful characteristics to their offspring.

Nerve A bundle of hundreds or even thousands of neurones.

Neurones Basic cells of the nervous system that carry minute electrical impulses around the body.

Non-communicable diseases Are not infectious and cannot be passed from one organism to another.

Nucleotide A molecule made up of a sugar, a phosphate group, and one of four different bases. They are key units in the structure of DNA and RNA.

Nucleus An organelle found in many living cells containing the genetic information surrounded by the nuclear membrane.

Oestrogen A female sex hormone that controls the development of secondary sexual characteristics in girls at puberty, and the build-up and maintenance of the uterus lining during the menstrual cycle.

Organ An aggregation (collection) of different tissues working together to carry out specific functions.

Organ system A group of organs that work together to carry out specific functions and and form organisms.

Osmosis The diffusion of water through a partially permeable membrane from a dilute solution (which has a high concentration of water) to a concentrated solution (with a low concentration of water|) down a concentration gradient.

Ovaries Female sex organs that produce eggs and sex hormones.

Ovulation The release of a mature egg (ovum) from the ovary.

Oxygen debt The extra oxygen that must be taken into the body after exercise has stopped to complete the aerobic respiration of lactic acid.

Palisade mesophyll The upper layer of the mesophyll tissue in plant leaves, made up of closely packed cells that contain many chloroplasts for photosynthesis.

Partially permeable membrane A membrane that allows only certain substances to pass through.

Pathogens Microorganisms that cause disease.

Permanent vacuole Space in the cytoplasm filled with cell sap.

Phenotype The physical appearance/biochemistry of an individual for a particular characteristic.

Phloem The living transport tissue in plants that carries dissolved food (sugars) around the plant.

Photosynthesis The process by which plants make food using carbon dioxide, water, and light.

Phototropism The response of a plant to light, controlled by auxin.

Pituitary gland Endocrine 'master gland' found in the brain that secretes a number of different hormones into the blood in response to different conditions, to control other endocrine glands in the body.

Placebo A medicine that does not contain the active drug being tested, used in clinical trials of new medicines.

Plasma The clear, yellow, liquid part of the blood that carries dissolved substances and blood cells around the body.

Plasmolysis The state of plant cells when so much water is lost from the cell by osmosis that the vacuole and cytoplasm shrink and the cell membrane pulls away from the cell wall.

Platelets Fragments of cells in the blood that play a vital role in the clotting mechanism of the blood.

Polydactyly A dominant inherited disorder that results in babies born with extra fingers and/or toes.

Preclinical testing Is carried out on a potential new medicine in a laboratory using cells, tissues, and live animals.

Primary consumers Animals that eat producers.

Producers Organisms, such as plants and algae, that can make food from raw materials, such as carbon dioxide and water.

Prokaryotic cells The cells of prokaryotic organisms, which have a cytoplasm surrounded by a cell membrane, and a cell wall that does not contain cellulose. The genetic material is a DNA loop that is free in the cytoplasm and not enclosed by a nucleus. Sometimes there are one or more small rings of DNA called plasmids.

Proteases Enzymes that speed up the breakdown of proteins into amino acids.

Proteins Molecules that contain carbon, hydrogen, oxygen, and nitrogen and are made of long chains of amino acids. They are used for building the cells and tissues of the body and to form enzymes.

Pulmonary artery The large blood vessel that takes deoxygenated blood from the right ventricle of the heart to the lungs.

Pulmonary vein The large blood vessel that carries oxygenated blood from the lungs back to the left atrium of the heart.

Punnett square A way of modelling a genetic cross and predicting the outcome using probability.

Quadrat A sample area used for measuring the abundance and distribution of organisms in the field.

Quantitative sampling Records the numbers of organisms, rather than just the type.

Range The maximum and minimum values for the independent or dependent variables – important in ensuring that any patterns are detected.

Recessive (allele) A phenotype that will only show up in the offspring if both of the alleles coding for that characteristic are inherited.

Receptors Cells that detect stimuli (changes in the internal or external environment).

Red blood cells Biconcave cells that contain the red pigment haemoglobin and carry oxygen around the body in the blood.

Reflex arcs Bring about a reflex action. They involve the sense organ, sensory neurone, relay neurone, and motor neurone.

Reflexes Rapid automatic responses of the nervous system that do not involve conscious thought.

Resolving power A measure of the ability to distinguish between two separate points that are very close together.

Ribosomes The site of protein synthesis in a cell.

Sample size The size of a sample in an investigation.

Secondary consumers Animals that eat primary consumers.

Selective breeding Speeds up natural selection by selecting animals or plants for breeding that have a required characteristic.

Selective reabsorption The process in the kidney where the materials needed in the body such as glucose, some mineral ions, and water are reabsorbed back into the blood from the filtrate.

Sensory neurone A neurone that carries impulses from the sensory organs to the central nervous system.

Sex chromosomes Carry the information that determines the sex of an individual.

Sexual reproduction Involves the joining (fusion) of male and female gametes, producing genetic variation in the offspring.

Sexually transmitted disease (STD) A disease transmitted from an infected person to an uninfected person by unprotected sexual contact.

Simple sugars Small carbohydrate units, for example, glucose.

Speciation The process by which two species evolve from a single original species by natural selection. Speciation often occurs in response to isolation or a change in the environment of one population.

Species The smallest group of clearly identified organisms in Linnaeus's classification system, often described as a group of organisms that can breed together and produce fertile offspring.

Sperm The male sex cells or gametes that carry the genetic material from the male parent.

Spongy mesophyll The lower layer of mesophyll tissue in plant leaves that contains some chloroplasts and many large air spaces to give a big surface area for the exchange of gases.

Statins Drugs used to lower blood cholesterol levels and improve the balance of high- to low-density lipoproteins in the blood.

Stem cells Undifferentiated cells with the potential to form a wide variety of different cell types.

Stent A metal mesh placed in a blocked or partially blocked artery. Stents are used to open up the blood vessel by the inflation of a tiny balloon.

Stimuli Changes in the external or internal environment that can be detected by receptors.

Stomata Openings in the leaves of plants, particularly on the underside, opened and closed by guard cells, allowing gases to enter and leave the leaf.

Suspensory ligaments The ligaments that connect the lens of the eye to the ciliary muscles.

Testosterone The main male sex hormone that controls the male secondary sexual characteristics at puberty and the production of sperm.

Therapeutic cloning A process where an embryo is produced that is genetically identical to the patient so the cells can then be used in medical treatments.

Thermoregulatory centre The area of the brain that is sensitive to the temperature of the blood.

Tissue A group of specialised cells with a similar structure and function.

Tissue culture A modern way of cloning plants that allows thousands of new plants to be created from one piece of plant tissue.

Transect A measured line or area along which ecological measurements are made.

Translocation The movement of sugars from the leaves to the rest of the plant through the phloem.

Transpiration The loss of water vapour from the leaves of plants through the stomata when they are opened to allow gas exchange for photosynthesis. It involves evaporation from the surface of the cells and diffusion through the stomata.

Trophic levels Feeding levels in an ecosystem.

Tropisms The responses of plant roots and shoots to environmental stimuli such as light or gravity.

Tumour A mass of abnormally growing cells that forms when the cells do not respond to the normal mechanisms that control growth and when control of the cell cycle is lost.

Turgor The pressure inside a plant cell exerted by the cell contents pressing on the cell wall.

Type 1 diabetes A disorder where the pancreas fails to produce sufficient insulin.

Type 2 diabetes A disorder where the body cells no longer respond to the insulin produced by the pancreas.

Urea The waste product formed by the breakdown of excess amino acids in the liver.

Vaccine Dead or inactive pathogenic material used in vaccination to develop immunity to a disease in a healthy person.

Vasoconstriction The constriction or narrowing of the blood vessels.

Vasodilation The dilation or opening up of the blood vessels.

Veins Blood vessels that carry blood towards the heart. They usually carry deoxygenated blood and have valves to prevent the backflow of blood.

Vena cava The large vein that brings deoxygenated blood from the body into the heart.

Ventilation Movement of air or water into and out of the gas exchange organ, for example, lungs or gills.

Ventricles Chambers of the heart that contract to force blood out of the heart.

Virus A pathogen, much smaller than a bacterium, that can only reproduce inside the living cells of other organisms.

White blood cells Blood cells involved in the immune system of the body. They engulf pathogens and make antibodies and antitoxins.

Xylem The non-living transport tissue in plants that transports water from the roots to the leaves and shoots.

Zygote The single new cell formed by the fusion of gametes in sexual reproduction

Answers

B1.1 The world of the microscope
1   a beam of light
2   length of cell = 12 mm = 12 000 μm

real size = $\dfrac{12\,000}{570}$

= 21 μm

range from 20–23 μm

B1.2 Animal and plant cells
1   mitochondria
2   to absorb light for photosynthesis
3   onion bulb cells do not contain chloroplasts for photosynthesis because they are underground and do not receive light.

B1.3 Eukaryotic and prokaryotic cells
1   in the cytoplasm as a long circle of DNA, and in plasmids
2   1 order of magnitude or 10^1

B1.4 Specialisation in animal cells
1   mitochondria transfer energy during aerobic respiration; muscle cells need energy to contract
2   the nervous system

B1.5 Specialisation in plant cells
1   to take up water and mineral ions from the soil
2   lignin

B1.6 Diffusion
1   the concentrations of the particles on either side of the membrane
2   the diffusion of oxygen and carbon dioxide in opposite directions

B1.7 Osmosis
1   partially permeable
2   isotonic
3   in **a**, the sugar solution inside the bag is more concentrated than the water outside the bag; water moves into the bag by osmosis in **b**, the solution outside the bag is more concentrated (a higher solute concentration, lower water concentration) than the water inside the bag, so water moves out of the bag by osmosis

B1.8 Osmosis in plants
1   when water enters the cell by osmosis, causing the vacuole to swell, which presses the cytoplasm against the cell wall
2   bigger, because water moves into the potato cells by osmosis

B1.9 Active transport
1   the particles are being absorbed *against* a concentration gradient
2   mineral ions (or a named mineral)

B1.10 Exchanging materials
1   large organisms have a small surface area to volume ratio; exchange surfaces allow materials to be passed to a transport system, which carries them to all the cells
2   leaves are flat and thin, and have internal air spaces and stomata
3   24:8 or 3:1

B1 Summary questions
1   [6 marks – all correct; lose 1 mark for each incorrect line]

Cell structure	Function	In animal cell?	In plant cell?	In prokaryotic cell?
nucleus	controls cell activities contains chromosomes	✓	✓	✗
cell membrane	controls entry and exit of substances	✓	✓	✓
cytoplasm	chemical reactions take place	✓	✓	✓
cell wall	rigid for support	✗	✓	✓
chloroplast	contains chlorophyll for photosynthesis	✗	✓	✗
permanent vacuole	contains sap to make cell rigid – gives support	✗	✓	✗
loop of DNA	contains genes	✗	✗	✓
plasmid	contains genes	✗	✗	✓
ribosomes	make proteins	✓	✓	✓
mitochondria	release energy in aerobic respiration	✓	✓	✗

2   10^3 **or** an order of magnitude of 3 [1]
3   to produce large quantities of proteins (such as enzymes) [1]
4   diffusion is the movement of all types of particle from a region of higher to lower concentration; [1] osmosis is the movement of water from a dilute solute solution to a more concentrated solute solution across a partially permeable membrane [1]
5   alveoli [1]
6   large surface area; [1] thin walls or short diffusion path; [1] good transport system [1]
7   active transport requires energy; [1] in active transport the movement of particles is against the concentration gradient; [1] **or** diffusion does not require energy; [1] in diffusion, particles move down the concentration gradient [1]
8   a solution with a lower concentration of solute molecules than another solution [1]
9   a   absorption of mineral ions by roots [1]
    b   absorption of glucose out of the gut or from kidney tubules into the blood [1]
10 water enters the vacuole in a plant cell, pushing the cytoplasm against the cell wall, creating a pressure called turgor pressure; [1] the cell becomes rigid and this helps to support the plant [1]
11 seawater contains salt [1] so the solution around the animal is hypertonic to its cells (higher solute concentration); [1] water leaves the cells [1] so chemical reactions in the cytoplasm stop [1]
12 water moves out of the cells [1] from a more dilute to the more concentrated solute solution; [1] the vacuole and cytoplasm shrink [1] so the cell membrane draws away from the wall / the cell becomes plasmolysed [1]

13 a   surface area of block: top and bottom: 4 cm $\times$ 6 cm $\times$ 2 = 48 cm^2 [1]

two long sides: 2 cm $\times$ 6 cm $\times$ 2 = 24 cm^2 [1]

two short sides: 2 cm $\times$ 4 cm $\times$ 2 = 16 cm^2 [1]

total surface area = (48 + 24 + 16) cm
= 88 cm^2 [1]

volume of block = 2 cm $\times$ 4 cm $\times$ 6 cm
= 48 cm^3 [1]

SA : V ratio = 88 : 48 = 11 : 6 [1]

b   roll out the plasticine so that it is very thin [1]

B2.1 Cell division
1   one set of chromosomes is pulled to each end of the dividing cell and the nucleus divides
2   each cell has 9 pairs or 18 chromosomes

B2.2 Growth and differentiation
1   an actively dividing tissue of a plant
2   every cell has a particular function; an organism needs a wide variety of specialised cells

B2.3 Stem cells
1   in the inner layers of the ball of cells that forms the embryo
2   in the meristems

B2.4 Stem cell dilemmas
1   one from: the embryo cannot give permission; the money could be used for other medical conditions
2   the cells are genetically identical to the person being treated and so are less likely to be rejected

B2 Summary questions
1   in the nucleus [1]
2   DNA [1]
3   mitosis [1]
4   23 [1]
5   meristem [1]

Answers

6 bone marrow [1] (this is the main source currently, though stem cells have been found in other places, such as the liver, blood, brain, and muscles)

7 two from: paralysis, type 1 diabetes, blindness, heart damage, bone damage [2]

8 an unspecialised cell changes into a specialised cell (such as a muscle cell or a nerve cell) [1]

9 two from: to save rare plants from extinction; for research using genetically identical plants; in horticulture, to produce large numbers of plants cheaply; in agriculture, to produce disease-resistant crops [2]

10 an embryo is produced that has the same genes as the patient [1] so the stem cells produced are not rejected (and may be used for medical treatment) [1]

11 two from: violation of embryo's rights; religious objections; money could be better spent on other medical research; process of differentiating stem cells is difficult and expensive; rapidly dividing stem cells could cause cancer; adult stem cells could transmit viruses or trigger an immune response [2]

12 it is difficult to work out the complex mechanisms that trigger the stem cell to differentiate [1]

B3.1 Tissues and organs
1 a group of cells with similar structure and function
2 to churn (mix up) the stomach contents

B3.2 The human digestive system
1 pancreas, salivary glands (the liver is also a gland)
2 small intestine

B3.3 The chemistry of food
1 a long chain of simple sugar units bonded / linked together
2 it changes shape and may be denatured
3 a iodine solution stays yellow-red (egg white does not contain starch)
   b Benedict's solution remains blue (egg white does not contain sugar)
   c Biuret solution turns purple (egg white contains protein)

B3.4 Catalysts and enzymes
1 active site
2 catalase works faster than manganese(IV) oxide; the graph for liver + hydrogen peroxide shows a steeper curve, and also reaches the end point before the manganese(IV) oxide graph

B3.5 Factors affecting enzyme action
1 the active site changes shape (so the substrate will not fit into the active site)
2 acidic, neutral, alkaline

B3.6 How the digestive system works
1 in the glands (of the digestive system – salivary glands, stomach, pancreas, and cells in the lining of the small intestine)
2 proteases

B3.7 Making digestion efficient
1 acidic
2 in the gall bladder

B3 Summary questions
1 pH; [1] temperature [1]
2 fatty acids; [1] glycerol [1]
3 amino acids [1]
4 a amylase [1] b protease [1] c lipase [1]
5 in the liver [1]
6 large, insoluble molecules [1] are changed into smaller, soluble molecules [1]
7 muscular tissue [1] to churn food; [1] glandular tissue [1] to produce digestive juices; [1] epithelial tissue [1] to line the inside and the outside of the stomach [1]
8 the molecules have more energy [1] so they move around faster [1] and collide more often [1] (so there are more collisions in a given time)
9 the enzyme and the substrate molecules move faster [1] so the substrate molecules collide with the active site more often [1]
10 the shape of other catalysts is not changed by increasing the temperature; [1] enzymes are denatured at high temperatures [1] (which stops them working)
11 bile neutralises the stomach acid, [1] makes the conditions in the small intestine slightly alkaline, [1] and emulsifies fats [1] to increase the surface area of the fats for lipase enzymes to act upon [1]
12 the pH changes the shape of the active site [1] by changing the forces that hold the protein together; [1] this can make the enzyme work efficiently [1] but the wrong pH denatures the enzyme [1]
13 a the hydrochloric acid alone has not digested the meat [1]
    b the pepsin has started the digestion of the meat but slowly [1] (there is still a large piece of meat)
    c the pepsin and hydrochloric acid have worked efficiently and digested the meat [1] because the low pH is the best / optimum pH for the pepsin to work [1]

B4.1 The blood
1 oxygen **or** carbon dioxide
2 to help the blood to clot at the site of a wound

B4.2 The blood vessels
1 arteries have thicker walls than veins; veins have valves along their length whereas arteries do not have valves along their length
2 to prevent the backflow of blood

B4.3 The heart
1 to prevent backflow of blood from ventricles to atria
2 to reduce blood cholesterol levels

B4.4 Helping the heart
1 right atrium
2 to prevent the blood from clotting

B4.5 Breathing and gas exchange
1 intercostal muscles, diaphragm
2 alveoli

B4.6 Tissues and organs in plants
1 photosynthesis
2 one from: stem, root, leaf

B4.7 Evaporation and transpiration
1 xylem, phloem
2 the movement of substances from one region of a plant to another

B4.8 Transport systems in plants
1 diffusion / transpiration
2 to control the size of the stomata (holes in the leaf surface)

B4.9 Factors affecting transpiration
1 the rate of evaporation increases because the rate of diffusion of water from the cells increases / the rate of evaporation inside the leaf increases
2 on the underside of the leaf

B4 Summary questions
1 valves [1]
2 epidermal tissue, [1] palisade mesophyll, [1] spongy mesophyll, [1] xylem, [1] phloem [1]
3 transport of food [1]
4 veins [1]
5 a red blood cells, [1] white blood cells, [1] platelets
   b plasma [1]
6 arteries have thick muscular walls and veins have thin muscular walls; [1] arteries do not have valves and veins have valves [1]
7 a in the right atrium (wall) [1]
   b it controls the resting rate (rhythm) of the heart [1]
8 it has a thicker muscular wall [1]
9 three from: large surface area; [1] thin walls / in close contact with blood capillaries (short diffusion path); [1] well supplied with blood capillaries (for transport); [1] to maintain a steep diffusion gradient [1]
10 vena cava → right atrium → right ventricle → pulmonary artery → lungs → pulmonary vein → left atrium → left ventricle → aorta [4 marks – complete sequence correct; 3 marks – chain of 5 correct; 2 marks – chain of 4 correct; 1 mark – chain of 3 correct]
11 if the cells lose a lot of water they become flaccid; [1] to reduce water loss the stomata close [1] and the leaves wilt, [1] which reduces their surface area, [1] so less water evaporates and diffuses out of the leaf [1]
12 the intercostal muscles contract [1] and the diaphragm contracts; [1] the ribcage moves up and out [1] and the diaphragm flattens; [1] this increases the volume inside the thorax [1] and decreases the pressure [1] (so air is forced into the lungs)
13 set up the potometer in an area without any air movement; [1] time how long it takes the bubble to move along the scale; [1] reset the potometer using the same plant; [1] place a fan or hairdryer near the plant; [1] time how long it takes the bubble to move to the same point on the scale [1]

Section 1 Practice questions
01.1 cell membrane [1]
01.2 to propel the sperm / for swimming [1]
01.3 they transfer energy / they respire [1] because energy is needed to move the tail [1]
01.4 the sperm must penetrate an egg; [1] the enzymes digest the outer layers of the egg [1]

01.5 a root hair cell has a nucleus, cell membrane, and cytoplasm [all 3 – 2 marks, 2 – 1 mark]

01.6 a root hair cell has a cell wall and vacuole [2]

01.7 30 mm = 30 000 μm [1]

$\dfrac{30\,000}{500}$ [1] = 60 μm [1]

02.1 **A** [no mark – can be specified in reason. If **B** given, no marks throughout. If unspecified plus two good reasons – 1 mark]

high(er) pressure in **A**; [1] (allow opposite for **B**, do not accept 'zero pressure' for **B**) pulse in **A** [1] (allow fluctuates / changes; allow reference to beats / beating; ignore reference to artery pumping)

02.2 17 [1]

02.3 68 [1] (accept incorrect answer from answer to 2.2 × 4)

02.4 oxygen / oxygenated blood; [1] (allow adrenaline; ignore air) glucose / sugar [1] (extra wrong answer cancels, for example, sucrose / starch / glycogen / glucagons / water; allow fructose as an alternative to glucose; ignore energy, ignore food)

02.5 carbon dioxide / CO_2 / lactic acid [1] (ignore water)

03.1 selectively permeable, [1] diffusion, [1] high, [1] cytoplasm, [1] osmosis, [1] low [1]

03.2 mucus blocks the surface of the intestine / stomach / pancreatic duct [1] so digestive enzymes cannot reach the food [1]

03.3 very little soluble food material can be absorbed [1] so cells cannot develop (idea of no growth); [1] oxygen cannot diffuse into the bloodstream [1] so little respiration [1]

B5.1 Health and disease

1 a disease caused by pathogens

2 one from: deficiency disease, obesity, cardiovascular disease, type 2 diabetes, cancer

B5.2 Pathogens and disease

1 viruses damage and destroy cells (when they reproduce inside them)

2 infection of an individual when they inhale droplets of water containing a pathogen, that have been coughed or sneezed out by another person

B5.3 Growing bacteria in the lab

1 the bacteria will multiply at a faster rate at the higher temperature, speeding up the industrial process

2 heat / sterilise the equipment, boil solutions, cover Petri dishes or flasks

B5.4 Preventing bacterial growth

1 256

2 the bacterial colony cannot grow there because the bacteria are killed by the disinfectant or antibiotic

B5.5 Preventing infections

1 no one knew about bacteria and viruses

2 plants do not have an immune system

B5.6 Viral diseases

1 by vaccination

2 the leaf cells are destroyed so they cannot photosynthesise

B5.7 Bacterial diseases

1 to kill all the *Salmonella* bacteria

2 sexually transmitted disease

3 new, undifferentiated, genetically modified cells (unspecialised cells)

B5.8 Diseases caused by fungi and protists

1 the leaves

2 a chemical that kills insects

B5.9 Human defence responses

1 (hydrochloric) acid

2 they ingest pathogens, make antibodies, and make antitoxins

B5.10 More about plant diseases

1 the sugar-rich sap in the phloem of the plant

2 the plant cannot make chlorophyll (which is green)

B5.11 Plant defence responses

1 cellulose cell wall

2 one from: poisons; thorns; hairy stems or leaves; drooping or curling when touched; mimicry

B5 Summary questions

1 air, [1] direct contact, [1] and water [1]

2 **A – 3,** [1] **B – 1,** [1] **C – 4,** [1] **D – 2** [1]

3 binary fission [1]

4 an animal that carries a pathogen (a disease-causing organism) from one organism (human) to another [1]

5 two from: poisons; thorns; hairy stems or leaves; drooping or curling when touched; mimicry [2]

6 the cellulose cell wall prevents microorganisms from entering the cell; [1] the waxy cuticle on the leaf is a barrier; [1] bark forms a protective layer; [1] in leaf fall, pathogens in the leaves fall off the plant [1]

7 sticky mucus [1] traps pathogens (bacteria); [1] cilia [1] waft mucus and the pathogen up [1] to be swallowed [1]

8 **a** nitrate deficiency causes stunted growth [1] because nitrate is needed for making protein [1] and protein is needed for growth [1]

b magnesium deficiency causes yellow leaves / chlorosis and the plant will not grow; [1] magnesium is needed to make chlorophyll [1] and chlorophyll is needed for photosynthesis, [1] therefore the plant cannot make the food it needs to grow [1]

9 add nutrients to water in a sterile flask; [1] boil the broth and stopper the flask; [1] flame a wire loop and then cool it (dip in alcohol to cool); [1] touch the colony with the loop; [1] transfer the bacteria quickly to the sterile broth (briefly dip the loop in the broth) [1] and stopper the flask [1]

10 **a** a clear area on an agar gel where bacteria have not grown [1]

b radius = 2 mm; [1] area = πr^2 [1]

area = 3.141 × 4; [1] = 12.6 mm [1]

(no mark for 12.564)

11 **a** their mouthparts penetrate the phloem vessels and suck the sap [1] so plants lose nutrients and cannot grow properly [1]

b the ladybird is a natural predator (of aphids) [1] so it does not pollute the environment; [1] an insecticide is a chemical [1] that can pollute air, land, and water [1] and also kills other insects that are not pests [1]

B6.1 Vaccination

1 introducing a dead or inactive pathogen into the body by injection or oral drops to stimulate the white blood cells to produce antibodies

2 by their shape

B6.2 Antibiotics and painkillers

1 viruses live inside body cells; destroying the virus would destroy the body cells

2 people would die of common bacterial infections if there were no effective antibiotics to treat them

B6.3 Discovering drugs

1 Alexander Fleming

2 foxglove

B6.4 Developing drugs

1 to make sure they are effective, safe, and stable, and can be taken into and removed from the body

2 a trial of a new drug using human subjects, both healthy volunteers and patients

B6.5 Making monoclonal antibodies

1 a protein that targets an antigen of a particular shape

2 a cell that has been formed from two different cells, for example, a mouse lymphocyte and a cancer (tumour) cell

B6.6 Uses of monoclonal antibodies

1 carry a radioactive substance or drug to a diseased cell; trigger the immune response to destroy the diseased cell; block receptors and stop the cell dividing.

2 monoclonal antibodies target specific cancer cells and do not damage healthy cells

B6 Summary questions

1 small amounts of a dead or inactivated pathogen [1]

2 **a** a drug that kills bacteria in the body [1]

b penicillin (accept others) [1]

3 digitalis, [1] aspirin [1] (accept others)

4 a good medicine is effective, [1] safe, [1] and stable, [1] and can be taken in and removed from the body easily [1]

5 the vaccination contains inactivated polio pathogens (viruses); [1] it triggers the white blood cells [1] to produce antibodies; [1] the antibodies target the polio antigens [1] and destroy them [1]; if you are infected with polio your white blood cells can make antibodies quickly [1]

6 viruses reproduce inside body cells [1] so antibiotics cannot reach them without damaging the cells [1]

7 many bacteria are now resistant to the antibiotics currently available [1] so they are not killed by them [1]

8 neither the doctor nor the patient knows [1] if they are given the drug or the placebo [1]

9 one from: side effects; expensive to produce [1]

Answers

10 he noticed that bacteria were not growing around the area where a mould was growing; [1] he realised the mould made a chemical that killed the bacteria [1]

11 a mouse cell that cannot divide [1] is stimulated to make antibodies; [1] the mouse cell is joined to a tumour cell [1] that can divide [1] to make a hybridoma; [1] the hybridoma divides many times to make a clone of cells [1]

12 the monoclonal antibodies bind [1] to antigens [1] on the cancer cell; [1] the antibodies produce a signal [1] and the white blood cells respond to this, [1] destroying the cancer cell [1]

B7.1 Non-communicable diseases
1 one from: ionising radiation, UV light from the sun, second-hand tobacco smoke (accept others, such as asbestos)

2 the two were linked together (correlation), and then scientists showed there was a biological process that caused the increase in lung cancer among smokers.

B7.2 Cancer
1 a mass of abnormally growing cells
2 skin cancer

B7.3 Smoking and the risk of disease
1 nicotine, carbon monoxide, tar
2 chronic obstructive pulmonary disease

B7.4 Diet, exercise, and disease
1 obesity
2 it has a better blood supply

B7.5 Alcohol and other carcinogens
1 the alcohol damages the fetus, causing fetal alcohol syndrome

B7 Summary questions
1 radiotherapy, [1] chemotherapy [1]
2 two from: UV light, radon gas, X-rays, radioactive materials (from nuclear power stations) [2]
3 it attaches to red blood cells [1] so they cannot carry oxygen to the body cells [1]
4 obesity [1]
5 liver, [1] brain [1]
6 a mitosis [1]
  b the cells mutate [1] and divide uncontrollably [1] to form an abnormal mass [1]
7 cancer cells (from a tumour) enter the bloodstream [1] and are carried to another part of the body [1] where they settle and start to divide again [1]
8 tobacco contains nicotine, [1] which is highly addictive [1]
9 a COPD; [1] lower respiratory infections; [1] trachea, bronchus, and lung infections [1]
  b lower respiratory infections [1]
  c 7.8 million [1]
  d 14.1 million deaths from coronary heart disease and stroke; [1] 14.1 : 7.8, so almost twice as many deaths from coronary heart disease and stroke **or** just over half as many deaths from lung diseases [1]

10 carbon monoxide [1] in the smoke attaches to fetal red blood cells, [1] which then cannot carry oxygen; [1] less oxygen passes to the fetus [1] so there is less oxygen for growth [1]

11 the alcohol enters the bloodstream; [1] the liver cannot break it down quickly enough [1] so it circulates throughout the body, [1] including the nervous system and brain; [1] here it causes slower reflexes / reaction times / thought processes; [1] it can lead to unconsciousness / coma / death [1]

12 chemicals in the smoke / named, e.g. tar, [1] build up in the lungs, [1] damaging the alveoli; [1] the alveoli break down, which reduces the surface area, [1] so there is less gas exchange, [1] leading to severe breathlessness [1] and then death

13 (doctors have observed that) among smokers, the blood vessels in the skin narrow; [1] nicotine increases the heart rate; [1] there is damage to the lining of blood vessels, increasing the risk of clots; [1] there is an increase in blood pressure [1]

B8.1 Photosynthesis
1 light from the Sun
2 the veins contain xylem and phloem; the xylem carries water to the leaf and the phloem transports the glucose made there to other parts of the plant

B8.2 The rate of photosynthesis
1 lower temperatures slow down the rate of enzyme-controlled reactions
2 bubbles can be different sizes; it can be difficult to count them accurately if the bubbles appear very quickly
3 heat from the lamp

B8.3 How plants use glucose
1 starch, fats, oils
2 a plant that captures animals (e.g., insects) and obtains nitrates from them by digesting them

B8.4 Making the most of photosynthesis
1 the enzymes in the plants need an optimum temperature to catalyse reactions as fast as possible.
2 the cost of energy / electricity for heating and lighting

B8 Summary questions
1 carbon dioxide + water [1] $\xrightarrow{\text{light}}$ glucose + oxygen [1]
2 chlorophyll [1]
3 light intensity, [1] temperature, [1] carbon dioxide concentration [1]
4 starch [1]
5 use a water plant [1] placed in water [1] and count the bubbles of oxygen produced **or** collect the oxygen in an inverted test tube [1]
6 three from: a leaf is thin, broad, and flat; [1] has air spaces inside; [1] has stomata (with guard cells); [1] has veins / xylem and phloem; [1] has mesophyll cells containing a lot of chloroplasts [1]
7 to convert glucose into amino acids / protein [1] for growth [1]
8 a a factor that stops photosynthesis increasing above a certain level [1]
  b one from: light intensity, colour of light, carbon dioxide concentration, temperature [1]

9 a light intensity [1]
  b number of oxygen bubbles [1]
  c temperature [1]
  d stand the boiling tube in a beaker of water [1]
  e carbon dioxide concentration [1]
  f provide fresh water and sodium hydrogencarbonate for each position of the lamp [1]
  g time [1]

10 an increase in intensity [1] of ¼ or 0.25 [1]

11 grow the tomatoes in greenhouses or polytunnels [1] and increase the temperature with heaters; [1] use lamps to extend the hours of light; [1] control the levels of carbon dioxide; [1] use hydroponics to supply nitrate and other essential ions [1]

12 costs of electricity, [1] of providing carbon dioxide, [1] of hydroponic solutions, [1] of computer technology to control the conditions, [1] of greenhouses / polytunnels and other equipment, [1] labour [1]

B9.1 Aerobic respiration
1 in the mitochondria
2 to combine the small amino acid molecules to make the large protein molecule
3 without oxygen the organism would die

B9.2 The response to exercise
1 glucose
2 the fit person's heart pumps more blood per beat at rest; the fit person has a bigger heart volume at rest, a lower breathing rate, and a lower pulse rate

B9.3 Anaerobic respiration
1 lactic acid
2 you breathe heavily after vigorous exercise to breathe in the extra oxygen needed to break down all the lactic acid that has formed by anaerobic respiration

B9.4 Metabolism and the liver
1 respiration
2 deamination

B9 Summary questions
1 glucose + oxygen [1] → carbon dioxide + water (energy transferred to the environment) [1]
2 in the mitochondria [1]
3 to transfer energy from glucose, [1] to contract [1]
4 no oxygen is used [1]
5 two from: cellulose, [1] starch, [1] protein [1]
6 the rate increases, [1] the depth of each breath increases [1]
7 the stored glycogen can be converted to glucose [1] for (aerobic) respiration, [1] so muscles have energy [1] to contract [1]
8 a anaerobic respiration (in yeast) [1]
  b carbon dioxide from fermentation [1] is used to make bread (rise); [1] fermentation produces ethanol [1] for alcoholic drinks [1]
9 allows increased supply of blood to muscle cells [1] to supply more oxygen [1] and glucose [1] more quickly; [1] removes carbon dioxide (more quickly) [1]

10 less energy is transferred from glucose; [1] lactic acid is produced, [1] which causes muscle fatigue [1]

11 the amount of oxygen needed [1] to break down the lactic acid [1] from anaerobic respiration [1]

12 three measurements and three reasons from: measure breathing rate at rest [1] – this is lower for a fitter person, indicating a larger lung capacity; [1] heart rate at rest [1] – this is lower for a fitter person, indicating that a larger volume of blood is pumped per beat; [1] the increase of both of these during exercise [1] – they are lower in a fitter person; [1] the time taken to return to the resting breathing and heart rates [1] is shorter in a fitter person [1]

13 a excess amino acids [1] are carried to the liver; [1] the amino group is removed [1] in the process of deamination, [1] producing ammonia, [1] which is toxic [1] and is converted to urea.

b urea in large amounts would be toxic; [1] it is transported by the blood to the kidneys [1] where it is filtered from the blood [1] and passes out in the urine [1]

Section 2 Practice questions

01.1 carbon dioxide [1]

01.2 glucose [1]

01.3 increase: light intensity, [1] carbon dioxide level, [1] temperature [1]

01.4 the gardener cannot see the oxygen given off (as tomatoes do not grow under water); [1] the gardener cannot see the glucose produced inside the plant [1]

02.1 some diseases are caused by bacteria; [1] antibiotics kill bacteria [1]

02.2 viruses reproduce inside body cells [1] so a drug that killed viruses would have to damage the cells to reach the viruses [1]

02.3 Example of student answer:

the fungus uses nutrients to grow during day 1 and produces penicillin after day 1; [1] after 2 days, the fungus has grown to optimum / run out of nutrients; [1] the rate of penicillin production increases; [1] between day 2 and day 3, the rate of penicillin production doubles; [1] after day 3, the rate of production slows down; [1] by day 5, the production of penicillin has reached a maximum [1]

03.1 a cell mutates, [1] leading to uncontrolled cell division [1]

03.2 four from: cells divide [1] and some of them push / break through the layers of skin; [1] the cancer / malignant cells enter the bloodstream and are carried to the liver; [1] the cells attach to the liver and divide here, [1] forming a new tumour (in the liver) [1]

03.3 UV light [1]

03.4 one factor influences another factor [1] by a biological process [1]

03.5 nicotine [1]

03.6 one from: they will not be inhaling carcinogens in smoke; [1] they will be less likely to get bronchitis / coughs; the e-cigarette

could help them to give up smoking; reduces risk of heart disease / stroke [1]

03.7 one from: they could encourage non-smokers / young people to start smoking; the effects of the other chemicals (name of one from list) are unknown [1]

04.1 protein [1]

04.2 lymphocytes [1]

04.3 a cell produced from a tumour and a mouse cell or other human cell [1]

04.4 lymphocytes are stimulated to make a particular antibody; [1] the lymphocyte is combined with a tumour cell; [1] the hybridoma reproduces rapidly [1] to form clones, [1] each of which produces the antibodies; [1] these are collected and purified

04.5 one from: pregnancy tests, diagnosing disease, measuring and monitoring hormones, treating disease / named example [1]

B10.1 Principles of homeostasis

1 one from: body temperature, water content, blood glucose concentration

2 muscles and glands

B10.2 The structure and function of the human nervous system

1 temperature, touch, pain

2 along a sensory neurone

B10.3 Reflex actions

1 to act as a coordinator, linking the sensory and motor neurones

2 muscle **or** gland

B10.4 The brain

1 the cerebellum

2 magnetic resonance imaging (MRI)

B10.5 The eye

1 to control the size of the pupil

B10.6 Common problems of the eye

1 the process of changing the shape of the lens to focus on near or distant objects

2 a concave

b convex

B10 Summary questions

1 muscles – which contract; [2] glands – which secrete hormones [2]

2 maintaining a constant internal environment [1]

3 a rapid [1] automatic response [1] to a stimulus [1]

4 a light [1] **b** retina [1]

5 chemicals released from one neurone [1] diffuse [1] to another neurone

6 enzymes work best at normal body temperature; [1] if the temperature is too high the enzymes denature; [1] if it is too low they work too slowly; [1] all the chemical reactions in the body are controlled by enzymes [1]

7 a cerebral cortex [1] **b** cerebellum [1]
c medulla [1]

8 (stimulus) → receptor [1] → sensory neurone [1] → relay neurone (coordinator) [1] → motor neurone [1] → effector [1] → (response)

9 cornea, [1] lens, [1] jelly in eye (vitreous humour) [1]

10 a myopia [1] **b** concave lens [1]

11 two from: electrical stimulation, [1] MRI scans, [1] studying people with brain damage [1]

12 the brain must receive impulses giving information about all the body's activities [1] so that all its movements and activities can be coordinated [1]

13 a the process of changing the shape of the lens [1] to focus on near or distant objects [1]

b the ciliary muscles contract [1] and the suspensory ligaments slacken; [1] this makes the lens thicker [1] to refract the light more strongly [1]

14 a lens is too thin / flat [1] or eyeball is too short, [1] so light rays focus behind retina [1]

b a convex spectacle lens, [1] to refract the light rays more (before they reach the eye); [1] laser treatment [1] to change the curvature of the lens; [1] lens replacement [1]

B11.1 Principles of hormonal control

1 in the bloodstream

2 in the pituitary gland

B11.2 The control of blood glucose levels

1 insulin

2 obesity (accept other correct answers)

B11.3 Treating diabetes

1 insulin injections (or pumps)

2 helps insulin to work better / helps the pancreas to make more insulin / helps to reduce the amount of glucose you absorb from your gut

B11.4 The role of negative feedback

1 it helps to maintain a steady internal environment (steady state)

2 in the pituitary gland

3 increased supply of oxygen and glucose to muscles allows more respiration there, providing more energy for muscles to contract so you can run fast

B11.5 Human reproduction

1 the release of an egg from the ovary

2 testosterone

B11.6 Hormones and the menstrual cycle

1 FSH, LH

2 Oestrogen

B11.7 The artificial control of fertility

1 oestrogen, progesterone

2 IUDs

B11.8 Infertility treatments

1 to stimulate eggs in the ovary to mature

2 one from: her general health; possibly a higher body weight as she ages; she will not have many eggs in her ovary as she is approaching the menopause; the success rate is only about 2%

B11.9 Plant hormones and responses

1 an unequal distribution of auxin causes unequal growth of the shoot

2 towards the hole

B11.10 Using plant hormones

1 two from: as a weed killer, to promote root growth, in tissue culture

2 they might harm useful plants as well as weeds

Answers

B11 Summary questions

1. **a** pituitary gland [1]   **c** ovary [1]
   b adrenal gland [1]   **d** pancreas [1]

2. **a** insulin injections (or pump) [1]
   b in type 1 diabetes, the pancreas [1] does not produce insulin [1]

3. three from: growth spurt; [1] development of pubic hair; [1] development of underarm hair; [1] external genitalia grow (and skin darkens); [1] brain matures [1]

4. they stop the sperm reaching the egg [1] so that fertilisation cannot take place [1]

5. **a** the response of a plant to light [1]
   b the response of a plant to gravity [1]

6. blood sugar concentration, [1] growing, [1] the menstrual cycle, [1] the metabolic rate, [1] sperm production [1]

7. when blood glucose concentration falls, [1] the pancreas detects this [1] and the pancreas releases glucagon, [1] which is transported to liver; [1] the liver converts glycogen to glucose, [1] which diffuses into the blood [1]

8. six from: adrenaline causes: the breathing rate to increase [1] so you can obtain more oxygen; [1] the liver to convert glycogen to glucose; [1] the heart rate to increase [1] to deliver oxygen and glucose to the muscles [1] for more respiration; [1] the transfer of energy [1] for muscles to contract [1] so you can run faster / you are stronger to fight / face the danger [1]

9. FSH is given to the woman, [1] which stimulates eggs to mature; [1] LH is then given [1] and eggs are collected (from the ovary); [1] these are fertilised by sperm (in the laboratory) and develop into embryos; [1] (healthy) embryos are selected and transferred to the uterus [1]

10. **a** to end seed dormancy [1] to speed up the germination (of barley) [1]
    b to promote flowering throughout the year; [1] to increase fruit size [1]

11. there is more auxin on the side of the shoot facing away from the light / facing the dark side, [1] which causes cells there to grow more [1] so the unlit / dark side of the shoot becomes longer [1]

12. six from: FSH is released from the pituitary gland, [1] which causes eggs to mature; [1] oestrogen is released from the ovary, [1] which stimulates the pituitary gland to release LH, [1] causing ovulation; [1] high levels of oestrogen and progesterone inhibit FSH production [1] (control) and maintain the uterus lining; [1] as levels of oestrogen and progesterone fall, FSH is no longer inhibited (control) [1]

13. six from: IVF is expensive; [1] different NHS areas may prioritise other needs (e.g. cancer treatment); [1] IVF requires a high level of skill (which may not be available) [1] and special equipment (which may not be available); [1] the age of the woman will be considered [1] as IVF is less successful in older women due to fewer eggs being available; [1] the woman's health will be considered [1] and IVF may not be offered if she is obese or has other health conditions; [1] the fertility of her partner may be a problem [1] if he does not produce healthy / enough sperm [1] (other relevant points may be valid)

B12.1 Controlling body temperature

1. in the thermoregulatory centre in the brain

2. the water in the sweat evaporates; energy is transferred from the skin to turn the water into water vapour so the skin cools

B12.2 Removing waste products

1. by respiration in the body cells

2. in the liver

B12.3 The human kidney

1. filtration and (selective) reabsorption

2. a hormone produced by the pituitary gland (that controls the amount of water in the urine, and so controls the concentration of water in the blood)

B12.4 Dialysis – an artificial kidney

1. to remove urea from the blood and restore normal concentrations of substances in the blood

2. a kidney transplant

B12.5 Kidney transplants

1. proteins on the surface of cells

2. the patient does not have to be attached to a machine every few days

B12 Summary questions

1. in the brain [1]

2. three from: carbon dioxide, [1] water, [1] urea, [1] mineral ions [1]

3. filtration / filtering [1]

4. **a** kidney [1]   **b** lung [1]   **c** skin [1]

5. for a transplant: the costs afterwards are much lower; [1] it is more convenient (fewer visits to hospital); [1] there is less risk of infection; [1] fewer dietary restrictions (description, e.g. protein not restricted); [1] the patient is not dependent on the availability of dialysis machines; [1] the main disadvantage is the need for immunosuppressant drugs [1]

6. in the winter you sweat less [1] because it is colder [1] so more water is excreted in the urine [1]

7. there is less radiation [1]

8. the athlete's core body temperature rises while they are running, [1] and sweating increases; [1] if too much water was lost without being replaced the core temperature would continue to rise [1] to dangerous levels [1] so water is needed to rehydrate the body and keep the water balance [1]

9. too little water in the blood is detected in the brain; [1] the pituitary gland [1] releases ADH, [1] causing the kidneys [1] to reabsorb more water; [1] as the water level (in the blood) rises, this stops the production of ADH [1] (negative feedback) (The reverse argument could be given for a high water content.)

Section 3 Practice questions

01.1 pulling your hand away from a very hot plate, [1] blinking when a bright light is shone in your eyes, [1] coughing when a crumb enters your trachea [1]

01.2 one from: breathing; moving food through your gut [1]

01.3 you do them automatically / you do not have to think about them [1]

01.4 cerebral cortex [1]

02.1 glucose passes into the villi [1]

02.2 pancreas [1]

02.3 glucagon [1]

02.4 the same order of magnitude [1]

02.5 (642 – 415) million = 227 million **or** 227 ÷ 415 × 100 [1]
54.7% [2] (2 marks for correct answer or 1 mark for correct working without correct answer)

02.6 obesity [1]

03.1 a decrease in the water content of the blood stimulates the pituitary gland [1] to produce ADH; [1] this causes the kidneys [1] to reabsorb more water (from filtrate into the blood), [1] causing the blood water content to rise; [1] this stops the release of more ADH (by the pituitary gland) [1]. (The pituitary gland should be mentioned at least once for either the first or the last mark.)

03.2 the blood water concentration would increase; [1] this would be detected and an impulse would be sent to the pituitary gland; [1] ADH would not be produced, [1] so less water would be reabsorbed by the kidneys; [1] therefore there would be a decrease in the water content of the blood / more water would be lost in the urine [1]

04.1 A [1]

04.2 A [1]

04.3 D [1]

04.4 C [1]

05.1 thyroxine [1]

05.2 testosterone [1]

05.3 progesterone [1]

05.4 LH (luteinising hormone) [1]

05.6 FSH (follicle stimulating hormone) [1]

05.7 FSH [1]

B13.1 Types of reproduction

1. mitosis

2. sexual reproduction

B13.2 Cell division in sexual reproduction

1. gametes

2. the cell divides twice – a body cell divides into two and each divides again

B13.3 The best of both worlds

1. the offspring are produced by mitosis from one parent

2. sexual reproduction

B13.4 DNA and the genome

1. a small section of DNA

2. the entire genetic material of an organism

B13.5 DNA structure and protein synthesis

1. sugar, phosphate, base

2. the order of bases in the DNA

B13.6 Gene expression and mutation

1. they are involved in switching genes, or parts of genes, on and off

2. the substrate will not attach to the enzyme so the enzyme cannot work to catalyse the reaction

B13.7 Inheritance in action

1 one form of a gene that can have different forms

2 it describes an organism that has two different alleles of a particular gene

B13.8 More about genetics

1 the proportions of the genotypes are $\frac{2}{4}$ or 50% heterozygous (Bb) and $\frac{2}{4}$ or 50% homozygous (bb); the proportions of the phenotypes are $\frac{2}{4}$ or 50% black and $\frac{2}{4}$ or 50% brown; the ratios for both genotypes and phenotypes are 2 : 2 (1 : 1)

2 X and Y

B13.9 Inherited disorders

1 polydactyly

2 50% or $\frac{2}{4}$ or $\frac{1}{2}$

B13.10 Screening for genetic disorders

1 DNA

2 one from: risk of miscarriage; possible damage to a healthy fetus; very expensive; an ethical issue described

B13 Summary questions

1 DNA [1]

2 a gene is a section of a chromosome / of DNA; [1] the genome is all the genetic material (of the individual) [1]

3 different forms of a gene [1]

4 it leads to variation in the offspring [1]

5 a mitosis [1]   b meiosis [1]

6 they only have one parent [1] and the cells divide by mitosis [1]

7 a 1 [1]   b 2 [1]   c 1 [1]   d 1 [1]

8 if both parents are heterozygous, [1] each parent will carry the recessive gene; [1] the child could inherit the recessive gene from each parent [1] and be homozygous recessive [1]

9 a nucleotide is (a unit of the DNA molecule) made up of a sugar, [1] a phosphate, [1] and a base [1]

10

Mitosis	Meiosis
one cell division	two cell divisions
two cells are formed	four cells are formed
number of chromosomes remains the same	number of chromosomes is halved
resulting cells are identical to parent cell and each other	resulting cells are genetically different from parent cell and each other

[1 for each comparison]

11 all the plants are identical / there is no variation; [1] if they cannot cope with the change, [1] all individuals will be affected by it [1]

12 a gene produces a template; [1] the template leaves the nucleus and attaches to a ribosome; [1] a carrier molecule carrying an amino acid [1] attaches to the template in a specific order; [1] the amino acids join and the completed protein detaches (from the carrier molecules) [1] and folds into the final protein shape [1]

13 the order of bases will be changed [1] so the template will be different; [1] the wrong amino acids may be carried to the template [1] which means the protein chain could have a different shape when folded [1]

B14.1 Variation

1 genes and environment

2 light, nutrients, space

B14.2 Evolution by natural selection

1 because of differences in their genes

2 they had a mutated gene that gave them immunity to the disease

B14.3 Selective breeding

1 because they produce more milk (so the farmers make more money) (or any other valid reason)

2 lack of variation in the offspring

B14.4 Genetic engineering

1 enzymes

2 they may not be killed by herbicides, so weeds can be sprayed, or they may be modified to kill pests that eat them

B14.5 Cloning

1 take cuttings from mature plants

2 animal cells must be split into groups of cells and then each group must be transplanted into a host mother, whereas individual plant cells can grow into new plants

B14.6 Adult cell cloning

1 an adult cell, such as a skin cell, and an egg cell

2 to save animals from extinction / to produce proteins for use in medicine

B14.7 Ethics of genetic technologies

1 GM crops give a higher yield so the farmers make more money

2 the beta carotene in the rice can be converted to vitamin A in the body

B14 Summary questions

1 genes, [1] the environment [1]

2 an organism that is genetically [1] identical to its parent [1]

3 a (skin) cell from the adult being cloned [1]

4 by mutation [1]

5 a human (pancreas) cell [1]

6 hormones [1]

7 to produce flowers with particular colours or strong scents [1] (or any other valid reason)

8 a few oysters survived because they had a mutation [1] that made them resistant to the disease; [1] these oysters bred; [1] some of their offspring were affected by the disease and died, [1] but those that were resistant survived and bred over many generations [1] until most of the population became resistant [1]

9 remove the nucleus from an unfertilised egg cell; [1] take the nucleus from a skin cell [1] and insert it into the 'empty' egg cell; [1] give the cell an electric shock so it starts to divide [1] to form an embryo; [1] insert the embryo into a host mother to develop [1]

10 (Individual plant cells can grow into new plants.) animal cells must be split into groups of cells [1] and then each group is transplanted (into a host 'mother'); [1] there have to be enough hosts [1] and some embryos may die during development; [1] it takes longer for the animals to develop [1]

11 of the insects feeding on plants that produce insecticide, a few insects will have a mutated gene [1] for resistance to the insecticide [1] and will not die; [1] these insects will reproduce and pass on their resistance gene [1]

12 the gene for insulin production [1] is cut from human DNA [1] using enzymes; [1] a bacterial plasmid is cut open with enzymes and the human gene inserted; [1] the plasmids are transferred to bacterial cells, [1] which then produce the insulin by protein synthesis [1]

B15.1 The history of genetics

1 genes

2 genes code for the production of proteins

B15.2 Theories of evolution

1 characteristics that we develop during our lifetime (e.g., well-developed muscles, hair colour due to dyeing it)

2 Charles Darwin

B15.3 Accepting Darwin's ideas

1 the theory of evolution by natural selection

2 finches

B15.4 Evolution and speciation

1 for example, islands can break away from mainland, new rivers can form, mountain ranges or craters can separate populations, the climate can change differently in two areas

2 the wide range of alleles that control the characteristics in a population

B15.5 Evidence for evolution

1 one from: bones, teeth, shells, claws

2 the fossils have been destroyed by earth movements or other climatic conditions, or the fossils were not formed in the first place due to unsuitable conditions

B15.6 Fossils and extinction

1 it can eat all the animals of that species

2 one from: volcano, earthquake, tsunami, collision by asteroid

B15.7 More about extinction

1 it may be too hot or too cold for the species to survive / the food supply might change

2 a new disease could have been introduced into the population; it is unlikely to have been caused by a new predator as dinosaurs were at the top of the food chain

B15.8 Antibiotic-resistant bacteria

1 very few people are immune to the new pathogen and no effective treatment is available yet

2 antibiotics kill the non-resistant strains, so if a resistant strain has evolved, it can survive and multiply without competition

B15.9 Classification

1 the members of a group that are very similar and can breed to produce fertile offspring

2 each organism is given two names (the genus name and the species name)

Answers

B15.10 New systems of classification

1   archaea, bacteria, eukaryota
2   they show the relationships between organisms

B15 Summary questions

1   **a**   Mendel [1]   **b**   Watson and Crick [1]
2   early organisms had soft bodies; [1] any fossils would be destroyed by geological activity [1]
3   4.5×10^9 [1]
4   the original species may be left with too little to eat [1]
5   **a**   a giant asteroid colliding with Earth; [1] sea ice melting and cooling the sea temperature by about 9 °C [1]
    b   new disease [1]
    c   dinosaurs are at the top of the food chain [1]
6   if the offspring are produced by sexual reproduction, [1] then the genes of both parents are inherited [1] in different combinations [1] when the gametes fuse [1]
7   doctors and nurses should wash their hands / use an alcohol cleanser [1] to kill microorganisms; [1] they should isolate patients / use disposable clothing / restrict visiting [1] to reduce the spread of the bacteria; [1] they should make sure visitors wash their hands on entering and leaving the hospital / maintain the highest standards of hygiene in the hospital [1]
8   three from: the climate may change – it could become hotter, colder, wetter, or drier; [1] a new predator may move into the area; [1] a new disease may affect the population; [1] a new competitor for the food supply may move into the area; [1] there may be a loss of habitat such as nesting sites [1]
9   Lamarck suggested that characteristics that developed during the lifetime [1] of the organism could be passed on; [1] Darwin said that organisms with the best characteristics [1] survived [1] to breed [1] and the offspring inherited the characteristic [1].
10 evolutionary trees show the relationships between organisms [1] and illustrate common ancestry [1]
11 two populations of an organism become separated [1] and live in two different regions, [1] for example, either side of a river / mountain range [1]
12 isolation of two groups; [1] there is genetic variation in the two populations; [1] alleles are selected that give an advantage; [1] interbreeding is no longer possible [1] (as the populations have diverged / become different); therefore a new species has formed [1]

Section 4 Practice questions

01.1   **1** [1]
01.2   **6** [1]
01.3   **8** [1]
01.4   **C** [1]
01.5   **A** [1]
01.6   **B** [1]
01.7   alleles [1]
01.8   asexual reproduction [1]
01.9   white [1]

02.1   from fossil evidence [1]
02.2   lack of light [1] so plants could not grow [1] so there was no food for animals [1]
02.3   two from: introduction of a new predator; [1] introduction of a new disease; [1] loss of habitat / food supply; [1] environmental / climate change [1]
02.4   two populations may become separated; [1] the populations have a wide range of alleles / genes; [1] this leads to variation of characteristics in the population; [1] some characteristics may be beneficial; [1] natural selection takes place and organisms (with the beneficial characteristic) survive to breed; [1] if the populations stay separated for a long time they become too different and cannot interbreed [1]
03.1   the gene for the bacterial protein is introduced into the corn; [1] this gene is a section of a DNA molecule; [1] enzymes are used to cut out the gene / section of DNA; [1] the gene is transferred, using a plasmid or virus; [1] this DNA section has a specific sequence of bases, which act as a code [1] for assembly of amino acids in the correct order to produce protein [1]
03.2   advantages: higher yield, less use of pesticides, only targets the corn borer; disadvantages: possible effect on other organisms, concerns about human health, may increase numbers of other pests; [3]
       reasoned conclusion [1]
       (For full marks at least one advantage and disadvantage and a reasoned conclusion must be given.)
04.1   in the liver [1]
04.2   carbohydrase / enzyme [1]
04.3   parent genotypes: Gg and Gg [1]

Gametes	G	g
G	GG	Gg
g	Gg	gg

       child with genotype gg will have the disease [1]
04.4   male is XY, [1] female is XX [1]
04.5   three from: the female will have two alleles; [1] there is a high chance that one is dominant (or described); [1] the male has only one X chromosome / one allele [1] so he will have the disease [1] as he has no other X chromosome to carry the dominant healthy allele [1]

B16.1 The importance of communities

1   one from: water, food, space, a mate, a breeding sit, materials to build shelters / nests
2   a community in which all the species and environmental factors are in balance, so the populations remain fairly constant

B16.2 Organisms in their environment

1   three from: carbon dioxide levels, light levels, wind, soil pH, presence of ions, water, temperature
2   organisms may not be resistant to the new disease and will be killed, wiping out the population

B16.3 Distribution and abundance

1   a square frame that may also be divided into a grid
2   a line drawn between two points to make ecological measurements

B16.4 Competition in animals

1   so they can find enough food and water; they also need space or shelter to protect and rear their young
2   the predator is put off by the warning colour of the caterpillar, which may be the same colour as a poisonous one

B16.5 Competition in plants

1   to reduce competition for light, water, mineral ions, and space
2   space if they are overcrowded; also light, mineral ions, and water

B16.6 Adapt and survive

1   a feature that allows an organism to live in its normal environment
2   organisms that live in extreme environmental conditions, such as extremely cold, extremely hot, very salty, or at high pressure

B16.7 Adaptation in animals

1   they have a small surface area : volume ratio
2   to stay cool, to conserve water

B16.8 Adaptations in plants

1   curled leaves; stomata situated away from heat and wind; waxy leaves; small leaves; water storage in the stems
2   thorns, poisonous chemicals, or warning colours to stop animals eating them

B16 Summary questions

1   a community is made up of the populations of different species of animals and plants (protista, fungi, bacteria, and archaea) [1] that are all interdependent (in a habitat) [1]
2   the mean is the total sum of all the readings divided by the number of readings; [1] the median is the middle value of the readings when written in order of value [1]
3   three from: water, [1] oxygen, [1] temperature, [1] light [1]
4   the birds lose nesting sites, [1] shelter, [1] and a possible food source [1]
5   very few plants grow there, [1] and those that do are very small; [1] they produce little food for herbivores, [1] so there are very few carnivores [1]
6   new predators eat prey [1] so there would be less food for other carnivores; [1] the numbers of prey would therefore go down [1] and the numbers of predators would also go down; [1] this could increase the plant populations [1] as there would be fewer herbivores to eat them [1]
7   a line is marked between two points; [1] the quadrat is placed at regular intervals along the line; [1] the organisms in the quadrat are counted at each position [1]
8   adaptations allow organisms to survive [1] in a particular habitat [1]
9   waxy cuticles; [1] stomata on undersides of leaves; [1] a thick shiny cuticle; [1] the ability to wilt [1] to reduce the surface area exposed; [1] desert plants have very small, spine-like leaves [1]

10 six from: use a 1 m² / 0.5 m² quadrat; [1] throw a quadrat randomly on the beach / use a random number calculator to determine the positions of quadrats; [1] count the number of casts inside each quadrat; [1] decide the system of counting casts on the edges of the quadrat [1] (e.g., N and E in, S and W out); [1] calculate the average number of casts per quadrat / per m² / per 0.5 m²; [1] multiply by 1000 / 2000 to find the abundance; [1] choose a time when the tide is low; [1] throw at least 15–20 quadrats; [1] repeat on another day(s) [1]

11 a 20 − 5 = 15 casts per m² [1]

b $\frac{143}{11}$ = 13 casts per m² [1]

c 11 casts per m² [1]

d 10 casts per m² [1]

e 13 × 1000 = 13 000 worms [1]

B17.1 Feeding relationships

1 any green plant or alga / phytoplankton; any primary consumer (e.g., fish) / herbivore

2 any carnivore / secondary or tertiary consumer that has to catch prey for food

B17.2 Materials cycling

1 bacteria, fungi

2 water falling as rain, sleet, or snow

B17.3 The carbon cycle

1 photosynthesis

2 respiration and combustion

B17.4 Rates of decomposition

1 warmth, moisture

2 optimum temperature (for enzymes), prevent oxygen entering (to keep it anaerobic), add water

3 use a data logger and probe to monitor the pH; make observations of the level of decay

B17 Summary questions

1 they photosynthesise [1] and produce glucose [1]

2 oxygen, carbon dioxide, water vapour [3]

3 the biological material in an organism (or organisms) [1]

4 pH [1]

5 herbivores [1]

6 warm, [1] moist, [1] plenty of oxygen [1]

7 respiration by cells [1] releases carbon dioxide, which diffuses from the leaves into the air [1] via stomata [1]

8 in the air breathed out; [1] in urine and faeces; [1] as sweat [1]

9 three from: materials are constantly used; [1] if they were not released from organisms, [1] the next generation would run out of materials to grow; [1] the waste would pile up [1]

10 (successful predators would) reduce the number of prey animals [1] by eating more of them; [1] fewer prey animals would mean less food for predators [1] so numbers of predators would fall; [1] this would allow the number of prey animals to increase again [1]

11 there will be several types of organism at each level of the food chain in a habitat / ecosystem; [1] one herbivore (primary consumer) could eat several types of plant, [1] and in turn the herbivore could be prey to several secondary consumers; [1] some animals eat both animals and plants [1]

12 nitrates are used by cells to make amino acids; [1] proteins are made by protein synthesis; [1] plant (protein) is eaten by animals [1] and is digested / built into animal tissue; [1] some is lost to the environment in the animal's waste products, [1] and some is released to the soil when the animal's body is decayed by microorganisms [1]

B18.1 The human population explosion

1 land has to be cleared, which destroys their habitats

2 a measure of the variety of all the different species of organisms on Earth

B18.2 Land and water pollution

1 to remove toxic chemicals and parasites

2 eventually there is no oxygen in the water

B18.3 Air pollution

1 sulfur dioxide

2 trees are damaged so there is a loss of habitat and food

B18.4 Deforestation and peat destruction

1 photosynthesis

2 respiration of microorganisms that decay the peat, burning of the peat

B18.5 Global warming

1 a forest or ocean that stores carbon dioxide so that it is not released into the air

2 because of an increase in the Earth's temperature, leading to the melting of the ice caps

B18.6 The impact of change

1 three from: temperature, rainfall, light, carbon dioxide level, oxygen level

2 one from: to provide habitats / food for other organisms; to increase the amount of photosynthesis / increase the amount of oxygen in the atmosphere / remove carbon dioxide from the atmosphere

B18.7 Maintaining biodiversity

1 to allow wild plants to grow in order to maintain / increase biodiversity

2 by taxing people on the waste taken to landfill sites

B18.8 Trophic levels and biomass

1 plants are producers, so they start every food chain

2 microorganisms

B18.9 Biomass transfers

1 respiration

2 insert a temperature probe into the flask, attached to a data logger

B18.10 Factors affecting food security

1 having enough food to feed a population

2 droughts and flooding resulting from global warming have caused the loss of crops

B18.11 Making food production efficient

1 to prevent them wasting energy when moving around, and to maintain their body temperature; more energy is then usefully transferred during growth (resulting in more meat production)

2 restricting the movement of cattle (or fish) is seen as cruel by many people

B18.12 Sustainable food production

1 the population could become extinct if the young fish do not grow and reproduce

2 the fungus *Fusarium*

B18 Summary questions

1 the mass of living material [1]

2 three from: use land for buildings / housing or roads; [1] use land for farming; [1] use land for quarrying; [1] pollute the land with waste [1]

3 waste from living organisms [1] containing carbon compounds (e.g., carbohydrates, fats, and proteins) [1]

4 three from: herbicides, [1] pesticides, [1] fertilisers, [1] toxic chemicals from landfill, [1] untreated sewage [1]

5 plants / algae / phytoplankton [1]

6 there is a loss of habitat [1] for all the animals that live in trees, (e.g., birds and insects) [1]

7 reduce the number of stages / eat plants or herbivores; [1] there is less energy available / more energy lost from the food chain if humans eat carnivores / organisms higher up the food chain than herbivores / organisms lower down the food chain [1]

8 acid rain affects leaves, flowers, and buds directly; [1] it kills roots, resulting in the death of plants; [1] the acid enters waterways and changes the pH there, [1] which kills fish / aquatic organisms [1]

9 a without food security, food will become scarce and a population will starve unless new sources of food are found [1]

b three from: increasing birth rates; [1] changing diets in developed countries; [1] new pests and pathogens; [1] environmental changes; [1] increase in the cost of agricultural inputs; [1] conflicts [1]

10 the trees may be burnt; [1] or microorganisms / decomposers [1] decay the tree's biomass (releasing carbon dioxide to the atmosphere through respiration) [1]

11 detritivores / decomposers [1] ingest / digest the biomass; [1] they respire, [1] transferring the energy from the biomass to the environment (which gets warmer) [1]

12 there are fewer stages in the food chain; [1] eating plants is the most efficient way of feeding the world population, [1] but if we eat meat, less energy is wasted (by eating herbivores rather than carnivores) [1]

13 there is undigested food in the calf's faeces (dung); [1] urea is lost in its urine; [1] the calf transfers energy to move around; [1] the calf produces methane which is lost to the atmosphere; [1] the energy transferred in respiration by the calf is eventually transferred to the surroundings [1]

14 sea levels would rise, [1] which would cause loss of habitat; [1] changing seasons [1] could lead to changes in distribution / migration patterns / reduced biodiversity [1]

15 when peat is removed from peat bogs and used in gardens, the microorganisms [1] in the garden soil decay the peat; [1] this releases carbon dioxide into the atmosphere (by respiration) [1] and the carbon that was 'locked up' in the peat is released; [1] the increased carbon dioxide in the atmosphere can contribute to global warming / climate change [1]

Answers

16 GM crops [1] provide higher yields of crop plants; [1] modified crops can supply particular nutrients, [1] for example, golden rice produces vitamin A; [1] fermenters are used [1] to produce mycoprotein from *Fusarium* [1]

Section 5 Practice questions

01.1 cube **A** – 3 : 1 [2; 24 : 8 or wrong answer but correct calculation – 1]

cube **B** – 2 : 1 [2; 96 : 48 or wrong answer but correct calculation – 1]

01.2 it is long / wide and flat [1]

01.3 (because smaller organisms have a large surface area : volume ratio) they transfer energy to the environment faster, [1] maintaining a suitable temperature for enzymes / metabolic reactions [1]

01.4 oxygen is required for respiration, [1] and energy from respiration is required for growth [1]

01.5 four from: mature organisms are larger; [1] larger organisms overheat more; [1] fewer larger organisms survive / mature [1] to reproduce [1] so the population will decrease [1] **or** mature organisms are larger; [1] the smallest mature organisms will survive [1] and will reproduce [1] so the numbers of smaller fish will increase [1]

02.1 grass [1]

02.2 two from: earthworm, [1] snail, [1] rabbit [1]

02.3 thrush [1]

02.4 a food chain shows only one set of links in a community; [1] a food web shows how the chains are interlinked, [1] for example, more than one organism feeds on the grass [1] (Other examples could be quoted.)

02.5 a balanced group of interdependent organisms in an ecosystem, whose population sizes remain fairly constant [1]

02.6 the thrushes have lost one source of food, [1] so they will eat more earthworms [1]

02.7 the numbers of all the consumers would fall [1] because they all depend on grass for the production of food; [1] fewer herbivores / primary consumers will mean fewer carnivores / secondary consumers can survive [1]

02.8 the concentration of the toxin in the organisms builds up through the food chain [1] because the toxin is not excreted / broken down by the consumers; [1] there is not enough toxin in the sea to kill the phytoplankton (concentration of toxin in phytoplankton 100 µg/kg), [1] but shrimp eat a lot of phytoplankton so they build up more poison in their bodies; [1] by the time the large fish eat the small fish there is a much higher concentration in their bodies (1500 µg/kg) which is sufficient to poison them [1]

03.1 two from: may cause changes in the Earth's climate; [1] may cause a rise in sea level; [1] may reduce biodiversity; [1] may cause changes in migration patterns; [1] may result in changes in distribution patterns [1]

03.2 large-scale deforestation, to clear areas for farming / agriculture, [1] reduces the uptake of carbon dioxide from the atmosphere; [1] (deforestation) releases carbon dioxide into the atmosphere due to burning of trees; [1] carbon dioxide is also released by microorganisms decaying the wood, as the microorganisms respire; [1] destruction of peat bogs releases carbon dioxide when the peat is burnt; [1] there is an increased need for food, and methane is released during rice growing and from cattle [1]

04.1 water would diffuse / move by osmosis out of the bacteria into the salty water / solution [1] due to the higher concentration of solutes / lower concentration of water in the salty water; [1] the cytoplasm would become dehydrated / chemical reactions in the cell would be disrupted [1]

04.2 they would swell / burst [1]

04.3 (they would expect) enzymes to denature, [1] so that no chemical reactions could occur [1]

Practical questions

01.1 independent variable – number of frames it took the hammer to move to the knee / speed of hammer; [1] dependent variable – distance moved by the toe; [1] control variable – distance hammer moved [1]

01.2 can measure very short times / fast speeds; [1] keeps a permanent record [1]

01.3 repeating the trial and calculating means [1]

01.4 the faster the speed of the hammer, the greater the movement, [1] up to a maximum of 10 cm movement [1]

02.1 the thermometers have to be lifted out of the peas to read them, [1] so the temperature reading will go down [1]

02.2 use a temperature probe [1] attached to a data logger [1]

02.3 the thermometers stick out of the flasks [1] so they can be read without removing them from the peas [1]

02.4 air / oxygen cannot diffuse into the flask / carbon dioxide cannot diffuse out of the flask [1]

02.5 microorganisms [1] will decay the peas; [1] respiration (of the microorganisms) releases more energy than respiration by the peas [1]

02.6 soak the peas in a disinfectant [1] to kill the microorganisms [1]

OXFORD
UNIVERSITY PRESS

Great Clarendon Street, Oxford, OX2 6DP, United Kingdom

Oxford University Press is a department of the University of Oxford. It furthers the University's objective of excellence in research, scholarship, and education by publishing worldwide. Oxford is a registered trade mark of Oxford University Press in the UK and in certain other countries

© Oxford University Press 2017

The moral rights of the authors have been asserted

First published in 2017

All rights reserved. No part of this publication may be reproduced, stored in a retrieval system, or transmitted, in any form or by any means, without the prior permission in writing of Oxford University Press, or as expressly permitted by law, by licence or under terms agreed with the appropriate reprographics rights organization. Enquiries concerning reproduction outside the scope of the above should be sent to the Rights Department, Oxford University Press, at the address above.

You must not circulate this work in any other form and you must impose this same condition on any acquirer

British Library Cataloguing in Publication Data
Data available

978-0-19-835940-1

10 9 8 7 6 5 4 3 2

Printed in Great Britain by Bell and Bain Ltd., Glasgow.

With thanks to **Faye Meek** for her contribution to the Practicals support section.

Acknowledgements

COVER: Shutterstock/Ethan Daniels
Header Photo: Marek Mis/Science Photo Library;
p2: Gerd Guenther/Science Photo Library; **p9(T)**: Michael Abbey/ Science Photo Library; **p9(B)**: Michael Abbey/Science Photo Library; **p14**: Biodisc/Visuals Unlimited/Science Photo Library; **p18**: Steve Gschmeissner/Science Photo Library; **p19**: Ism/Science Photo Library; **p25**: Martyn F. Chillmaid/Science Photo Library; **p29**: Raphael Gaillarde/ Getty Images; **p32**: Steve Gschmeissner/Science Photo Library; **p39**: Nature'S Geometry/Science Photo Library; **p43(T)**: Lowell Georgia/ Science Photo Library; **p43(B)**: Norm Thomas/Science Photo Library; **p47(T)**: Dimijana/Shutterstock; **p47(B)**: Nigel Cattlin, Visuals Unlimited/ Science Photo Library; **p48(L)**: Anthony Short; **p48(CL)**: Anthony Short; **p48(C)**: Symbiot/Shutterstock; **p48(CR)**: Skyprayer2005/Shutterstock; **p48(R)**: Geoff Kidd/Science Photo Library; **p56**: Anthony Short; **p60**: Andrew Lambert Photography/Science Photo Library; **p63**: Lukasz Szwaj/Shutterstock; **p92**: Bluiz60/Shutterstock; **p104(L)**: Sari Oneal/ Shutterstock; **p104(R)**: Valentina Photo/Shutterstock; **p110**: Linn Currie/ Shutterstock; **p111**: Zoonar Gmbh/Alamy Stock Photo; **p116**: Golden Rice Humanitarian Board www.Goldenrice.Org; **p120**: Anthony Short; **p131**: Lkordela/Shutterstock; **p132**: Flpa/Alamy Stock Photo; **p136**: Dea/L.Romano/Getty Images; **p138(TL)**: OUP/Corbis; **p138(TR)**: Martin Fowler/Shutterstock; **p138(BL)**: Chris2766/Shutterstock; **p138(BR)**: Peter Louwers/Shutterstock; **p141**: Anthony Short; **p144**: Michael Marten/ Science Photo Library

Artwork by Q2A Media

MIX
Paper from
responsible sources
FSC® C007785